Engineering Geometrical Drawing

L B COOK

BA (Hons), MIED, Cert Ed, HNC (Mech Eng)
Lecturer in Drawing and Design
Stafford College of Further Education

R S RHODES

MWeld I, Diploma in Advanced Studies
in Education, HNC (Mech Eng)
Lecturer responsible for Engineering Drawing
Stafford College of Further Education

Pitman

PITMAN BOOKS LTD
128 Long Acre London WC2E 9AN

Associated Companies
Pitman Publishing New Zealand Ltd, Wellington
Pitman Publishing Pty Ltd, Melbourne

© L B Cook and R S Rhodes 1982

First published in Great Britain 1982

ISBN 0 273 01821 3

Printed and bound in Great Britain
at The Pitman Press, Bath

PREFACE

This book has been written primarily for O-level students of technical drawing. However, any other students of the subject should find it helpful.

The topics covered are those that appear in the geometrical section of the technical drawing syllabus of every one of the major examining boards, together with several topics which, though not common to all syllabuses, we feel are worthy of inclusion.

The first part of the book deals with PLANE (two-dimensional) geometry, i.e. with figures (drawings) which have no depth — circles, triangles, quadrilaterals, etc. The second part concentrates upon SOLID (three-dimensional) geometry. It deals with prisms, pyramids, cones, etc.

All topics have been covered clearly and comprehensively and dealt with in a logical and orderly sequence. The information has been presented graphically as well as in words wherever possible because experience has taught us both that, in this subject, this is the best method for "getting the message across". To assist the student we have tried to contain each separate item of information (definition, construction, instruction, etc.) within one page. Furthermore, diagrams (drawings) have been placed adjacent to the corresponding text throughout the book because we feel that nothing is more distracting than having to refer to a diagram which is pages away from the relevant text.

LBC & RSR

Publishers note
The publisher and authors wish to express their gratitude to William Keel for the illustration work in this book.

CONTENTS

Drawing Equipment

Very few tasks can be completed satisfactorily without the necessary "tools for the job".
For the successful preparation of technical diagrams, sketches and drawings, it is essential to possess, or at least have access to, a comprehensive set of carefully chosen and well maintained drawing equipment.
The student draughtsmans "tool kit" should, ideally, include the following instruments, equipment and publications.

ESSENTIAL EQUIPMENT

1 PENCILS

Good quality pencils, of reasonable length, are essential for producing neat, accurate constructions, sketches and drawings. The grade of pencil which should be used depends to a large extent on the quality of the drawing paper available, but as a general recommendation HB and F (medium grade pencils) are suitable for sketching, and H and 2H (slightly harder pencils) are suitable for producing geometrical constructions and machine drawings. The H pencil is generally used for outlines, notes, dimensions, etc. and the 2H for construction lines, leader lines, dimension lines, etc., on technical drawings.

Standard wooden pencils to be used for sketching, lettering and numbering should be sharpened to a conical point, as shown opposite.

Standard wooden pencils to be used for line work — on both geometrical constructions and machine drawings — are often sharpened to a chisel "point" by experienced draughtsmen. In the early stages of a drawing course, a chisel point may not be an advantage, however. Pencils with a conical point can be, and in fact often are, used quite successfully for line work.

Conical point   Chisel point

Sharpening ordinary wooden pencils is a dirty, time-consuming and wasteful process, so experienced draughtsmen generally prefer to use a much more sophisticated type of pencil. Many proprietary brands are manufactured under various descriptions such as "Semi-automatic draughting pencils" "Drawing lead holders", "Fine-line lead holders", etc. All of these pencils are based upon the same basic principle — a retracting lead. A selection of the more commonly used sophisticated draughting pencils is shown below.

Sharpener

Chuck pencil

Fine lead holder (0.7mm)

Fine lead holder (0.3mm)

These pencils are cleaner to use, much more convenient to use, and are more likely to produce a line of consistent thickness, than the standard wooden pencil.

A lead of appropriate grade (HB, F, H, 2H etc) and diameter, or width (0.3mm, 0.7mm, etc) is loaded into the pencil and a simply operated feed mechanism pushes the lead forward in a constant length sufficient for draughting. Some of these pencils accept rectangular cross-section leads.

The main disadvantage from the students viewpoint is that these sophisticated pencils are all relatively expensive — ten to twenty times the cost of an ordinary wooden pencil. Fineline lead holders, in particular, though convenient to use, prove rather costly because a different pencil has to be used for each of the lead diameters (widths) required.

2 PENCIL SHARPENER

Pencils should always be kept reasonably sharp. A purpose-made plastic or metal pencil sharpener, sharp penknife or scalpel can be used for initial sharpening of wooden pencils. A typical example of each of these sharpeners is shown opposite.

A separate sharpener is not required if a sophisticated pencil is used because these are usually manufactured with a built-in sharpener.

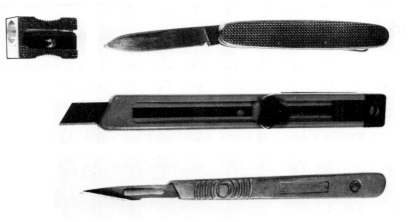

3 GLASS PAPER (SANDPAPER) BLOCK

A glasspaper, or sandpaper block is a very useful piece of equipment. It is used initially to obtain the final shape of the pencil point and used frequently to maintain the desired sharp point or wedge.

Students should avoid using either the striking strip on the edge of a matchbox or an old nail file as a substitute for glasspaper. The surfaces of these generally are too rough for the intended purpose.

Note Students should take care not to sharpen pencils over, or near to, the drawing sheet or drawing equipment, particularly the set-squares.

4 SET-SQUARES

Either a fairly large plastic adjustable set-square OR a fairly large 45° set-square AND also a 30°/60° square are essential for any drawing student. The shortest side should be at least 150 millimetres long. Small squares are not very useful.

An adjustable square will probably cost more than the alternative pair of set-squares. However, an adjustable set-square can be extremely useful for drawing lines parallel to each other and also for drawing "non-standard" angles, i.e. angles other than 30°, 45° and 60°.

Note Set squares should be used only whilst in good condition. They should be discarded immediately they become "bowed" chipped, cracked or broken.

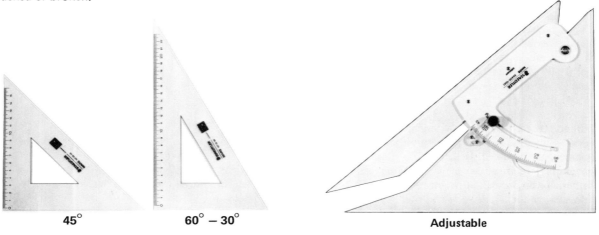

45°   **60° — 30°**   **Adjustable**

5 COMPASSES

A pair of good quality compasses with a radius range of approximately 5 millimetres to 150 millimetres is required for this class of work.

Two typical instruments which would be suitable are shown opposite. Those on the left are a relatively inexpensive and popular pair. Check that the centre screw is both strong and rigid in the more expensive and theoretically, more accurate type shown on the right.

The much cheaper and cruder pair of compasses shown far right, which many students initially think are adequate for technical drawing, should not be bought. They are not suitable for producing lines of the desired quality. However, these simpler compasses are useful for drawing circles in other subjects.

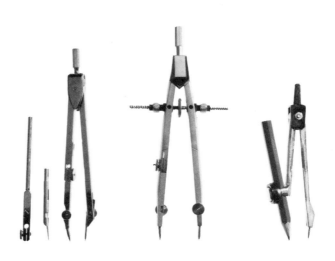

6 COMPASS LEADS

The grade of lead inserted in the compasses should, ideally, be the same as that in the pencil being used in conjunction with the compasses, if even line density and acceptable line blending are to be achieved. Compasses are used mainly for drawing outlines and construction lines. Therefore, a box of H leads and a box of 2H leads should be sufficient.

Note Compass leads should be sharpened initially as shown in the adjacent sketch.

This wedge shape should be maintained by frequently "touching-up" the lead with glasspaper.

The lead should be lowered periodically so that it just touches the drawing paper when the compasses are closed and held vertically.

Wedge point   Chisel point

7 RULE

A relatively inexpensive plastic rule, similar to either of those shown below, is perfectly adequate.

It should be at least 300 millimetres long and clearly marked in millimetres and multiples of millimetres. It should be kept clean and in good condition.

A rule should be replaced if the markings become indistinct, if it is broken or becomes badly bowed through misuse, or if the long edges become badly worn, chipped or pitted.

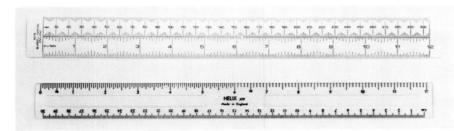

8 ERASER (RUBBER)

A good quality soft eraser will be used very frequently, especially in the early part of the study course.

It may be made of rubber or plastic. The required "softness" is determined by the surface hardness of the paper upon which it is used.

A block or "pencil" eraser can be used, the latter being probably better because the holder permits greater control.

After using the rubber for a while it will become dirty and make a mess of the drawing. It can easily be refurbished by washing it in hot, soapy water, then drying it with a clean cloth.

Rubber

Plastic

"Pencil" chuck grip plastic eraser with refill

9 BOARD CLIPS

At least two board clips, similar to those shown opposite, are required to hold the drawing sheet in place on the drawing board.

Draughting tape, masking tape or sellotape can be used instead, but the latter two, particularly, tend to peel off part of the top layer of the drawing sheet unless they are removed very carefully.

Drawing pins should NOT be used to secure the drawing sheet in position. They quickly ruin the surface of the drawing board.

10 PROTRACTOR

A protractor is required, particularly for use in plane geometry. It should be fairly large (50 mm minimum radius,) transparent and clearly marked. A suitable one is illustrated opposite.

A circular (360°) protractor, though not absolutely essential, is preferable to the standard semi-circular (180°) type.

11 INSTRUMENT CASE

A well-made, sufficiently large, lockable case or box should be acquired in which to keep all of these items and instruments conveniently and safely. They should, ideally, be kept together and they should not be slipped randomly into the nearest available plastic bag, box or pocket at the end of each drawing lesson.

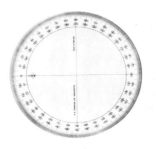

12 PUBLICATIONS

B.S. 308 : 1972 *Engineering drawing practice*
Much of parts 1 and 2 of the students' edition of this publication (often referred to as the "draughtsman's bible") is invaluable. These parts contain a great amount of basic information which must be fully mastered in order to prepare drawings correctly.

BSI PD 7308 *Engineering drawing practice for schools and colleges*
This is an abridged version of B.S.308, containing all the necessary information about engineering drawing standards that the student is likely to require. This condensed publication, very much cheaper than B.S.308, can be obtained from BSI Sales Department, 101 Pentonville Road, London N1 9ND.

Note Drawing boards, tee-squares (or drawing arms), and drawing and sketching paper, though essential, have been excluded from the list of equipment above as they are all usually provided by the school or college which the student attends.

USEFUL but NOT essential equipment

1 DRAWING BOARD

It is obviously an advantage, though not essential, for the student to own a drawing board.
It is particularly useful for doing homework quickly and accurately and also for obtaining additional drawing practice at home.
A small (A4) board, complete with drawing arm, similar to the one shown here, is ideal, for the relatively small geometrical drawings but not big enough for some of the larger machine drawings.

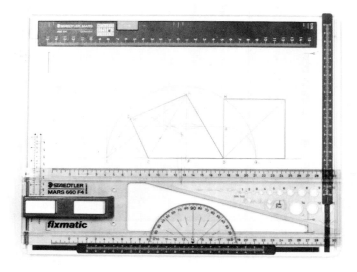

A4 Drawing Board for paper 297mm x 210mm

2 SMALL COMPASSES

An additional, small pair of compasses, or spring-bows, similar to the pairs shown here, can prove useful. They can be used for drawing accurately the very small radii (up to 5mm) occasionally required — those for which the larger compasses illustrated previously would not be suitable. They can also be a time-saver when used in conjunction with the larger pair for those constructions which require a fixed radius and a variable radius repeatedly.

3 DIVIDERS

Dividers are used as a stepping-off tool. They are used, for example, for stepping off a set distance from one view to another, accurately, or for stepping a set distance along a line several times in geometrical constructions.
Compasses can be used as a substitute for dividers to perform these tasks but they tend to leave unwanted, often untidy, pencil marks — dividers do not.
Dividers are, generally, more accurate to use and less messy.

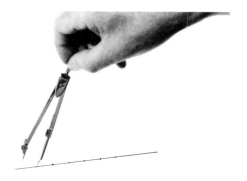

4 ERASING SHIELD

A thin metal or plastic erasing shield, a typical example of which is shown opposite, is used to try to ensure that only incorrect or unwanted lines are removed.

If a shield is not used, it is all too easy to erase not only mistakes but also adjacent features on the drawing which should be retained. This not only wastes time, for they have to be redrawn, but often looks messy.

5 RADIUS CURVES

A good quality template of radius curves is a most useful tool. It is used for drawing relatively small radii approximately to size.

It is a time-saver. It proves particularly useful for drawing small fillet radii on castings, etc., relatively quickly.

Various types and sizes are marketed. The one shown opposite is a typical medium-sized plastic template.

6 FRENCH CURVES

These plastic templates, of which there are many various shapes and sizes, are used for drawing neat, smooth curves relatively quickly — through a series of plotted points for example.

A selection is shown opposite.

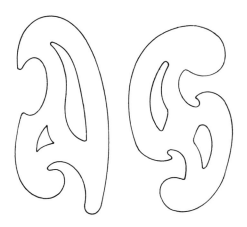

7 FLEXI-CURVE

A flexi-curve is merely a flexible plastic-coated rod. It can be used instead of French curves, since it also is used for drawing neat, smooth curves quickly. The rod is bent to the desired shape in-situ. Two typical flexi-curves are shown here.

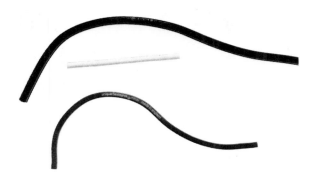

Note The drawing student should attempt to obtain every item listed above as "essential".
Without them it is not possible to prepare drawings properly.
Continually borrowing equipment from fellow students is not a good idea.
This not only wastes precious time but also disrupts the work of the other student.

CLEANLINESS Technical drawings should always be presented neatly. The student should try to keep hands and equipment clean at all times. Hands should be washed before starting to draw and also immediately after sharpening pencils. The drawing arm or tee-square should be cleaned frequently, with a clean soft cloth or by rubbing the surface periodically with clean scrap paper. The rule, protractor and set-squares should, when soiled, be washed in soapy water and carefully dried. If the drawing is left on the board for an extended period, it should be covered with a dust sheet.

Lines, Letters and Numbers

To avoid misunderstanding, all technical drawings — including geometrical and machine drawings — should be prepared using the universally accepted standards and conventional representations.

Engineering drawing practice (BS. 308 : 1972) clearly illustrates and explains both the recommended types of line (Part 1 : section 4) and lettering (Part 1 : section 5) to be used on technical drawings.

Extracts are presented in detail below.

TYPES OF LINE AND THEIR APPLICATIONS

	LINE	TYPE	COMMENTS	TYPICAL APPLICATIONS
A	————————	Thick, continuous		Final shape, or line, on a geometrical construction. Visible outlines and edges on machine drawings.
B	————————	Thin, continuous		Construction lines on both geometrical and machine drawings. Dimension, projection and leader lines. Section or hatching lines. Outlines of adjacent parts.
C	∼∼∼∼∼∼	Thin, continuous, irregular		Limits of partial views when line is not an axis.
D	– – – – – – –	Thin, short dashes. (It is NOT a *dotted* line!)	Dashes should be of consistent length and spacing, approximately to the proportion shown.	Hidden outlines and edges. Fold or bend lines.
E	—— – —— – ——	Thin chain	Should comprise long dashes alternating with short dashes — not dots! Proportions generally as shown here.	Centre lines. Extreme positions of movable parts.
F	▬— – — –▬	Chain (thick at ends and change of direction; thin elsewhere.)	Long dashes alternating with short dashes. Proportions as shown.	Cutting planes. Traces.

Typical applications of the various types of lines

(a) Plane geometry   (b) Solid geometry

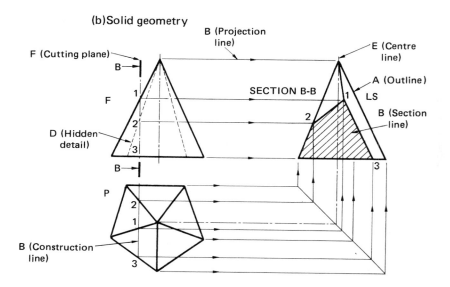

General Notes

1 All lines on a technical drawing should be of consistent density and reflectance.

2 The lines on any one drawing sheet should be entirely in pencil or entirely in ink. (The O-level student will rarely, if ever be asked to draw in ink. Biro should NEVER be used on a drawing, for either lining or printing.)

3 Each type of line should be of consistent thickness (width). Only two thicknesses of lines are recommended in B.S.308:1972 0.7 millimetres for thick lines and 0.3 millimetres for thin lines.

However, these rather precise recommended line thicknesses can reasonably be ignored by treating "thick" and "thin" merely as relative terms and making "thick" lines about two to three times thicker (wider) than "thin" lines.

All CHAIN lines should start and finish with a LONG dash. When thin chain lines are used as centre lines they should cross one another at the solid parts of the lines.

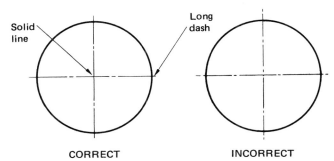

Centre lines should extend only a short distance beyond the outline of the feature.

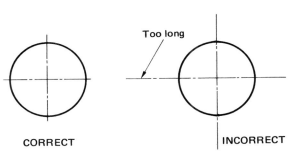

Centre lines should NOT extend through the space(s) between views.

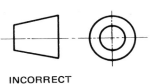

Centre lines should NOT terminate at another line on the drawing.

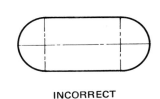

Where angles are formed with chain lines, the LONG dashes should meet at the corners.

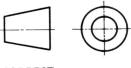

The dashes in dashed lines should also meet at the corner.

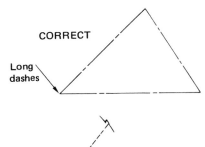

Where a dashed line or chain line meets a full line the dash should touch the full line, as shown.

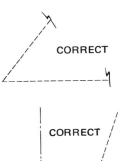

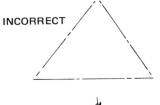

7

Note Neat, correct linework of consistent thickness is difficult to achieve in the early stages of a technical drawing course. Typical errors made by students with little drawing experience are illustrated in the view immediately below.

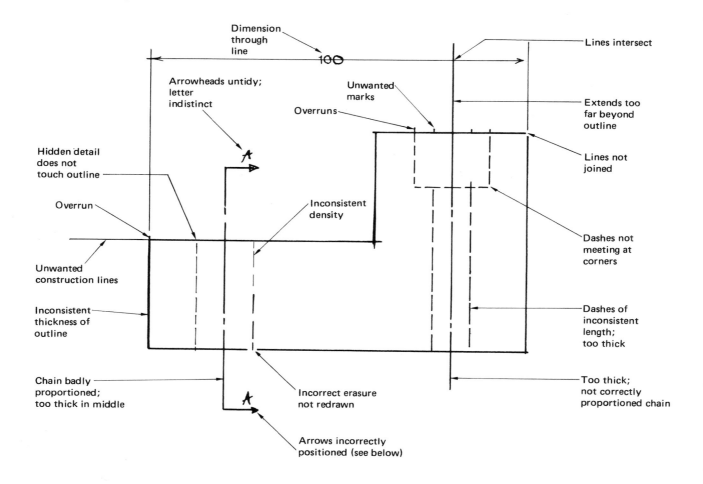

Frequent "lining" practice is essential in the first few weeks of a course.
A "corrected" view, with comments, is presented below to reinforce the "rules" of linework detailed previously.

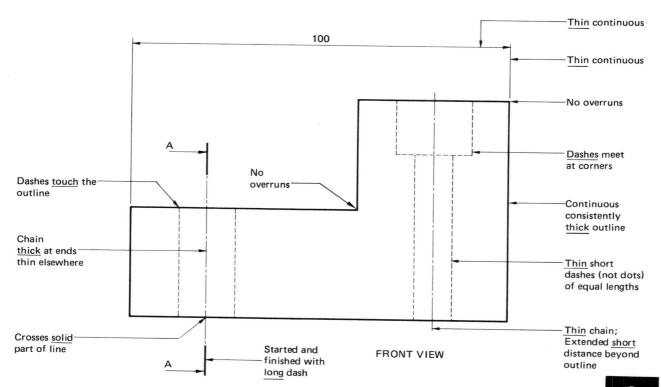

FRONT VIEW

LETTERS and NUMBERS

Printing is generally more legible than handwriting. All lettering on drawings should, therefore, be printed.

Characters — letters and numbers — should be uniform, i.e. style, height and spacing should, ideally, be identical on drawings sheets of the same size.

It is helpful to print between feint, suitably spaced parallel guide lines in the early stages to practice uniformity of lettering and numbering.

Characters should be printed clearly and sufficiently large so that they remain legible when photo-copied ("printed" in draughtsman's terminology).

Clarity, style, size and spacing are all important when lettering and/or numbering. Characters should be of open form for maximum clarity, i.e. they should be devoid of serifs (cross-lines) and other embellishments, e.g.

A	not	*A*		1	not	*1*	
B	not	*B*		2	not	*2*	etc.

Characters should be of consistent density, compatible with the associated line work on the drawing. The thickness (width) of the characters should be approximately the same as that of the outlines on the drawing. The letters in the title may, perhaps, be a little thicker than those on the drawing for they are usually slightly larger.

No particular style is recommended for use on technical drawings. The primary aim is to produce legible and unambiguous characters. Either vertical or sloping characters are acceptable but whichever style is used it should be consistent on any drawing. Vertical AND sloping characters should NOT be used on the same drawing. The vertical style is probably the better one to use as this presents no problems about varying slopes.

Use either vertical characters   DRILL JIG
                                                a b c d
                                                1 2 3 4

or uniformly sloping characters   *DRILL JIG*   but NOT   DRILL *JI*G
                                         a b c d   a mixture   a *b* c d
                                           1 2 3 4   *1 2* 3 4

Generally, upper-case (capital) letters are used on technical diagrams, sketches and drawings in preference to lower-case letters as they are less congested and also less likely to be misread when reduced in size by photo-copying. Lower-case letters can be used, for example, to designate the sides of triangles, to label lines in true length of line constructions, etc.

Minimum character heights are recommended in B.S. 308 : 1972 (Part 1, 5 : 3) in some detail. They are dependent upon the application and the size of the drawing sheet used. They need not be memorized or adhered to rigidly, merely serving as a guide.

Generally speaking, if all letters and numbers on the drawing can be easily "read", even after photo-copying, then height and spacing is satisfactory.

To facilitate the reading of drawings, all notes (lettering) and dimensions (numbering) should be placed so that they can be easily read when looking from the bottom right-hand corner, or right-hand side of the drawing sheet, as shown opposite.

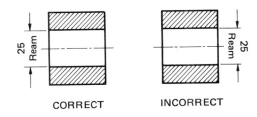

CORRECT   INCORRECT

Untidy, indistinct lettering and numbering can spoil an otherwise well prepared drawing. The aim is to produce a neat clear and, of course, correct drawing. Draughtsman's instructions (views, lettering, numbering etc.) must NOT be misunderstood by anyone reading the drawing. Ambiguity cannot be tolerated.

Note Intensive practice is usually necessary in the early stages of a technical drawing course if the art of lettering and numbering both legibly and rapidly is to be mastered.

Lines used in Geometrical Drawing

General note:

It is important that the lines used in geometrical drawing are always referred to correctly.
The following definitions are a useful addition to the vocabulary needed to describe and comprehend geometrical constructions.

Definitions:

Straight line: A line which lies between two points and does not deviate in any way.

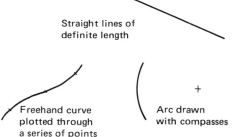

Straight lines of definite length

Curved line: A line of which no part is straight. It may be formed by an arc or a series of joining radii.
A curve is often formed by joining together a number of points freehand or by using a french curve.

Freehand curve plotted through a series of points

Arc drawn with compasses

Horizontal line: A straight line which is parallel to the ground (or level with the horizon).

Horizontal line

Vertical line: A straight line which is at 90° to the ground (or 90° to the horizon).

Vertical line

Perpendicular: A straight line which forms an angle of 90° with another straight line. In each case shown on the right, the lines marked OP are perpendiculars and should not be confused with vertical lines.

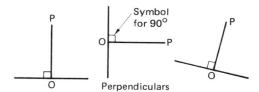

Symbol for 90°

Perpendiculars

Oblique line: A straight line which is neither horizontal nor vertical.

Oblique lines

Diagonal line: A straight line which is drawn between opposite corners of a plane figure.

Diagonal

Parallel lines: Lines which are always the same distance apart. They may be straight or curved.
Arrowheads are frequently used to indicate that lines are parallel to each other.

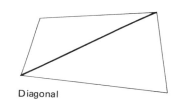

Parallel straight lines

Parallel curved lines

Converging lines: Straight lines which meet at a common point if extended far enough as shown on the right. AB and CD are converging on O.

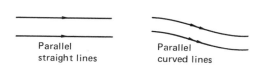

Converging lines

Diverging lines: Straight lines which will never meet when extended from a common point.
AB and CD are diverging away from O.

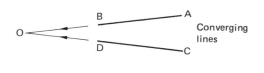

Diverging lines

Basic Line Constructions

General Note The following examples include several line constructions which may be carried out either by using 45°, 60° and adjustable set-squares, or geometrically. The latter method should be used whenever possible to ensure accuracy. For examination purposes, set squares may be used for line constructions unless the question states otherwise.

A. GEOMETRICAL CONSTRUCTIONS

1. To draw a perpendicular from a point P on a given straight line AB.

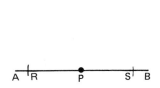

Draw line AB and from a given point P on AB set out equal arcs of any radius to R and S.

From R and S set out equal arcs of any radius to intersect at C.
Join CP. ∠SPC = 90°.

2. To draw a perpendicular from a point P on a given straight line AB.

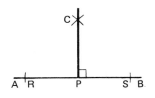 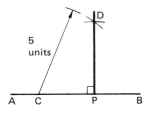

From P set out 3 units of length, PC, along AB. With centre P draw an arc of radius 4 units.

With centre C, draw an arc, 5 units radius, to intersect the 4 unit arc at D. Join PD to obtain the perpendicular.

3. To draw a perpendicular from a point P to a given straight line AB.

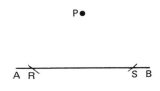 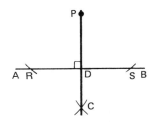

From the given point P set out equal arcs of any radius to cut the given line at R and S.

From R and S set out equal arcs of any radius to intersect at C. Join PC.

4. To draw a perpendicular from a point P to a given straight line AB.

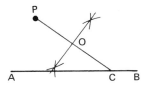 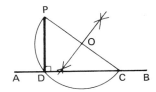

Draw a line from P to any point C on line AB. Bisect PC at O.

With centre O and radius OP draw a semi-circle on PC cutting line AB at D. Join PD to obtain the perpendicular.

5. To draw a perpendicular from a point P on the end of a given straight line.

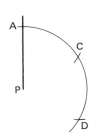 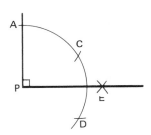

With centre P set out an arc of any suitable radius PA.
Set out an arc of the same radius from A to C and from C to D.

From C and D set out equal arcs to intersect at E. Join PE to obtain the perpendicular.

6. To draw the perpendicular bisector of a given straight line AB.

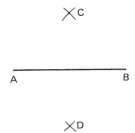 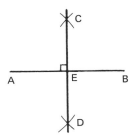

From A and B draw equal arcs of any suitable radius to intersect at C and D.

Join CD to cut AB at E to obtain the perpendicular bisector.

All the above constructions are useful for setting out lines at right angles to each other but number 2 is used extensively in practical situations. For example, when marking out large fabrications, setting out foundations for buildings, surveying offsets and even for marking out football pitches when a 30m, 40m, 50m triangle ensures square corners and accuracy.

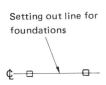

Setting out line for foundations

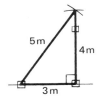

11

7. To draw a line parallel to a given line AB at a given distance d from it.

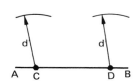 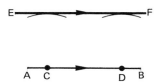

From two suitable points C and D on line AB draw arcs equal to the required distance d.

Draw a line EF tangential to the two arcs to obtain a line parallel to AB.

8. To draw a line through a given point P and parallel to a given straight line AB.

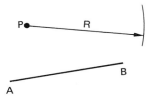 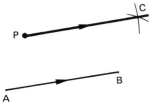

From P set out an arc, R, equal in length to the given line AB.

From B set out an arc, radius equal to AP, to cut the first arc at C. Join PC.

B. SET-SQUARE CONSTRUCTIONS

A set-square should be checked for accuracy before it is used for setting out lines at 90° to each other. The adjoining sketch shows how an error can be recognized.

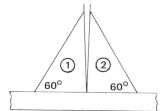

Draw a vertical line with the set-square in position ①. Turn the set-square over and repeat in position ②. If the two lines do not lie on each other, the angle is not 90°.

9. To draw a perpendicular bisector to a given line AB using a straight-edge and a set-square.

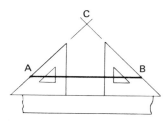 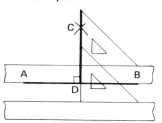

Ensure that the straight edge is parallel to the given line AB.
From A and B draw lines with the set-square to meet at C.

Draw, with the set-square, a vertical line passing through C. DC is the required perpendicular bisector of AB.

10. To draw lines perpendicular to a given line AB using a straight-edge and set-square

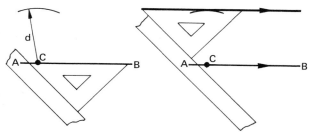 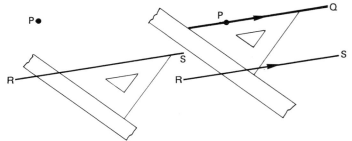

(a) Set a straight-edge slightly below the given line AB and slide a set-square until it is in the required position to draw the perpendicular CD.

(b) Move the set-square until it lines up with the line AB. Then slide it along the straight-edge until it is in the required position to draw the perpendicular CD.

(c) Move the set-square on the straight-edge up to the line AB, then revolve it around its 90° corner. Slide it along the straight-edge so that the required perpendicular may be drawn along CD.

Blade of tee-square

11. To draw a line parallel to and at a distance d from a given straight line AB using a set-square.

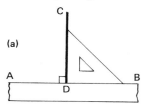 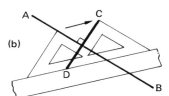

From a suitable point C on AB draw an arc equal to the required distance, d. Place a set-square on AB as shown.

Slide the set-square along the straight-edge and up to the arc. Draw a line tangential to the arc and hence parallel to and distance d from AB.

12. To draw a line parallel to a given straight line RS and passing through a given point P using a set-square.

Position the tee-square so that one edge of the set-square lines up with the given line RS.

Slide the set-square along the tee-square up to point P. Draw line PQ parallel to RS.

C. DIVISION OF LINES

When a straight line lies across a series of parallel straight lines the following is true:

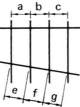

If a = b = c
Then e = f = g

In the figure on the right, the distances between the parallel lines are not equal.

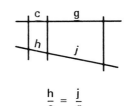

$$\frac{h}{c} = \frac{j}{g}$$

The following constructions are based on the above geometrical principles.

EQUAL PARTS

13. **To divide a given straight line AB into a number of equal parts (say 6)**

Method 1

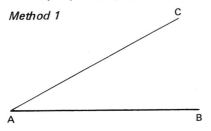

Draw a line AC at any angle to AB (but not *too* acute an angle). A set-square angle (60° 30° or 45°) can be used to save time.

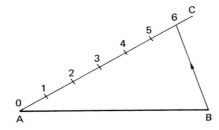

Set out 6 equal divisions along AC using a scale, spring-bows or dividers. Join B to 6.

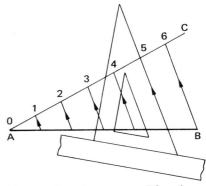

Line up the set-square on B6 and then draw lines parallel to B6 through each division in turn, as shown.

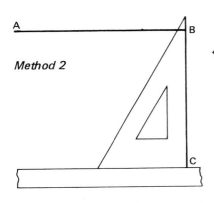

Method 2

Draw a vertical line, BC, at one end of the given line AB.

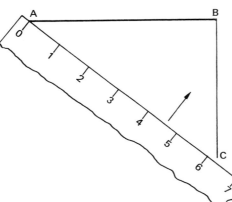

Set the 0 value of a scale on the other end of the line, A, and swing the scale towards BC.

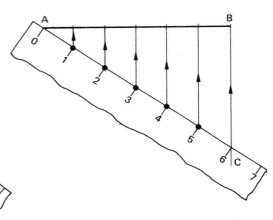

Locate the 6 scale divisions on BC and mark the points 1 to 5. Draw vertical lines from these points to divide AB into 6 equal parts.

DIVISION OF LINES – PRACTICAL APPLICATIONS

To divide the distance between two parallel lines into a given number of equal parts (say 7).

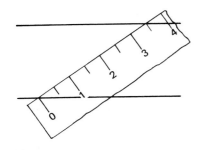

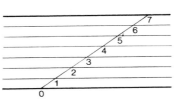

To set out the pitch lengths of a compression spring when represented diagrammatically.

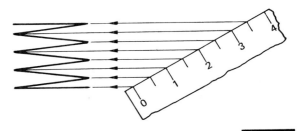

PROPORTIONAL PARTS

14. To divide a given straight line AB in a given ratio, say 4 : 3.

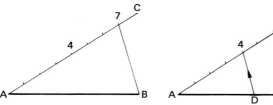

Draw AC at any angle to AB and mark off
A - 4 = 4 equal parts
4 - 7 = 3 equal parts
(A total of 7 equal divisions).
Join 7 to B.

Draw 4 - D parallel to 7 - B.

$$\frac{AD}{DB} = \frac{4}{3}$$

15. To extend a given straight line AB in a given ratio, say 7:5

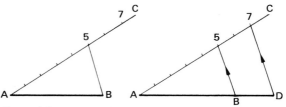

Draw AC at any angle and mark off
A - 5 = 5 equal parts
5 - 7 = 2 equal parts
(A total of 7 equal divisions).
Join 5 to B.

Extend line AB.
Draw 7 - D parallel to 5 - B

$$\frac{AD}{AB} = \frac{7}{5}$$

16. To divide a line AB into a given number of proportional parts, say 3, 2, 4.

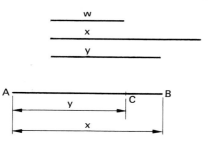

Draw a straight line, CD, at a convenient distance from and parallel to AB.

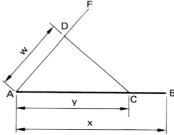

Set off 3, 2 and 4 units with a scale as shown (a total of 9 units).
In this case 1 unit is represented by 0.5 cm.
Join 0 to A and 9 to B and extend the lines to intersect at E.

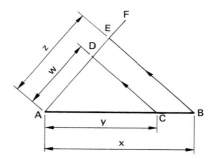

Draw lines from E, through AB to 3 and 5 to obtain the required proportional parts on AB.

Note: In surveying this construction may be utilized to plot contour lines.

17. To construct a fourth proportional, of length z, to three given lines of length w, x and y.

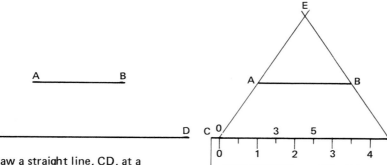

Draw line AB = x and on AB mark off AC = y

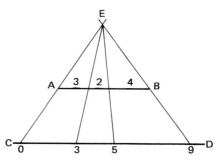

Draw line AF at any angle to AB.
Mark off AD = w.
Join CD.

Draw a line from B parallel to CD to meet AF at E.
AE is the 4th proportional.

$$\frac{y}{x} = \frac{w}{z}.$$

Note: In the above construction the ratios $\frac{y}{x} = \frac{w}{z}$ may be expressed in different ways.

a)   In words,   y is to x as w is to z.

b)   In the form   y : x : : w : z
                    means
                  └─extremes─┘

18. **To find the third proportional, of length c, to two lines of lengths a and b.**

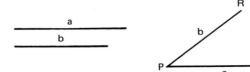

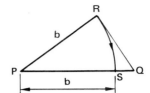

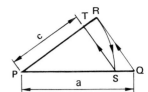

Set out PQ = a.
Draw PR = b at any acute angle to PQ.

With centre P draw an arc of radius b to meet PQ at S.
Join RQ.

Draw a line from S parallel to RQ to meet PR in T.
PT is the third proportional length c.

The result of this construction is that $\dfrac{a}{b} = \dfrac{b}{c}$

a : b : : b : c

b is common to both ratios and is referred to as the *mean proportional* between a and c.
Notice that a x c = b^2

19. **To divide a line, length a, in extreme and mean ratios.**

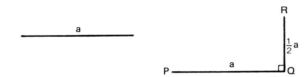

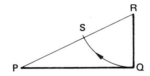

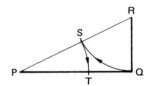

Draw PQ = length a.
Draw QR at 90° to PQ and equal to $\frac{1}{2}$ a.

Join PR.
With centre R draw an arc of radius RQ to cut PR in S.

With centre P draw an arc of radius PS to cut PQ in T.

The result of this construction is that
    PQ : PT : : PT : TQ
where PT is the mean proportional between PQ and TQ.

20. **To find the mean proportional between two given lines of lengths a and b.**

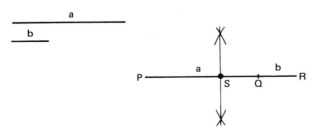

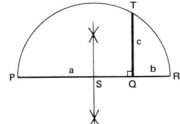

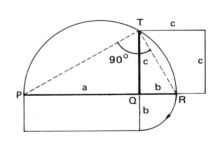

Set out a straight line
PR = a + b.
Bisect PR in S.

With centre S draw a semi-circle on line PR.
Draw a perpendicular at Q to meet the semi-circle at T.
PQ : QT : : QT : RQ
or a : c : : c : b

Note: QT (c) is the mean proportional between PQ and RQ.
It is also known as the *geometric mean*.

The ratios can be written
    $\dfrac{a}{c} = \dfrac{c}{b}$ or ab = c^2

This means that the rectangle drawn on a is equal in area to the square drawn on c.
Notice that angle PTR = 90° (angle in a semi-circle).

Note: This construction using the geometric mean is frequently used in problems relating to areas. (See p. 46).

Construction and Use of Scales

The use of a scale for any kind of drawing or diagram is made necessary by the simple fact that the component being represented is usually either too large or too small to be shown on the limited sizes of paper available. The choice of a suitable scale depends on a number of factors, but, in general:

1. Objects and diagrams should be drawn full size whenever possible.
2. Very large objects in engineering, buildings in architecture, surveys and topographical features need to be scaled down but nevertheless, should be drawn on as large a standard size drawing sheet as is practical, convenient and economical. Normally the scale should be one recommended in British Standards, for example B.S. 308 and B.S. 1192, but it may be necessary of course to use scales other than these.
3. The marking of the scale should conform to the recommendations of B.S. 1347.
4. Very small components need to be scaled up using, wherever possible, the recommended multipliers of 2, 5 and 10.

Note   1. The scale of the drawing should *always* be stated in an appropriate manner.
2. Lengths and distances should not normally be scaled or measured from a drawing or a plan. Sizes may be altered without the drawing itself being modified and, in the case of old drawings and plans, shrinkage of the paper may have occurred. It is fair to say, however, that maps produced by the Ordnance Survey are usually very accurate and thus permit scaling.

The student should be able to construct and use two types of scale — the PLAIN scale and the DIAGONAL scale — and, in addition, be able to demonstrate understanding of the term   Representative Fraction, usually abbreviated R.F. Each of these topics is dealt with in this section.

PLAIN SCALES
Full Size (designated 1:1)

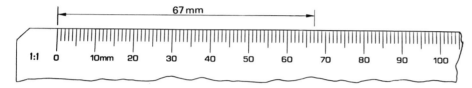

The scale shown on the left is FULLY-DIVIDED, i.e. divided into the smallest sub-division along its whole length.
It has two main divisions: mm and multiples of 10 mm.
Multiples of 5 mm are indicated but not actually labelled.
The mm symbol states the unit of the scale.

A convenient method of stating the ratio of a scale is by its REPRESENTATIVE FRACTION (R.F.) which is found as follows:

Representative Fraction = $\dfrac{\text{Drawn size of component}}{\text{Actual size of component}}$ For a FULL SIZE scale   R.F. = $\frac{1}{1}$ or 1 : 1

For a HALF SIZE scale   R.F. = $\frac{1}{2}$ or 1 : 2

The scale shown above is accurate to 1 mm, any fraction of a mm having to be judged by eye. Full size scales may be purchased, with each millimetre sub-divided into 2 parts of 0.5 mm each as shown below.

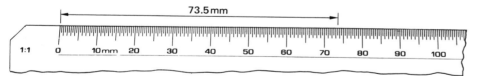

Note On manufactured METRIC scales the 0 position is always on the left of the scale.

To construct a scale to measure FULL-SIZE in millimetres up to 100 mm.

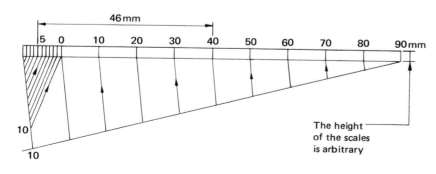

The height of the scales is arbitrary

> *The scales presented in this section are for illustration only.*
> *The dimensions shown may be read as correct but lengths may be slightly inaccurate due to photographic distortion.*

A full size scale would not normally be constructed — a ruler could be used to draw full size.
This one has been drawn, however, to illustrate the method of construction.
The scale shown on the left is called an OPEN DIVIDED scale. It consists of 10 mm divisions from 0 mm to 90 mm and only the last division to the left of 0 mm being sub-divided into 1 mm divisions. This is also referred to as the ARMSTRONG pattern.
Notice that the r.h. end division is labelled 90 mm and not 100 mm.

Draw a line 100 mm long and divide it into 10 equal parts.
Divide the l.h. 10 mm division into 10 equal parts, geometrically, and with great care, number the divisions as shown.

REDUCTION PLAIN SCALES

These scales are used to draw components that are too large to be drawn full size on the largest available standard drawing sheet. In the metric system, the recommended scale divisors are 2, 5 and 10. This means that each 1 mm unit on the scale represents 2 mm, 5 mm, 10 mm respectively. The ratio of each scale is clearly marked in each case and the mm or m symbol indicates the unit of measurement.

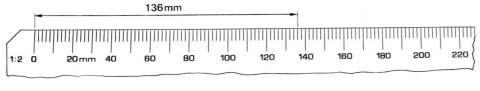

Scale 1 : 2
R.F. = $\frac{1}{2}$ ($\frac{1}{2}$ full size)

1 mm represents 2 mm

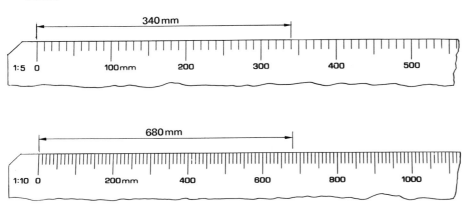

Scale 1 : 5
R.F. = $\frac{1}{5}$ ($\frac{1}{5}$ th full size)

Note the smallest sub-division is 2 mm representing 10 mm.

Scale 1 : 10
R.F. = $\frac{1}{10}$ ($\frac{1}{10}$ th full size)

1 mm represents 10 mm

To construct a reduction scale of 1 : 5 to measure to 10 mm, up to a length of 600 mm.

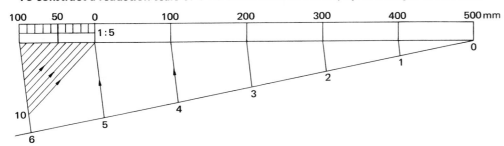

Scale 1 : 5 R.F. = $\frac{1}{5}$
Note there are 2 basic units: 100 mm and 10 mm

Divide the maximum length of 600 mm by 5 (= 120 mm). Draw a line 120 mm long and divide it into 6 equal parts, geometrically.
Divide the l.h. end division into 10 equal parts, each to represent 10 mm.

Note The small divisions are 2 mm each in length and could, of course, be marked out with a ruler rather than geometrically. The Armstrong pattern is preferred because it would be a tedious and lengthy process to sub-divide the whole length of the scale. Notice that the r.h. end division is labelled **500** and not **600**.

COMBINED REDUCTION SCALES

Many commercially produced scales economize by showing two different scales on one set of divisions as shown in the examples below. Care must be taken not to confuse the scales.

Scales 1 : 10 and 1 : 100

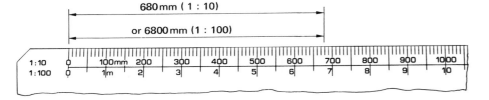

Scale 1 : 10 R.F. = $\frac{1}{10}$
1 mm represents 10 mm on the upper scale.

Scale 1 : 100 R.F. = $\frac{1}{100}$
1 mm represents 100 mm on the lower scale.

The following combined reduction scales are also to be found on the same scale rule as the 1 : 10 and 1 : 100

| 1:20 | 0 | 200mm 400 | 600 |
| 1:200 | 0 | 2 m   4 | 6 |

| 1:5 | 0 | 100mm |
| 1:50 | 0 | 1 m |

| 1:500 | 0 | 5 m 10 | 15 |
| 1:1000 | 0 | 10 m 20 | 30 |

R.F.s $\frac{1}{20}$ and $\frac{1}{200}$

R.F.s $\frac{1}{5}$ and $\frac{1}{50}$

R.F.s $\frac{1}{500}$ and $\frac{1}{1000}$

All the reduction scales shown so far are based on what are fundamentally 1 mm divisions with the appropriate values of multiples of millimetres clearly displayed. There are, however, a number of reduction scales, commonly used for construction site plans and maps for which the sub-divisions are *not* in millimetres.

Scales 1 : 1250 and 1 : 2500

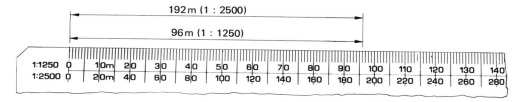

R.F.s $\frac{1}{1250}$ and $\frac{1}{2500}$
These scales are used for distances in metres.

Two further scales which are also used by the Ordinance Survey are the 1 : 1000 and 1 : 10560 (still retained, 6 inches to 1 mile).

ENLARGEMENT PLAIN SCALES

These are used to draw very small components larger than their actual size, enabling them to be visualised more clearly and dimensioned more easily. The recommended scale multiples are 2, 5 and 10. This means that each 1 mm unit on the scale represents 0.5mm, 0.2mm and 0.1mm respectively.

Enlargement scales are not normally manufactured. Enlarged sizes may be obtained simply by multiplying by the required factor and drawing with a full size scale. Scales may, of course, be constructed geometrically.

To construct an enlargement plain scale 2 x full size to measure to the nearest millimetre, up to 60 mm.

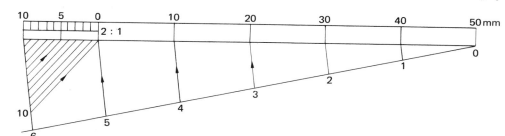

Scale 2 :1 R.F. = $\frac{2}{1}$
1mm represents 0.5mm.
Note: The smallest sub-division is 2mm.
There are 2 basic units:
10mm and 1mm.

Multiply the maximum size of 60 by 2 (=120mm). Draw a line 120mm long and divide it into 6 equal parts.
Divide the l.h. end division into 10 equal parts, each to represent 1mm. Label the divisions as shown.

Note   1. The divisions of this scale are *exactly* the same as the 1 : 5 reduction scale so it is important that the scale and its units be clearly marked, as shown, to avoid any misunderstanding.
2. If the l.h. end division were to be sub-divided further into 20 parts, then the scale would be used to measure the 0.5mm, i.e. a *third* unit.

DIAGONAL SCALES

The name of this type of scale is derived from the use of a diagonal line to divide the l.h. end division of the scale into the required number of parts. The DIAGONAL scale shown below could be used as an alternative to the PLAIN scale shown above. Both could be used to measure 2 x full size in 10mm units and 1mm sub-units, i.e. in TWO basic units only.

To construct a diagonal scale 2 x full size to measure to the nearest millimetre, up to 60mm

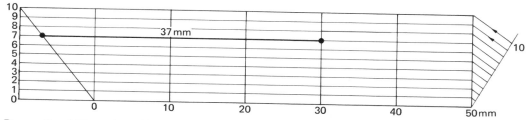

Note the 10 equal divisions on the r.h. end perpendicular may be more readily marked out with a ruler.

Draw a line 120mm long (2 x 60) and divide into 6 equal parts as shown previously.
Draw a perpendicular at the r.h. end of the line and mark out *any* convenient height — its length is arbitrary.
Divide the perpendicular into 10 equal parts and draw lines parallel to the original line.
Draw further perpendiculars to complete a grid as shown.
Draw a diagonal line across the l.h. end division and number as shown. As the diagonal crosses 10 equal spaces, it effectively divides the l.h. end division into 10 equal parts.
Dimensions are taken off the appropriate horizontal line with compasses or dividers, e.g. 37mm as shown.

A diagonal scale is most useful when a greater degree of accuracy in measurement is required, i.e. when a third unit or sub-unit is added to the scale. In the Armstrong pattern 2 : 1 plain scale on the previous page, it was noted that a third unit (0.5mm) could be obtained by further division of the l.h. end but this would be a tedious exercise. On a 2 : 1 diagonal scale, a third unit is achieved by one of the constructions shown below.

To construct a diagonal scale 2 x full size to measure to 0.5mm, up to 40mm

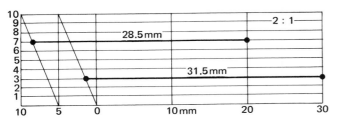

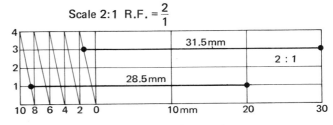

28.5 is made up of (2 x 10) + (1 x 5) + (7 x 0.5) units

31.5 is made up of (3 x 10) + (3 x 0.5) units

A modified 2 unit scale
Multiply the maximum required size (40mm) by 2 (=80mm).
Draw a line 80mm long.
Divide this line into 4 equal parts and sub-divide the l.h. end division into 2 equal parts.
Draw a perpendicular and divide it into 10 equal parts as before. Draw lines parallel to the original 80mm line.
Draw diagonal lines across each l.h. end division and number as shown.

An alternative construction
Draw a line 80mm long and divide it into 4 equal parts
Sub-divide the l.h. end division into 5 equal parts.
Draw a perpendicular and divide it into 4 equal parts.
Draw lines parallel to the original 80mm line.
Draw diagonal lines across each l.h. end sub-division, and number as shown.

Note In both cases, extreme care must be taken in selecting the correct line from which to take off the required dimension with compasses or dividers. It should be clear that the 3-unit diagonal scale is more accurate than either a 2 unit diagonal scale or a plain scale. A diagonal scale may also be used, of course, to construct an accurate reduction scale.

To construct a diagonal reduction scale of 1 : 5 to measure to 5mm, up to 600mm (R.F. = $\frac{1}{5}$)

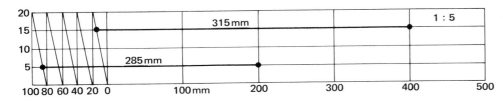

285 is made up of (2 x 100) + (4 x 20) + (1 x 5) units

Note The divisions on this scale are *exactly* the same size as those on the 2 : 1 enlargement scale shown above. It is the stated ratios and actual division markings that distinguish them.
There are 3 basic units marked on this scale: 100mm, 20mm, and 5mm. The 10mm division is at the mid-point of each diagonal line.

Divide the maximum required size (600mm) by 5 (= 120mm).
Draw a line 120mm long and divide it into 6 equal divisions.
Draw a perpendicular at the r.h. end of the line. Divide it into 4 equal parts and draw lines parallel to the original 120mm line.
Draw further perpendiculars to complete the grid as shown.
Divide the l.h. end division into 5 equal parts. Draw diagonal lines across each sub-division and number as shown.

Metric Scales — a Summary
This summary is included to show the range of scales available and the fields in which they are used.

Scale to B.S. 1347				Used in	Nearest Imperial Equivalent	Preferred Metric
1	1 : 1		1 : 2	Mechanical and	Full Size	1 : 1
	1 : 5		1 : 10	production engineering	Half Size	1 : 2
					2″ to 1 ft (1 : 6)	1 : 5
2	1 : 5	1 : 50	1 : 10 1 : 100	Engineering, shipbuilding	1″ to 1 ft (1 : 12)	1 : 10
	1 : 20	1 : 200	1 : 500 1 : 1000	architecture	$\frac{1}{2}$″ (1 : 24)	1 : 20
					$\frac{1}{4}$″ (1 : 48)	1 : 50
3	1 : 1	1 : 100	1 : 20 1 : 200	Architecture, quantity	$\frac{1}{8}$″ (1 : 96)	1 : 100
	1 : 5	1 : 50	1 : 1250 1 : 2500	surveyors	$\frac{1}{16}$″ (1 : 192)	1 : 200
					1 : 500	1 : 500
						1 : 1000
4	1 : 1250 1 : 2500		1 : 10000 1 : 10560*	Land surveys, planners	1 : 1250	1 : 1250
	(Ordnance Survey ratios)			*included until all	1 : 2500	1 : 2500
				6″ to 1 mile maps replaced.	1 : 10560 (6″ to 1 mile)	1 : 10000

Angles and their Construction

Definitions When two straight lines are drawn from the same point, they are said to contain a **plane angle**. The straight lines are called the *arms* of the angle and the point is called the **vertex**. The symbol used to represent an angle is $\angle$, e.g. $\angle ABC$ when B is at the vertex.

Right angle

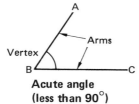

Acute angle
(less than 90°)

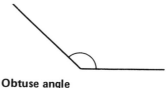

Obtuse angle
(between 90° and 180°)

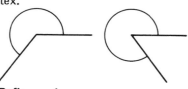

Reflex angles
(between 180° and 360°)

$\angle a$ and $\angle b$ are referred to as **adjacent angles**.

$\angle c + \angle d = 90°$ and are referred to as **complementary angles**.

$\angle x + \angle y = 180°$ and are referred to as **supplementary angles**.

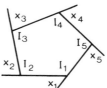

In a polygon angles x_1, x_2, x_3 are **exterior angles**. Angles l_1, l_2, l_3 are **interior angles**.

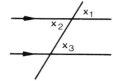

When a straight line cuts two parallel lines
$\angle x_1 = \angle x_2$ - **opposite angles**
$\angle x_2 = \angle x_3$ - **alternate angles**
$\angle x_1 = \angle x_3$ - **corresponding angles**

To bisect a given angle

a) When the arms of the angle meet at a point

With centre A set out equal arcs to cut the arms of the angle at B and C.

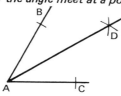

With centres B and C set out equal arcs to meet at D. Line AD bisects the angle.

b) When the arms do not meet at a point.

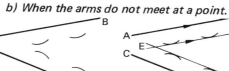

From points on AB and CD draw equal arcs.

Draw lines parallel to AB and CD and meeting at E.

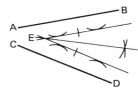

Bisect the angle at E.

To construct angles by continuous bisection

1

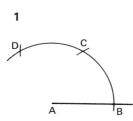

From A draw an arc of convenient radius AB. From B set out the same arc to C and again from C to D.

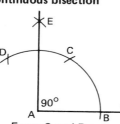

From C and D set out equal arcs to meet at E. Join AE. $\angle BAE = 90°$ This is the standard construction for a right angle.

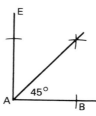

Bisect $\angle BAE$ to obtain an angle of 45°.

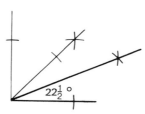

Bisect the 45° angle to obtain an angle of $22\frac{1}{2}°$.

Note: This method has limitations but may be useful for dividing a circle into 4, 8, 16, 32 or even 64 parts.

2

From A draw an arc of convenient radius AB. From B set out the same arc to C.

Join AC. $\angle BAC = 60°$. This is the standard construction for a 60° angle.

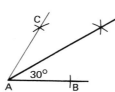

Bisect $\angle BAC$ to obtain an angle of 30°.

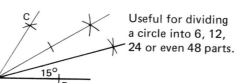

Bisect the 30° angle to obtain an angle of 15°.

Useful for dividing a circle into 6, 12, 24 or even 48 parts.

To copy a given angle using compasses.

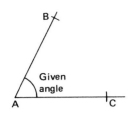 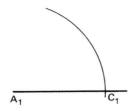 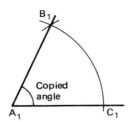

Note:
This construction becomes less accurate.
1. as an acute angle becomes smaller.
2. as an obtuse angle becomes larger.

From the vertex of the given angle draw any convenient arc to meet the arms of the given angle at B and C.

Draw a straight line and from one end A_1 draw an arc of radius AC.

From C_1 set out arc of radius CB to cut the first arc in B_1
Join $A_1 B_1$ to give $\angle B_1 A_1 C_1 = \angle BAC$

To trisect an angle of 90°

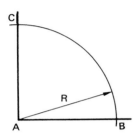 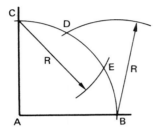 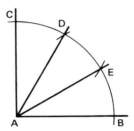

Draw an angle of 90°.
From the vertex A draw an arc of convenient radius R to cut the arms of the angle at B and C.

With centres B and C, draw arcs of radius R to cut the arc BC at D and E respectively.

Join AD and AE.
$\angle CAD = \angle DAE = \angle EAB = 30°$

To draw angles using a 60°/30° set-square.

The 60°/30° set-square can be used to draw angles of 30°, 60°, 120°, 150°, 210°, 240°, 300°, 330° and, of course, 90°.
In each case the line drawn with the set-square must be related to a point, O, and another straight line, usually either a horizontal axis X, or a vertical axis Y. The angle may be read clockwise or anti-clockwise from the given axis.

The following sketches illustrate how 9 different angles may be obtained with a single 60°/30° set-square.
Note that, when two lines intersect, opposite angles are equal.

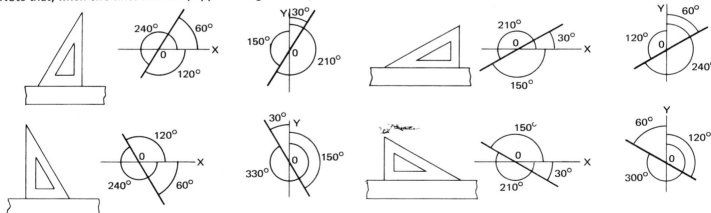

To draw angles using a 45° set-square.

The 45° set-square can be used to draw angles of 45°, 135°, 225°, 315° and 90°.

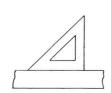 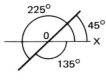 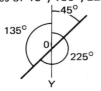 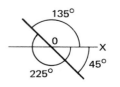 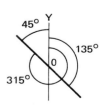

To draw angles using 60° and 45° set-squares combined.

The angles of the 45° and 60° set-squares are all multiples of 15° and they can be used together to construct angles which are also multiples of 15°. These extra angles, which can be drawn from either a horizontal or vertical axis, are:

15°   75°   105°   165°   195°   255°   285°   345°

The examples below illustrate how several of these may be obtained. Only two basic positions of the set-squares are required.

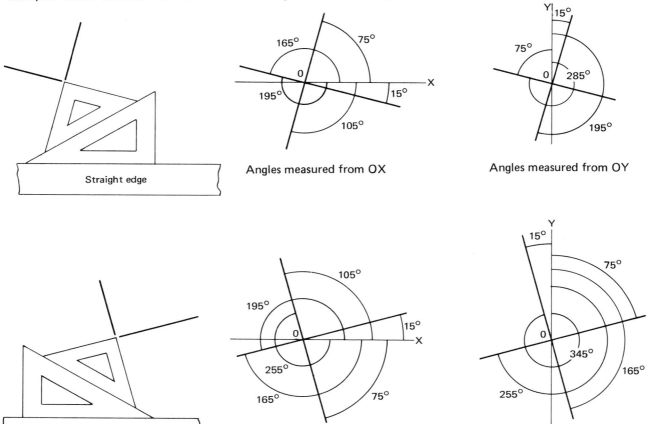

Straight edge   Angles measured from OX   Angles measured from OY

Straight edge   Angles measured from OX   Angles measured from OY

To draw angles using an adjustable set-square
Most adjustable set-squares are accurate to $\frac{1}{2}°$ but extreme care must be taken when reading the quadrant scale since it is double-marked. Because of the tightening screw, the square cannot be turned over to obtain identical angles in adjacent quadrants.

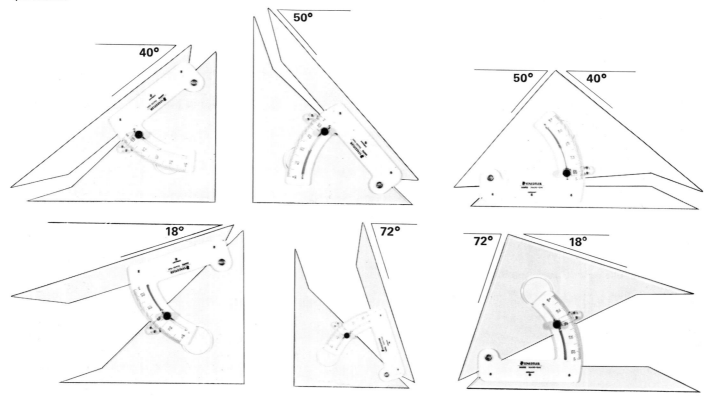

To construct a scale of chords for use in setting out angles.

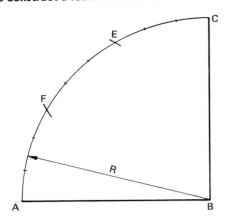

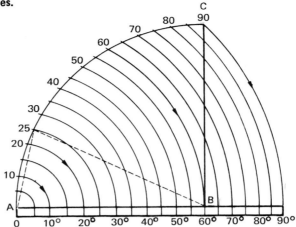

Draw a line AB of any convenient length.
With centre B draw an arc of radius R=BA.
Draw a line at 90° to AB to meet the arc at C.
Trisect the 90° angle.
Divide each of the 30° sectors into three equal parts by stepping off equal chords along the arc to divide the quadrant ABC into 10° sectors.

With centre A draw arcs of radii A10, A20, A30, etc to meet AB.
Note that the radius A60 = AB and represents an angle of 60° on the horizontal scale.
Points 70, 80 and 90 are swung down from the arc to the horizontal scale to meet AB extended.
Label the horizontal division 0° — 90°
The scale can be sub-divided into 5° divisions as shown if required.

Note: The range of a scale of chords can be further extended if the 0° — 60° radius is increased sufficiently to allow the arc AC to be sub-divided into single degrees.

To draw an angle of 25° using the above scale of chords.

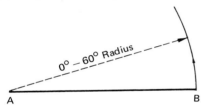

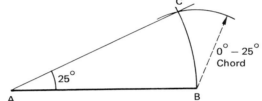

Draw a straight line AB equal in length to the 0° — 60° radius.
With centre A draw an arc of radius AB.

With centre B draw an arc with radius equal to the 0° — 25° chord (taken from the scale of chords) to cut the 0° — 60° arc at C. Join AC. ∠BAC = 25°.

Note: This is basically the same construction as for copying a given angle.

To set out angles using trigonometrical ratios.

This method is extremely accurate if the triangles used are drawn to a large enough scale. It is used, for example, for the accurate layout of large items of structural steelwork and for setting out certain angles in surveying. To enable the arms of the required angles to be set out to a convenient size, it is necessary to multiply the numbers derived from trigonometric tables by a suitable factor, e.g. 10 as used in the examples below.

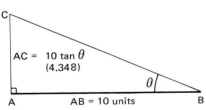

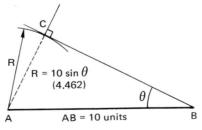

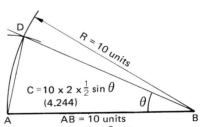

To set out an angle of 21° 30' using the TANGENT.
Look up tan 21°30' = 0.4348
Multiply 0.4348 by 10 to give AC = 4.348
Set out AB = 10 units
Set out AC = 4.348 units at 90° to AB
Join BC. ∠ABC = 21°30'.

To set out an angle of 26°30' using the SINE.
Find sine 26°30' = 0.4462
Multiply by 10 to give R = 4.462
Set out AB = 10 units and from A draw an arc R = 4.462 units.
From B draw a line touching the arc.
∠ABC = 26°30'

To draw an angle of 24°30' using the CHORD.
Find sine $\frac{24°30'}{2}$ = sin 12°15' = 0.2122
Chord C = 2 × 0.2122 = 0.4244
Multiply by 10 to give C = 4.244
Set out AB = 10 units and from B draw an arc R = 10 units also.
From A draw an arc radius C = 4.244 to cut the first arc in D.
Join BD to give ∠ABD = 24°30'.

Circles and their Construction

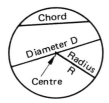

Circumference	— A line always equi-distant from the centre of a circle.
Chord	— Any straight line drawn across the circle and touching the circumference at both ends.
Diameter	— A chord drawn through the centre of the circle.
Radius	— Any straight line drawn from the centre of the circle to touch the circumference. $R = \frac{1}{2}D$.

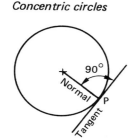

Arc	— Any part of the circumference of a circle.
Sector	— A part of a circle enclosed by two radii and the arc of a circle.
Quadrant	— A sector in which the angle between the two radii is $90°$.

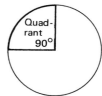

Segment	— A part of a circle enclosed by a chord and an arc of a circle.
Minor segment	— The smaller segment.
Major segment	— The larger segment.
Semi-circle	— A segment with the diameter as the chord.

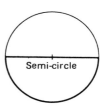

Note: When either the minor or major segment is referred to simply as "the segment of a circle", the other segment may be called the *alternate* segment.

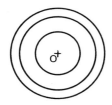

Concentric Circles	— Circles drawn about the same centre 0 but with different radii.
Eccentric Circles	— Circles drawn about different centres 0_1 and 0_2 and with different radii.

Concentric circles

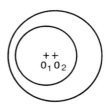

Eccentric circles

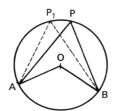

Tangent	— A straight line which touches a circle at only one point on the circumference, P, called the *point of tangency*.
Normal	— The normal to a tangent is a line drawn from the centre of a circle to cut, or meet, the tangent at right angles.

Several geometrical properties relating to the circle are required for the completion and understanding of a number of the constructions which follow. Four of these properties are shown below.

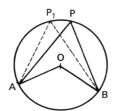

Angles in the same segment are equal.
$\angle APB = \angle AP_1B$ *and* the angle at the centre of the circle is twice the angle at the circumference
$\angle AOB = 2\angle APB$

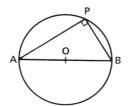

When AOB is a diameter
$\angle AOB = 180°$
$\therefore \angle APB = 90°$
or The triangle *on* a semi-circle is always right-angled.

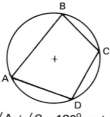

$\angle A + \angle C = 180°$ and
$\angle B + \angle D = 180°$

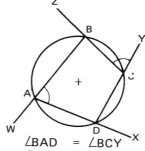

$\angle BAD$	$=$	$\angle BCY$
$\angle ADC$	$=$	$\angle ABZ$
$\angle DCB$	$=$	$\angle DAW$
$\angle CBA$	$=$	$\angle CDX$

Note: ABCD is known as a cyclic quadrilateral because it is drawn inside a circle and all four corners touch the circle.

1.   To find the centre of a given circle

Mark 3 points A, B and C well spaced out on the circumference.
Bisect the chord between one pair of points (AB)

Bisect the chord between the second pair of points (BC). The intersection at O is the centre of the circle.

2.   To construct a circle to pass through 3 points E, F, G

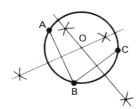 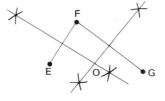

Join EF and FG.
Bisect EF and FG to intersect at O.

From the centre O describe the circle to pass through all three points.

Note: There is no need to draw in the chords or the lines joining the points.

---

3.   To draw a tangent to a given point P on a circle of radius R

 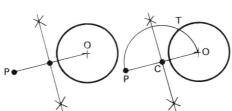

Join OP and extend beyond P

With centre P describe an arc of radius R

Construct a right angle at P.
PT is the required tangent.

4.   To draw tangents from a given point P outside a circle

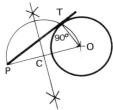

Join OP
Bisect OP

With centre C draw a semi-circle on OP to cut the circle at T.

Join PT. PT is a tangent because OPT is a triangle in a semi-circle and $\angle PTO = 90°$

---

5.   To draw a common external tangent to two given circles with radii R and r

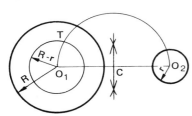 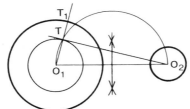 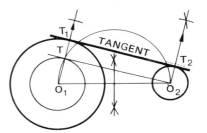

Draw 2 circles with radii R and r.
With centre O_1 draw a circle of radius R – r. Join $O_1 O_2$.
Bisect $O_1 O_2$ to obtain centre C.
With C as centre draw a semi-circle of radius CO_1 to cut the inner circle at T.

Draw a line from O_1 through T to locate T_1 on the outer circle.
Draw the tangent $O_2 T$ to the inner circle.

Draw a line from O_2 parallel to $O_1 T_1$ to cut the small circle at T_2.
Draw a line through T_1 and T_2 to obtain the external tangent to the two circles.

Note: $O_2 T$ has been included as a check. $T_1 T_2$ *must* be parallel to $O_2 T$.

---

6.   To draw a common internal tangent to two given circles with radii R and r

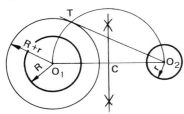 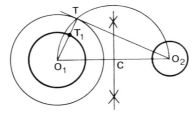 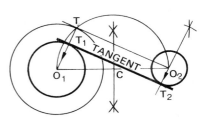

Draw 2 circles with radii R and r. With centre O_1 draw a circle of radius R + r.
Join $O_1 O_2$.
Bisect $O_1 O_2$ to obtain centre C. With C as centre draw a semi- circle of radius CO_1 to cut the outer circle at T.

Draw a line from O_1 to T to cut the inner circle at T_1.
Draw the tangent $O_2 T$ to the outer circle.

Draw a line from O_2 parallel to $O_1 T_1$ to cut the small circle at T_2
Draw a line through T_1 and T_2 to obtain the internal tangent to the two given circles.

7. To draw a circle to pass through a given point A and a point B
on the circumference of a given circle

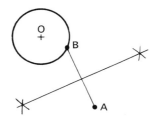

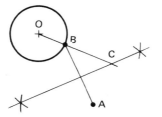

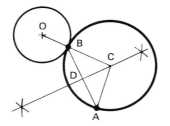

BD = DA
DC is common
$\therefore \triangle$ CDA = $\triangle$ CDB
$\therefore$ CB = CA
= radius of
the circle

Join AB and bisect AB

From centre O, join OB
and extend to meet
the bisector at C.

With centre C draw a circle
which passes through A and
touches the given circle at B.

8. To draw a circle to touch a given circle and a given line at B

$\triangle$ OCD = $\triangle$ PCD
$\therefore$ OC = CP
but OT = BP
$\therefore$ CT = CB

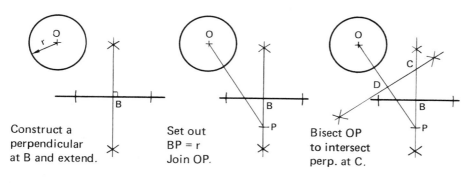

Construct a
perpendicular
at B and extend.

Set out
BP = r
Join OP.

Bisect OP
to intersect
perp. at C.

With centre C
draw a circle
which touches the given circle
at T and the line at B.

9. To draw a circle to pass through a given point P_1 and enclose a given circle
touching it at a given point P_2 on its circumference.

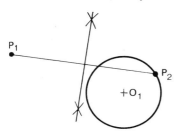

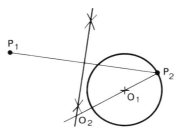

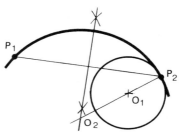

Draw a line from P_1 to P_2
Bisect P_1 P_2.

Draw a line from P_2, through
centre O_1 and extend to intersect
the bisector at O_2.

With centre O_2 draw a circle of
radius O_2 P_2 to pass through P_1
and touch the given circle at P_2.

10. To draw a circle to touch and enclose 2 given circles

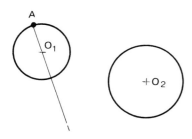

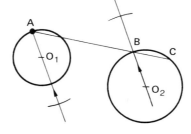

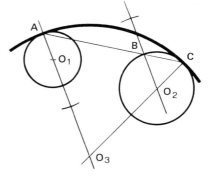

Mark any point A on the
circumference of one of the
given circles. Draw a line
from A through O_1.

Construct a line parallel to O_1A
through O_2 to meet the circumference
of the second circle at B.
Join AB and extend to C
Note: The position of point C will
depend on the position
chosen for point A.

Draw a line from C through O_2
and extend to meet AO_1
extended at O_3
With centre O_3 draw a circle of
radius O_3A to enclose the given
circles.

11. **To draw a circle to pass through two given points A and B and to touch a given line EF.**

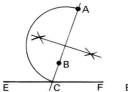

Join AB and extend to meet EF at C. Bisect AC and draw a semi-circle on AC.

Erect a perpendicular at B to cut the semi-circle at P. On line EF set out CD = CP Join BD

Bisect BD and AB to meet at O With centre O draw a circle to pass through points A and B, and touch EF at D.

Alternative construction. On line EF set out CD_1 = CP. Join BD_1. Bisect BD_1 and extend to meet the bisector of AB at O_1

With centre O_1 draw a circle to pass through points A and B, and touch line EF at D_1.

12. **To construct a circle to pass through two given points A and B and to touch a given circle K.**

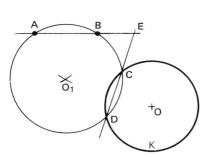

Draw any circle with centre O_1 to pass through A and B and to cut circle K at C and D. Draw lines joining AB and CD. Extend AB and DC to intersect at E.

Join OE and draw tangent EP to the given circle K. Construct the perpendicular bisector of AB from O_1.

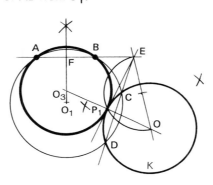

Extend PO and FO_1 to intersect at O_2.

Draw a circle with centre O_2 to pass through points A and B and touch the given circle K at tangential point P

Alternative construction:
Draw the tangent EP_1 to the given circle K. Draw a line from O through P_1 to cut the perpendicular bisector of AB at O_3. Draw a circle with a centre O_3 to pass through points A and B and touch the given circle at the tangential point P_1.

Note: In both these constructions extreme accuracy is required in locating the centres O_2, O_3.

13. **To draw 3 circles which touch each other, given the positions of their centres O_1, O_2 and O_3.**

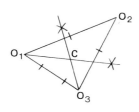

Join O_1, O_2 and O_3 to form a triangle. Bisect two angles to find the 'centre' of the triangle C.

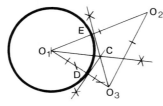

Construct a perpendicular from C to cut $O_1 O_3$ at D. With centre O_1 and radius $O_1 D$ draw a circle which cuts $O_1 O_2$ at E.

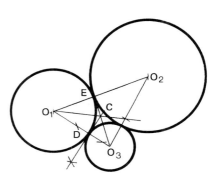

With centre O_2 and radius $O_2 E$. draw a second circle. With centre O_3 and radius $O_3 D$. draw a third circle to touch the other two.

14. **To draw a circle to pass through a given point P and to touch two lines AB and AC**

Note:
OD is extended
to facilitate the
construction of
parallel lines.

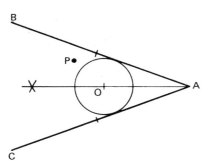

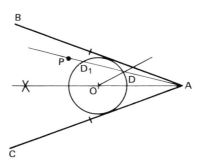

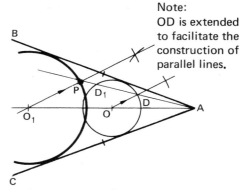

Bisect the angle between the lines.
With centre O anywhere along the
bisector draw a circle to touch
AB and BC.

Draw a line from A through P
cutting the circle at D and D_1
Join OD and extend.

Draw a line parallel to OD which passes
through P and cuts the bisector at O_1.
With centre O_1 and radius O_1P draw a
circle to pass through P and touch AB
and AC.

Alternative construction.
Join OD_1 and extend.
Draw line parallel to OD_1 which
passes through P and cuts the
bisector at O_2.
With centre O_2 and radius O_2P
draw a circle to pass through
P and touch AB and AC.

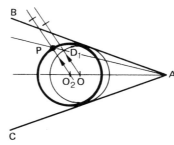

Note: In both these constructions
extreme accuracy is required
in locating the centres O_1 and O_2.

15. **To draw a circle to touch two lines AB and AC, touching one of the lines at a given point P.**

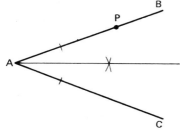

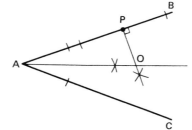

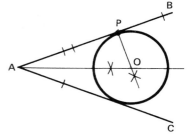

Bisect the angle at A

Construct a perpendicular
at P to cut the bisector at O.

Draw a circle with centre O
and radius OP to touch AC,
and AB at point P.

16. **To draw a circle to touch a given circle and to touch two lines AB and AC.**

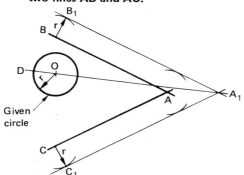

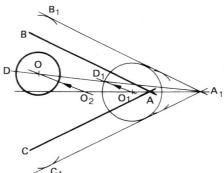

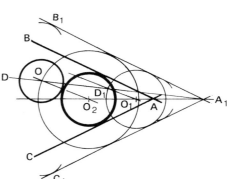

Draw two lines A_1B_1 and A_1C_1
parallel to and distance r from
AB and AC respectively.
Draw a line A_1D passing
through centre O.

Bisect the angle between
A_1B_1 and A_1C_1
With centre O_1 anywhere along the
bisector draw a circle to touch
A_1B_1 and A_1C_1 cutting A_1D at D_1
Draw a line from O_1 through D_1.
Draw OO_2 parallel to O_1D_1.

With centre O_2 and radius O_2O.
draw a circle to pass through O
and touch A_1B_1 and A_1C_1.
Reduce radius OO_2 by r and
with centre O_2 draw a circle
which will now touch AB, AC
and the given circle

17. To draw a circle which touches both a given circle K and also two tangents to circle K.

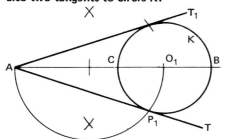 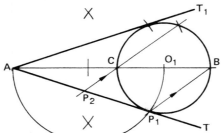 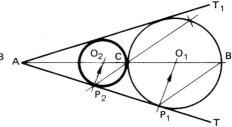

Draw the tangents to the given circle K, so that they intersect at A. Draw a line from A through O_1 cutting the circle at B and C.

Draw a line from P_1 to B. Draw a line parallel to P_1B passing through C on the circle and cutting the tangent AT at P_2

Join O_1P_1
Draw a line parallel to O_1P_1 passing through P_2 and cutting AB in O_2
Draw a circle with centre O_2 and radius O_2P_2 which touches the given circle and the tangents AT and AT_1

18. To construct a segment of a circle on a given straight line AB with an angle of segment equal to a given angle θ.

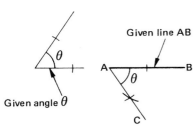 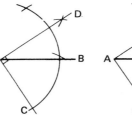 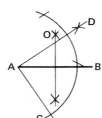 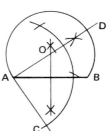 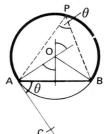

Copy angle θ from and below line AB.

Construct a right angle $\angle CAD$

Bisect line AB to cut AD at O.

With centre O and radius OA draw an arc to form a segment on AB.

The circle passes through A and B. (OA = OB) AC is a tangent $\angle CAB$ is the angle in the alternate segment.

Note: In the completed construction, any angle in the major segment is equal to $\angle\theta$
e.g. $\angle APB = \angle CAB = \angle\theta$

19. To construct a triangle in a given circle equi-angular to a given triangle.

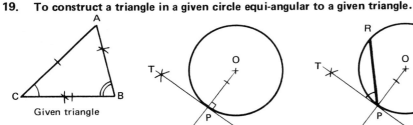 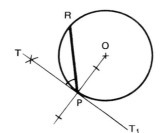

Given triangle

Draw a tangent TT_1 to any point P on the given circle

Construct $\angle ACB$ from the given triangle at P. Draw chord PR. $\angle TPR = \angle ACB$

Construct $\angle ABC$ from the given triangle at P. Draw chord PS. $\angle T_1PS = \angle ABC$. Join RS to complete the required triangle.

Required triangle

20. To draw a triangle about a given circle equi-angular to a given triangle.

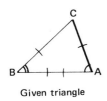 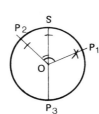 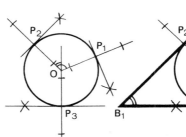 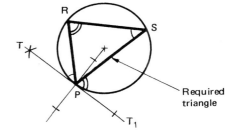

Given triangle

Construct $\angle SOP_1$ equal to $\angle CAB$, at centre O of the given circle.

Construct $\angle SOP_2$ equal to $\angle ABC$ at centre O

Draw tangents to the the circle at P_1 P_2 and P_3.

Extend the tangents to form the required triangle $A_1B_1C_1$.
Note: The quadrilateral $A_1P_1OP_3$ is cyclic because the angles at P_1 and P_3 are both 90°.

29

21. **To draw the INSCRIBED circle for a given triangle ABC.**

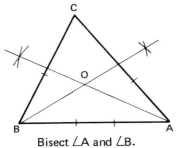

Bisect ∠A and ∠B.
Extend the bisectors
to meet at O.

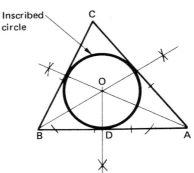

Construct a perpendicular
from O to cut AB at D.
With centre O and radius OD
draw the *inscribed* circle
of the △ABC.

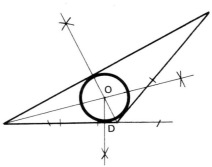

The sequence of constructions is
the same for an obtuse-angled
triangle.

22. **To draw the ESCRIBED circle for a given △ABC.**

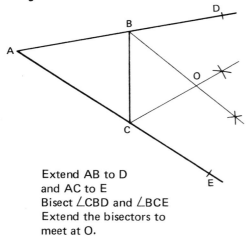

Extend AB to D
and AC to E
Bisect ∠CBD and ∠BCE
Extend the bisectors to
meet at O.

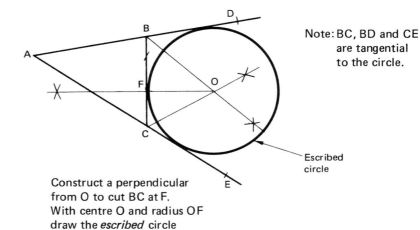

Construct a perpendicular
from O to cut BC at F.
With centre O and radius OF
draw the *escribed* circle
of the △ABC.

Note: BC, BD and CE
are tangential
to the circle.

23. **To draw the CIRCUMSCRIBED circle for a given triangle ABC.**

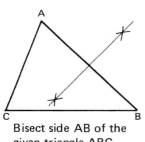

Bisect side AB of the
given triangle ABC.

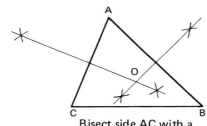

Bisect side AC with a
line which meets the
first bisector at O.

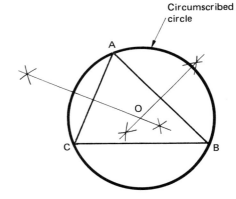

With centre O draw a circle
of radius OA which also passes
through C and B. This is the
circumscribed circle and
OA = OB = OC.

Note: For certain
triangles centre O
may be *outside*
the triangle.

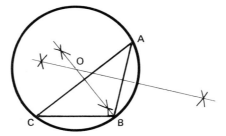

Note: The final required
figures should ALWAYS
be drawn with relatively
thick lines.

Blending of Arcs

For accurate geometric and machine drawing, the centres for arcs should be constructed so that the arc blends neatly with joining lines. Where speed rather than accuracy is essential a radius gauge or curve should be used.

Arc in a right angle

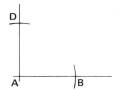
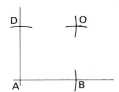
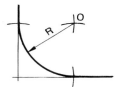
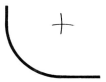

Set out feint intersecting lines at 90°. From A set out AB and AD equal to the required radius R.

From B and D set out arcs of radius R to intersect at O.

From O draw an arc radius R to blend with the straight lines.

Erase unwanted lines, leave arcs at centre. Darken the outline.

Arc in an acute angle

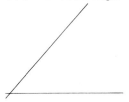
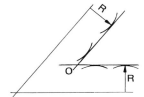
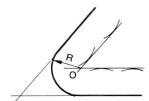

Set out feint intersecting lines at the required angle.

Construct lines parallel to and distance R from the given lines to intersect at O.

From O draw an arc radius R to blend with the straight lines.

Erase unwanted lines, leave lines at centre, Darken the outline.

Arc from a given point to meet a straight line

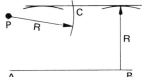
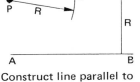
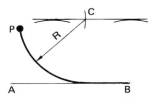
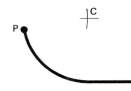

Draw feint line AB and position point P.

Construct line parallel to and distance R from AB. Describe arc, radius R from P to cut line at C.

From C draw an arc radius R to touch P and blend with line AB.

Erase unwanted lines, leave arcs at centre. Darken the outline.

Arc from a point to a circle of radius r

1. *To blend with the near side.*

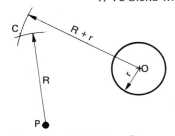

Set out radius R from P and radius R + r from O to meet at C.

From C draw an arc radius R to touch the circle and point P

2. *To blend with the far side.*

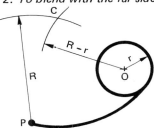

Set out radius R from P and radius R − r from O. From C draw an arc radius R to touch the circle and point P.

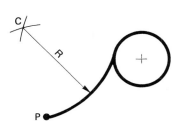

In both cases, if a line is drawn between the centre of arc C and centre of circle O, it will pass through the point of common tangency T. This line is called a NORMAL (N)

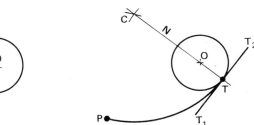

Note: T_1T_2 is the common tangent to both the circle and the arc.
The tangent touches both curves at the point of common tangency T, and is 90° to the normal.

Arc from a straight line to a circle

1. *To blend with the near side*

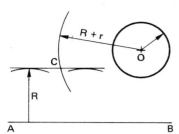

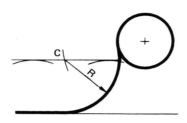

Draw line parallel to AB and distance R from AB. Set out radius R + r from O to meet line at C.

From C draw arc radius R to blend with the line and the circle.

2. *To blend with the far side*

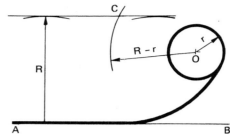

Draw line parallel to AB and distance R from AB. Set out radius R - r from O, to cut this line at C. From C draw an arc radius R to blend with the line and circle.

Arc from a circle to a circle — 3 cases

1

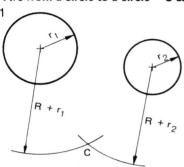

Set out R + r_1 and R + r_2 to intersect at C.

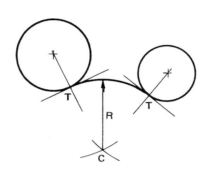

Draw an arc radius R from C to blend with the circles at points of common tangency T.

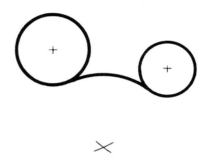

Erase unwanted lines and darken the outline.

2

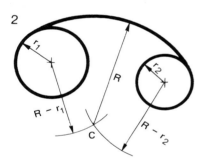

Set out R – r_1 and R – r_2 to intersect at C.
Draw an arc radius R from C.

3

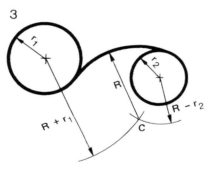

Set out R + r_1 and R – r_2 to intersect at C. From C draw an arc radius R to blend with both circles.

Note: Construction lines are not *always* erased. It may be required to leave them in for geometrical solutions.

Practical hints for "blending"

1) Ensure that both the pencil lead and compass lead are sharp and of the same grade and diameter.
2) Always draw construction lines FEINTLY.
3) Measure lengths of radii CAREFULLY. A slight error will lead to an untidy and/or inaccurate "blend".
4) Ensure that construction lines which are meant to be parallel ARE parallel. An adjustable set-square is most helpful for achieving this.
5) Complete the "blend" with feint (thin) lines initially. If it is inaccurate it can then be erased easily, without permanently dirtying the drawing sheet.
6) Carefully erase any unwanted construction lines. An eraser shield should prove useful when doing this.
7) Finally, "heavy-in" the "blend" with lines of consistent thickness and density.

Triangles and their Construction

The first section of this chapter identifies and defines different types of triangle and also terms associated with triangles, e.g. base, vertex, altitude, median, etc.

The second section illustrates and explains a wide selection of the constructions which an O-level student could reasonably be expected to follow and remember. To fully understand the geometric principles under-lying the more complicated constructions presented, towards the end of the text, needs a careful study of the relevant theorems of Euclid.

General note for all triangles:

A triangle is a plane figure with 3 straight sides. Any one of these sides may be termed the base.

Each corner of a triangle is referred to as a *vertex* which is usually designated by a capital letter.

The same letter, but in lower case is often used to label the side opposite the angle.

In any triangle ABC, if AC is the base, then B may be referred to as the *apex* and the angle at B as the *apex angle*

It is sometimes called the "vertical" angle. Also, h is called the *altitude* or *vertical height*.

Sides of equal length are often identified by "equal" marks as shown in the equilateral and isosceles triangles below.

Types of Triangle

Scalene   All the sides are unequal in length and all the angles are unequal.
Triangle ① is an obtuse-angled triangle because the angle at C is greater than 90°.
Triangle ② is an acute-angled triangle because all the angles are less than 90°.

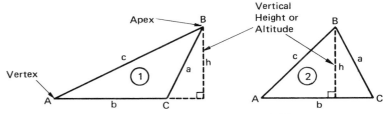

Both triangles have 3 unequal sides
and 3 unequal angles

Equilateral   All three sides are equal in length and all three angles are equal.

3 equal sides
3 equal angles

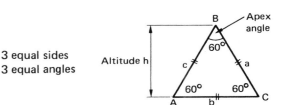

Isosceles   The two base angles are equal and the sides opposite the base angles are equal.

2 base angles equal.
2 sides opposite
the base angles equal.

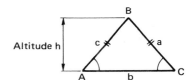

Right-angled   One angle is equal to 90°. The side opposite that angle is known as the hypotenuse.

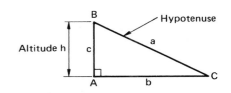

The Median   A line drawn from the corner of a triangle to the mid-point of the side opposite that corner is known as a *median*. Any two medians intersect at the *centroid* of the triangle.
If AC is the base and h the vertical height, then $\frac{h}{3}$ = distance of the centroid from the base.

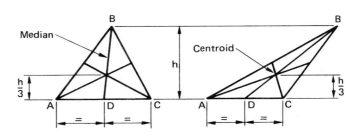

A median divides a triangle into two equal areas

Area of $\triangle$ ABC $=$ Area $\triangle$ ABD + Area $\triangle$ CBD

$\therefore$ $\frac{1}{2}$ AC.h $=$ $\frac{1}{2}$ AD.h + $\frac{1}{2}$ DC.h but AD = DC = $\frac{1}{2}$ AC

$\therefore$ $\frac{1}{2}$ AC.h $=$ $\frac{1}{4}$ AC.h + $\frac{1}{4}$ AC.h = $\frac{1}{2}$ AC.h

1. To draw a triangle given the lengths of 3 sides, a, b and c.

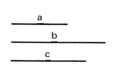 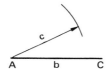 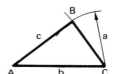

Draw line AC equal to length b.
With centre A draw an arc of radius c.

With centre C draw an arc of radius a to intersect the first arc at B.
Join AB and BC.

2. To draw a triangle given the lengths of 2 sides, f and g, and the altitude h.

 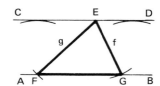

Draw any line AB.
Draw a line CD parallel to AB at a distance h from AB.

From any convenient point E on CD draw arcs of radii f and g cutting AB at G and F respectively.
Join EF and FG.

3. To draw a triangle given the lengths of 2 sides and the angle between those sides (the included angle).

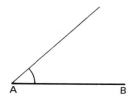 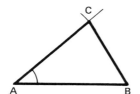

Draw a line AB equal to the length of one of the sides.
At A set out the given base angle with a protractor.

From A draw a line AC equal to the length of the second side.
Join BC to complete the triangle.

4. To draw an isosceles triangle given the length of the base p and the altitude h.

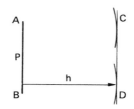 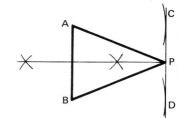

Draw line AB equal to base length p.
Draw a line CD parallel to AB at a distance h from AB.

Draw the perpendicular bisector of AB cutting CD at P.
Join PA and PB.

5. To draw an isosceles triangle given the altitude h and the apex angle.

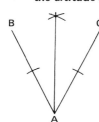 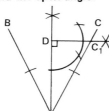 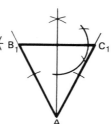

Set out the apex angle at any point A with lines AB and AC.
Bisect ∠BAC.

Set out AD equal to h on the bisector.
Draw a perpendicular at D to cut AC at C_1.

Extend the perpendicular to cut AB at B_1 to obtain the required triangle AB_1C_1.

6. To draw an isosceles triangle given the perimeter and the altitude h.

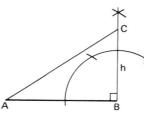 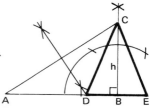

Draw a line AB equal in length to half the perimeter.
Construct a perpendicular at B and set out BC equal to h.
Join AC.

Draw the perpendicular bisector of AC to cut AB at D.
Join CD and from C draw CE equal to CD to obtain the required triangle CDE.

7. To draw an equilateral triangle given the altitude h.

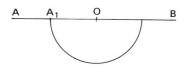 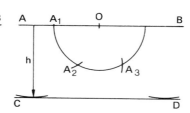 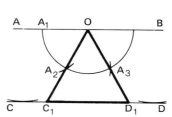

Draw a straight line of any length AB. From any centre O draw a semi-circle of any convenient radius OA_1.

From A_1 set out the same radius to A_2 and from A_2 to A_3.

Draw a straight line CD parallel to and distance h from AB.

Draw lines from O through A_2 and A_3 to meet CD at C_1 and D_1 respectively to obtain the required triangle C_1OD_1.

8. To draw a triangle given the base length c, the base angle, and a, the length of the side opposite the base angle.

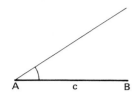 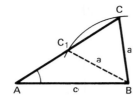

Draw line AB equal to the length of the base c.
Set out the given angle at A with a line of any length.

With centre B set out an arc of radius a cutting the opposite side at C and C_1.
Join BC to obtain the required triangle (or BC_1 for an alternative triangle).

9. To draw a triangle given the base length e, the altitude h, and the base angle.

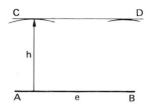 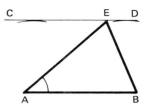

Draw line AB equal to base length e.
Draw a line CD parallel to, and distance h from AB.

Set out the given base angle at A with a line cutting CD at E.
Join BE to complete the triangle.

10. To draw a triangle given the base length, c, and the two base angles.

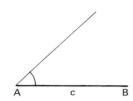 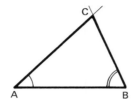

Draw line AB equal to the base length c.
Set out the base angle at A by a line of any length.

At B set out the second base angle with a second line which cuts the first at C.

11. To draw a triangle given two base angles and the altitude h.

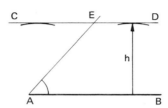 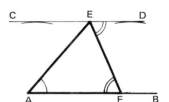

Draw a line AB of any length.
Draw a line CD parallel to and distance h from AB.
At A set out the base angle with a line to cut CD at E.

Set out the second base angle at E with a line as shown to cut AB at F.
AEF is the required triangle.
Notice that $\angle AFE = \angle DEF$. (Alternate angles).

12. To draw a triangle given base angle θ, the apex angle α, and the altitude h.

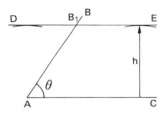 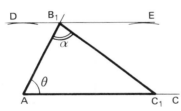 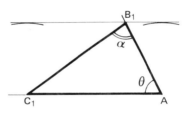

Set out the base angle θ with lines AB and AC of any length.
Draw a line DE parallel to and distance h from AC cutting AB at B_1.

Set out the apex angle on AB_1 with a line cutting AC at C_1 to obtain the required triangle AB_1C_1.

Alternative solution (Opposite hand)

13. To draw a triangle given the length of the perimeter and the ratio of the 3 sides (say 5 : 4 : 6)

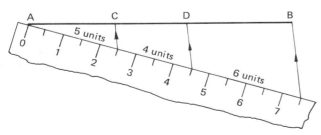

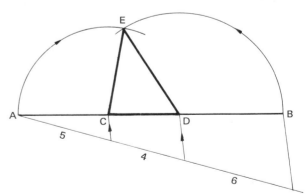

Draw a straight line AB equal in length to the perimeter.
Divide AB in the given ratio 5 : 4 : 6 by the method described on page 14.

With centre C draw an arc of radius equal to CA.
With centre D draw an arc of radius equal to DB to intersect the first arc at E.
Join CE and DE to obtain the required triangle.

14. To draw a triangle given the length of the perimeter and the two base angles

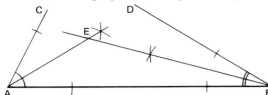

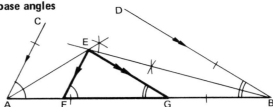

Draw a straight line AB equal in length to the perimeter. At A and B set out the given base angles with lines AC and BD respectively. Bisect the angles at A and B and let the bisectors intersect at E.

From E draw a line parallel to AC cutting AB at F. From E draw a line parallel to BD cutting AB at G. Join EF and EG to obtain the required triangle EFG. Notice that ∠EFG = ∠CAF and ∠EGF = ∠DBG (corresponding angles).

15. To draw a triangle given the base length d, the sum of the other two sides (a+b), and the base angle.

16. To draw a triangle given the length of one side a, the angle opposite that side, and the ratio of the other two sides (say 5 : 7)

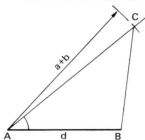

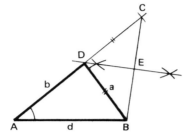

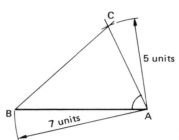

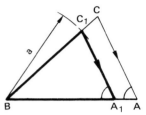

Draw a line AB equal to the base length d. At A set out the base angle with a line AC equal to the combined lengths of a and b. Join BC.

Draw the perpendicular bisector of BC to cut AC at D. Join BD to obtain the required triangle ADB. DC = DB because triangles CDE and BDE are identical.

Draw line AB of length 7 units and arc AC of length 5 units. Set out the given angle at A. Join BC.

From B draw an arc BC₁ equal to the length of the given side a. From C₁ draw a line C₁A₁ parallel to CA. A₁BC₁ is the required triangle.

17. To draw a triangle given the apex angle, the length of the perimeter, and the altitude.

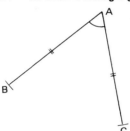

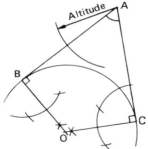

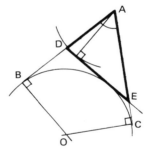

Set out the given apex angle at A and make lines AB and AC each equal in length to half the perimeter.

From B and C construct perpendiculars to meet at O. With centre O and radius OB draw an arc through B and C. With centre A draw an arc radius equal in length to the altitude.

Draw a tangent common to the two arcs cutting AB at D and AC at E. ADE is the required triangle.

18. To draw a triangle given the base length d, one base angle, and the radius of the inscribed circle r.

19. To draw a triangle given the base length d, and 3 angles in a given ratio (say 2 : 3 : 5)

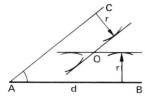

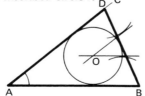

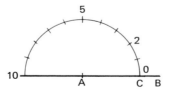

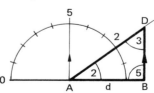

Draw a line AB equal to the base length d. Set out the given angle at A. Draw lines parallel to and distance r from AB and AC to meet at O.

With centre O and radius r draw the inscribed circle. From B draw a tangent to the circle to cut AC at D. ABD is the required triangle.

Draw line AB equal to the base length d. With centre A draw a semi-circle of any radius cutting AB at C. Divide the semi-circle into 10 equal parts (i.e. 2 + 3 + 5 = 10) with protractor.
Note: 1 part = $\frac{180°}{10}$ = 18°.

From A draw lines A2 and A5 through the second and fifth division. From B draw a line parallel to A5 cutting the A2 line extended at D, to obtain the required triangle ABD.

20. **To draw a triangle given the base length p, the apex angle θ**
and either i) one other side b
or ii) the altitude h

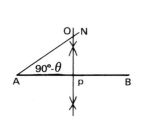 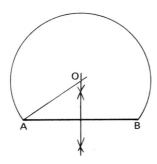 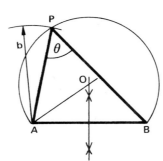 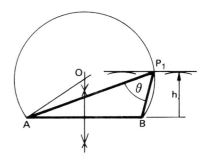

Draw line AB equal to
base length p.
At A set out an angle of
$90°-\theta$ with line AN.
Draw the perpendicular
bisector of AB to cut
AN at O.

With centre O and radius
OA draw the segment of
a circle on AB.

Case ① . With centre A
and radius b, the length
of the given side, draw
an arc to meet the
segment at P.
Join AP and BP to obtain
the required triangle APB.

Case ② . Draw a line
parallel to and distance h
from AB to cut the
segment at P_1.
Join AP_1 and BP_1 to
obtain the required
triangle AP_1B.

---

21. **To draw a right-angled triangle given the length of one**
side a, and the length of the hypotenuse, H.

22. **To draw a right angled triangle given the lengths of the**
two shorter sides b and c.

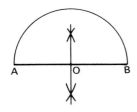 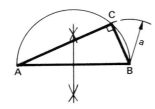 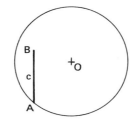 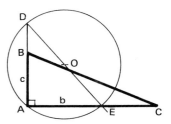

Draw a line AB equal in
length to the hypotenuse H.
Draw the perpendicular
bisector of AB to cut AB
at O.
With centre O and radius OA
draw a semi-circle on AB.

From B set out arc radius
equal in length to the given
side a, cutting the semi-
circle at C.
Join AC and CB to obtain
the required triangle ACB.

Draw AB equal to length c.
From *any* centre O draw a
circle which touches one
end of AB (in this case A).

Extend AB to touch the circle
at D.
From D draw a diameter
through O to cut the opposite
side of the circle at E.
Set out the length of the
second side b, along AE
extended (AC = b). Join BC.
ABC is the required
triangle.

---

23. **To draw a triangle given the lengths of the 3 medians,**
x, y and z.

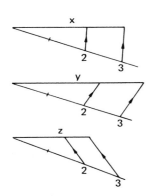 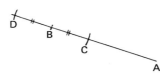 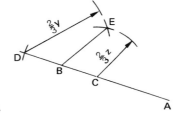 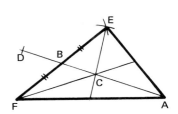

Draw line AB equal in length
to the median x.
Mark off BC = $\frac{1}{3}$x and
extend AB to D so that
BD = BC.

From D and C draw arcs
of radii $\frac{2}{3}$y and $\frac{2}{3}$z
respectively to intersect
at E.
Join BE.

Extend EB to F so that BF = BE.
Join EA and FA to obtain the
required triangle AFE.

The following examples illustrate how the required figures depend on a progressive series of constructions, all of which have been explained previously.

24. **To draw a triangle given the base length p, the ratio of the other two sides (say 3 : 2), and the altitude h**

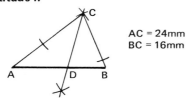

AC = 24mm
BC = 16mm

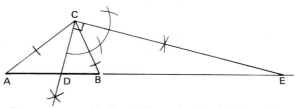

Draw AB equal to base length p and on AB draw *any* triangle ABC with the sides AC and BC in the given ratio (3 : 2).
Bisect ∠ACB with a line which cuts AB at D.

Draw a perpendicular to CD and extend the line to meet AB produced at E.

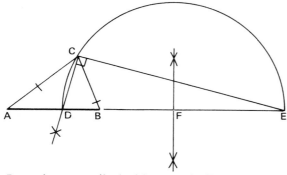

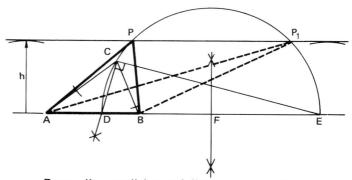

Draw the perpendicular bisector of DE to cut DE at F.
With centre F and radius FD draw a semi-circle on DE.

Draw a line parallel to and distance h from AE to cut the semi-circle at P and P_1.
Join AP and BP to obtain the required triangle APB.
Join AP_1 and BP_1 to obtain an alternative triangle AP_1B.

25. **To draw a triangle given the length of the base p, the ratio of the other two sides (say 3 : 2), and the apex angle θ (say 55°)**

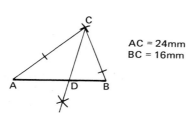

AC = 24mm
BC = 16mm

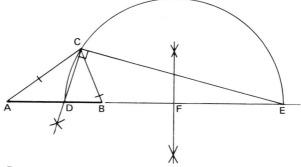

Draw AB equal to the base length p and on AB draw *any* triangle ABC with the sides AC and BC in the given ratio (3 : 2).
Bisect ∠ACB with a line which cuts AB at D.

Draw a perpendicular to CD and extend the line to meet AB produced at E.
Draw the perpendicular bisector of DE to cut DE at F.
With centre F and radius FD draw a semi-circle on DE.

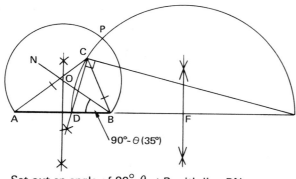

90°- θ (35°)

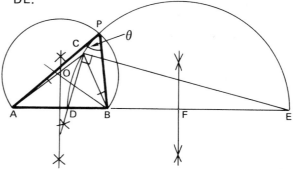

Set out an angle of 90°-θ at B with line BN (90°-θ = 35°).
Draw the perpendicular bisector of AB to meet BN at O.
With O as centre draw the segment of a circle on AB to cut the semi-circle at P.

Join AP and BP to obtain the required triangle APB
Note: AC = 24 mm and BC = 16 mm
24 : 16 : : 3 : 2
AP = 31 mm and BP = 20.67mm
31 : 20·67 : : 3 : 2

Construction of Quadrilaterals

Any plane figure with four straight sides is called a *quadrilateral.* The general term used for figures with more than four sides is a *polygon.* If all the sides and all the angles are equal, it is then referred to as a *regular polygon.*

Quadrilaterals - definitions

  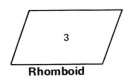 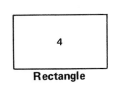 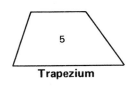

1	2	3	4	5	6
Square	**Rhombus**	**Rhomboid**	**Rectangle**	**Trapezium**	**Trapeziod**

All sides equal
Opposite sides parallel.
All angles =90°.

All sides equal.
Opposite sides parallel.

Opposite sides equal.
Opposite sides parallel.

Opposite sides equal.
Opposite sides parallel.
All angles = 90°.

One pair of opposite sides parallel.

No sides parallel.

These figures are usually referred to as irregular quadrilaterals.

Note: 1, 2, 3 and 4 are known as regular quadrilaterals.
         2 and 3 are commonly known as parallelograms.

1.   To draw a square given the length of side

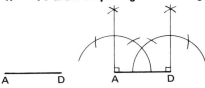 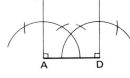 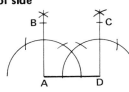 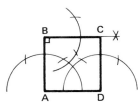

Note: A similar construction is also used to draw a rectangle.

Draw a straight line AD of given length.

Draw perpendiculars at A and D.

Mark off AB = AD and DC = AD.

Draw a perpendicular at B to obtain the fourth side BC.

2.   To draw a parallelogram

The construction of a parallelogram depends on how its shape is described.

a)   By lengths of sides and internal angle.

b)   By length of side, vertical height h, and position of top relative to bottom, x.

c)   By lengths of sides and diagonal.

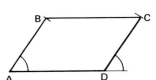 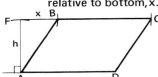 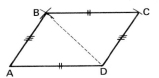

Draw straight line AD of given length.
Draw given angle at A and D.
Mark off AB and DC of given length.
Join BC to obtain the parallelogram.

Draw straight line AD of given length.
Draw AF = h perpendicular to AD.
Set out FB = x horizontally.
Draw BC parallel to and equal to AD.
Join AB and DC to obtain the parallelogram.

Draw straight line AD of given length.
With centre A, draw an arc, radius AB, the length of the other side, and from D draw an arc, radius DB, the length of the diagonal.
With centres B and D, set out BC and DC to complete the parallelogram.

3.   To draw a trapezium

A similar construction to *2b* may be used for setting out a trapezium but, when this section is used for a cutting or embankment, for a road or railway, the shape is often defined in terms of the width of base, b, the slope of sides, and formation width w.

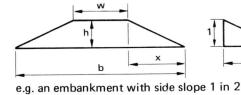

Slope is the ratio $\frac{h}{x}$ or, in this example, $h : x : : 1 : 2$

Note: When drawing any 4-sided figure, two sides and a diagonal can be used first to construct an accurate triangle on to which the remaining two sides can easily be added to complete the figure. Triangulation such as this is the basis of good surveying practice.

e.g. an embankment with side slope 1 in 2

4.   To draw any quadrilateral ABCD given the lengths of sides and a diagonal, BD

 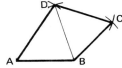

Note: Any polygon may be constructed from given lengths of sides and internal angles.
In an examination, it is usually stated that protractors and set squares may be used to draw angles.
Students should *construct* angles only if required to do so.

Draw one side AB. With centre A draw an arc, radius AD. With centre B, draw an arc, radius BD to intersect the first radius at D. Join AD.

With centres B and D draw arcs, radii equal to the sides BC and DC, intersecting at C, to complete the quadrilateral.

or With two sides AB and AD and the diagonal BD draw a triangle ABD.

Construction of Regular Polygons

A number of methods exist for the construction of regular polygons and, in general, the student should be familiar with those which require the polygon to be drawn

a) Given the length of side, when, in some cases, it is necessary to construct a *circumscribing* circle in which to draw the polygon.

b) *Inside* a circle of known diameter

c) *Outside* a circle of known diameter.

REGULAR PLANE FIGURES GIVEN THE LENGTH OF SIDE

1A **To draw a regular 5-sided polygon (PENTAGON) given the length of side**

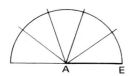 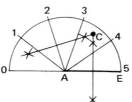 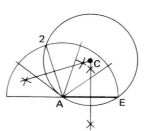 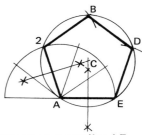

Draw a straight line AE equal to the given length of side. With centre A and radius AE draw a semi-circle on AE extended.
Divide the semi-circle into 5 equal parts with a protractor, if possible, or by trial and error, with compasses.

Number the divisions in the order shown above. Draw the bisectors of A2 and AE to intersect at C.

With centre C and radius CA draw a circle touching A, E and point 2.

With centre E set out an arc radius AE to cut the circle at D, and from 2 set out the same arc to cut the circle at B.
Join 2B, BD and ED to obtain the required regular pentagon.

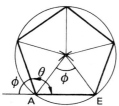

The above construction depends on the following:
If the internal angle of a regular pentagon $= \theta$
Then the sum of all the internal angles $= 5\theta$
and $5\theta =$ the sum of all the angles in 5 triangles minus the angle at the centre
$\therefore \quad 5\theta = (5 \times 180°) - 360°$
$\quad\quad\quad = 900° - 360° = 540°$
$\therefore \quad \theta = \dfrac{540°}{5} = 108°$ and $\phi = \dfrac{360°}{5} = 72°$.

Note: When 180° is divided into 5 equal parts, 2 divisions give a total of 72° which equals the supplement ϕ of the angle θ. A regular pentagon could be constructed accurately, therefore, by setting out ϕ to the left of A and the right of E.

1B

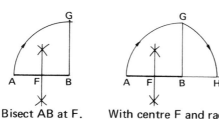 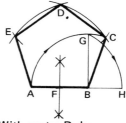

Draw one side AB. With centre B and radius BA draw an arc. Draw a perpendicular at B to cut the arc at G.

Bisect AB at F.

With centre F and radius FG draw an arc to cut AB produced at H. (AH is the diagonal of the pentagon.)

With centres A and B draw arcs of radius AH to intersect at D. Extend the arcs as shown.

With centre D draw arcs of radius AB to intersect the previously drawn arcs at E and C respectively.
Join ABCDE.

1C

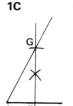 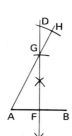 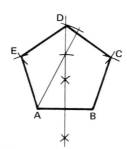

Draw the perpendicular bisector of given side AB. Set out FG = AB. Join AG and extend.

With centre G and radius AF set out GH. With centre A and radius AH draw an arc to cut the bisector at D.

With centres A, B and D draw arcs of radius AB to intersect at E and C. Join BC, CD, DE and AE to obtain the required pentagon.

2. **To draw a regular pentagon given the diagonal**

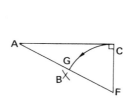 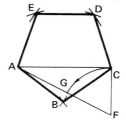

Draw the given diagonal AC and a perpendicular CF $= \frac{1}{2}$AC. Join AF.
With centre F and radius FC draw an arc to cut AF at G.
With centres A and C draw arcs of radius AG to intersect at B.

AB is the length of one side.
With centres A, B and C draw arcs of radius AC to intersect at E and D.
Join A B C D and E to obtain the required pentagon.

40

3. To draw a 6-sided polygon (HEXAGON) given the length of side

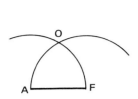 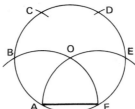 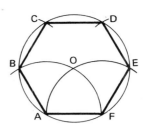

Draw a straight line AF equal to the given length of side.
With centres A and F, draw arcs of radius AF to intersect at O.

With centre O, draw a circle of radius OA to cut the arcs at B and E.

With centres B and E, draw arcs of radius AF to cut the circle at C and D respectively.

Join the points on the circle to obtain the required regular hexagon.

4. To draw a regular hexagon using a 60° – 30° set-square given the distance across the corners.

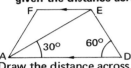 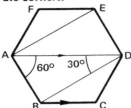

Draw the distance across the corners, AD.
From A and D draw lines at 30° and 60° to AD, respectively, to meet at E.
Draw a second line at A, at 60° to AD, to meet a line drawn from E, parallel to AD, at point F.

Repeat the procedure for the lower half of the hexagon.

5. To draw a regular hexagon using a 60° – 30° set-square given the length of side and distance between the parallel sides of the hexagon.

 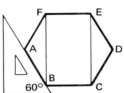

Draw line BC to the given length.
Draw perpendiculars at B and C.
Draw FE equal and parallel to BC at the given distance between the parallel sides.

From B, C, E and F draw lines at 60°, as shown, to complete the hexagon.

6. To draw a regular 7-sided polygon (HEPTAGON) given the length of side

The method used is similar to that used for the regular pentagon but in this case the second division of 7 equal parts of the semi-circle is used to construct the second side of the figure, the 7 equal parts being obtained by trial and error.

The sum of the internal angles = $(7 \times 180°) - 360° = 900°$

∴ The internal angle $\theta = \frac{900°}{7} = 128\frac{4}{7}° = 128.57°$ and $\phi = 180° - 128\frac{4}{7}° = 51\frac{3}{7}° = 51.43°$

In this case it would be difficult to set out accurate angles unless the trigonometrical methods described on page 23 were used. To obtain an accurate heptagon, extreme care must be taken in setting out the length of side around the circumference of the constructed circle.

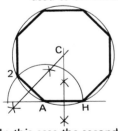

7. To draw a regular eight-sided polygon (OCTAGON) given the length of side

a) Using a method similar to that used to construct a pentagon

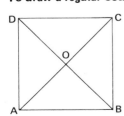

In this case the second of 8 equal divisions is used to construct the second side.

b) Using a 45° set square

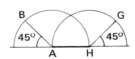 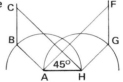 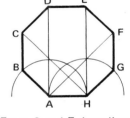

Draw a straight line AH equal to the given length of side.
With centres A and H, draw arcs radius AH.
From A and H draw lines at 45° with the set-square to cut the radii at B and G respectively.

From B and G draw lines perpendicular to AH, and from A and H draw lines at 45° with the set-square to meet these lines at F and C respectively.

From C and F draw lines at 45°, and from A and H draw lines perpendicular to AH to meet these lines at D and E.
Join DE to complete the required regular octagon.

8. To draw a regular octagon given the distance between the parallel sides

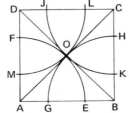 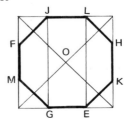

Draw a square ABCD with length of sides equal to distance between the parallel sides of the octagon.
Draw the diagonals to obtain O, the centre of the square.

With centre A and radius AO, draw an arc to cut AB at E and AD at F. Repeat using centres B, C and D.

Join the points on the square, EK, GM, FJ and HL to obtain the required regular octagon.

Note: These constructions are useful, practically, for drawing hexagonal nuts and, less commonly, octagonal nuts.
8-sided nuts are used, for example, for fixing domestic heating pipework.

9. To draw any regular plane figure given the length of side

This construction depends on obtaining the centre of the circumscribing circle on which the corners of the required polygon can be set out. In the case of the square and the hexagon the method is accurate, but for other regular polygons there are slight inaccuracies which may be obscured by line and centre point thicknesses but which can be shown to exist by a simple trigonometrical calculation, the results of which are shown below graphically.

When answering examination questions, it is important to realise that any solutions offered should be geometrically correct.

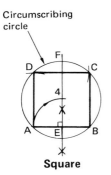

Square

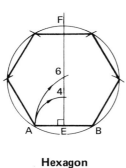

Hexagon

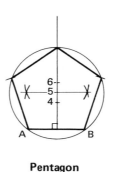

Pentagon

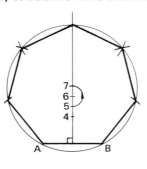

Heptagon

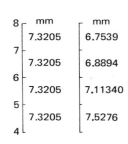

mm	mm
7.3205	6.7539
7.3205	6.8894
7.3205	7.11340
7.3205	7.5276

Draw the perpendicular bisector, EF, of the given side AB. With centre E and radius EA draw an arc to cut the bisector at 4. This is the centre of a circumscribing circle for a 4-sided figure. Step off length AB around the circle.

With centre B and radius AB, draw an arc to cut EF at 6. With centre 6 draw a circle to touch A and B. Set off lengths equal to AB around the circle to obtain the required hexagon.

Position centres for 4 and 6 sided figures from the previous construction. Bisect the line between 4 and 6 to obtain centre 5. Complete the pentagon in the same way as for the square and hexagon.

Position points 4, 6 and 5. Set off distance 5-6 above centre 6 to fix centre 7. Complete the heptagon as before.

Assume AB = 40 mm. In the table above the figures on the left are distances between circle centres obtained by the construction method. The figures on the right are those obtained by calculation. They indicate clearly the slight inaccuracies of the construction method.

REGULAR PLANE FIGURES DRAWN OUTSIDE GIVEN CIRCLE

10. Regular plane figures drawn outside a given circle

1) Angles at centre

Note: In all cases, this construction depends on using an accurate protractor or adjustable set-square to divide the angle at the centre (360°) into the same number of equal parts as the required number of sides. Tangents are then drawn at the points where the arms of the angles touch the circumference of the circle.

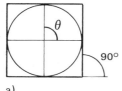

a)
Angles at centre = θ

$\theta = \dfrac{360}{4} = 90°$

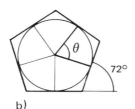

b)

$\theta = \dfrac{360}{5} = 72°$

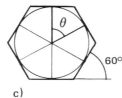

c)

$\theta = \dfrac{360}{6} = 60°$

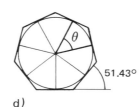

d)

$\theta = \dfrac{360}{7} = 51.43°$

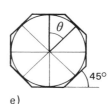

e)

$\theta = \dfrac{360}{8} = 45°$

2) Using Set-squares

a) a hexagon

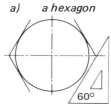

b) an octagon

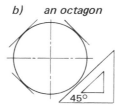

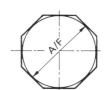

Draw the given circle. Using a 60°-30° set-square, draw lines at 60° to the horizontal and tangential to the circle as shown.

Draw horizontal lines tangential to the top and bottom of the circle to complete the hexagon.

Draw the given circle and using a 45° set-square, draw lines at 45° to the horizontal and tangential to the circle as shown.

Draw horizontal and vertical lines tangential to the top, bottom and sides of the circle to complete the octagon.

Note: This method can be used to draw hexagonal and octagonal nuts. In both cases, the diameter of the circle is equal to the distance across the flats of the nut — designated A/F.

42

REGULAR PLANE FIGURES DRAWN INSIDE A GIVEN CIRCLE

11. Square

Draw the given circle.
Draw the diameter AC with a 45° set-square.

Draw horizontal lines AB and DC with a straight-edge and vertical lines AD and BC with a set-square.

12. Regular pentagon

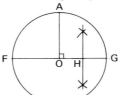 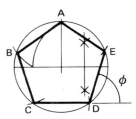

Draw a diameter FG and a perpendicular at the centre O to cut the circle at A.
Bisect OG at H.

With centre H and radius HA, draw an arc to cut FG at J.
With centre A and radius AJ, draw an arc to cut the circle at B.

AB is the length of one side.
Step off length AB around the circle to obtain the required pentagon ABCDE.
Note: $\phi = 72°$.

13. Regular hexagon - using compasses mainly

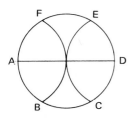 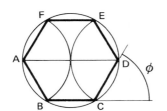

Draw the given circle.
Draw a horizontal diameter AD.
With centres A and D draw arcs, of the same radius as the circle, to cut the circle at B, C, E and F.

Join the points on the circle to obtain the required hexagon A B C D E F.
Note $\phi = 60°$

14. Regular heptagon — using compasses mainly

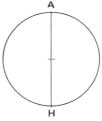 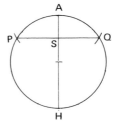 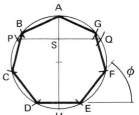

Draw the given circle.
Draw the vertical diameter AH.

With centre A draw arcs equal to the radius of the circle to cut the circle at P and Q. Join PQ to cut AH at S.
SP is the length of side.

Step off lengths equal to SP around the circle to obtain the required heptagon ABCDEFG.
Note: $\phi = 51° 43'$.

15. Any regular Polygon, in this case, a regular pentagon

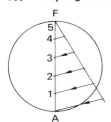 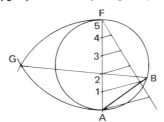 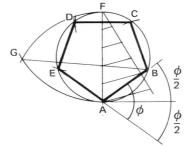

Draw diameter AF vertically and divide it into 5 equal parts (the same number of sides as the required polygon).

With centres A and F, draw arcs of radius AF to meet at G.
From G draw a line through point 2 to cut the circle at B.
Join AB to obtain the first side of the pentagon.

Step off BC, CD, DE and EA, all equal to AB, to obtain the required pentagon.
Note: $\phi = 72° \therefore \frac{\phi}{2} = 36°$.

Note: This method may be used to draw any regular polygon e.g. for a 7-sided figure AF would be divided into 7 equal parts. Accuracy and care are essential if a regular shape is to be achieved. In all cases the line GB passes through the point marked 2. It is more useful for polygons with odd numbers of sides than for the hexagon and octagon for which simpler constructions are available.

16. Regular octagon - using compasses mainly

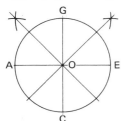 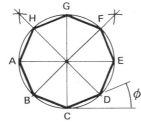

Draw the given circle.
Draw horizontal and vertical diameters AE and CG to intersect at O.
Bisect ∠AOG and ∠GOE.
The circle is now cut into 8 equal sectors.

Join the points on the circle to obtain the required octagon ABCDEFGH.
Note: $\phi = 22\frac{1}{2}°$

Notes on the constructions on this page

1. Construction 12 can only be used for a regular pentagon.
2. Construction 14 can only be used for a regular heptagon. It is not exact mathematically.
3. Construction 15 is accepted geometrically even though it is not exact mathematically.

General

Constructions for the following regular plane figures are not included.

the *nonagon* – 9 sides
the *decagon* – 10 sides
the *dodecagon* – 12 sides

This is because they are not commonly encountered

43

PLANE FIGURES DRAWN INSIDE GIVEN PLANE FIGURES OTHER THAN CIRCLES

It should be noted that in all cases, the inscribed figure is the *largest* that will fit inside the given plane figure.

17.   To draw a square inside a given triangle.

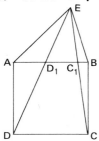 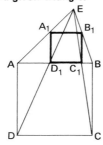 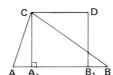 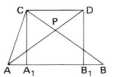 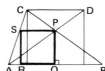

a) Draw a square ABCD on base AB of the given triangle. Join EC and ED cutting AB at C_1 and D_1 respectively.

Draw perpendiculars at D_1 and C_1 to cut AE at A_1 and BE at B_1. Join A_1B_1 to complete the required square.

b) Draw a line CA_1, from C, perpendicular to AB. Draw a square A_1CDB_1 on A_1C.

Draw a line from D to A cutting BC at P.

Draw a line PQ from P, perpendicular to AB, and a horizontal from P to S, on AC. Draw a line SR, from S, perpendicular to AB. PQRS is the required square.

Note: In both cases, the square is the largest which will 'fit' inside the given triangle. The constructions can be based on any side of the triangle but the largest side is the most convenient to use. Notice that one side of the square lies on one side of the triangle.

18.   To draw a quadrilaterals similar in shape to a given quadrilateral DEFG, inside a given triangle ABC.

 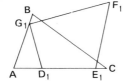 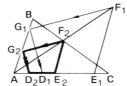

Given quadrilateral DEFG

Draw a quadrilateral $D_1E_1F_1G_1$ of any size similar in shape to given quadrilateral. D_1E_1 lies on AC and G_1 must touch AB.

Join AF_1 to cut BC at F_2. Draw lines from F_2 parallel to F_1G_1, F_1E_1 and G_1D_1 to obtain the required quadrilateral $D_2E_2F_2G_2$.

19.   To draw a square inside a given regular polygon — a pentagon.

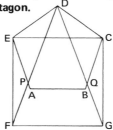 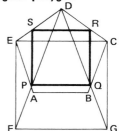

Draw the diagonal EC and on EC draw a square ECGF. Join FD to cut AE at P. Join GD to cut BC at Q.

Join PQ and draw lines perpendicular to PQ at P and Q to cut ED at S and CD at R. Join SR to obtain the required square.

20.   To draw a square inside a given sector

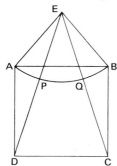 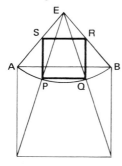

Draw the chord AB. Draw a square ABCD on AB. Join DE and CE to cut the arc AB at P and Q respectively.

Join PQ and draw perpendiculars to PQ at P and Q to cut AE at S and BE at R. Join SR to obtain the required square.

21.   To draw a semi-circle inside a given square

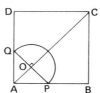 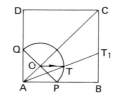 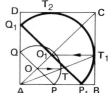

Draw the diagonal AC. At any point O on AC draw a line at right angles to AC, touching AB at P and AD at Q. With centre O and radius OP, draw a semi-circle on PQ.

Draw a horizontal from O to cut the semi-circle at T. Draw a line from A through T to meet BC at T_1.

Draw a horizontal from T_1 to cut AC at O_1. With centre O_1 and radius O_1T_1 draw a semi-circle to touch the square at T_2, P_1 and Q_1. Join P_1Q_1 to obtain the required semi-circle $P_1T_1T_2Q_1$.

22.   To draw a semi-circle inside a given triangle

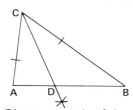 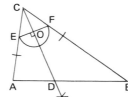 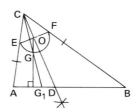 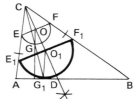

Bisect any angle of the given triangle ABC — in this case C. The bisector cuts AB in D.

From any point O on CD draw a semi-circle so that its diameter is at $90°$ to CD and touches CA and CB at E and F respectively.

From O draw a line perpendicular to AB cutting the semi-circle at G. Join CG and extend to meet AB at G_1.

From G_1 draw a line perpendicular to AB cutting CD at O_1. With centre O_1 and radius O_1G_1 draw a semi-circle to touch AC at E_1, AB at G_1, and BC at F_1.

Areas of Plane Figures

Triangles

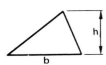 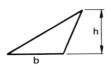

Area of acute-angled triangle $= \frac{1}{2}$ bh

Area of obtuse-angled triangle $= \frac{1}{2}$ bh

The area of a triangle $= \frac{1}{2}$ base x vertical height.

Triangles between parallel lines

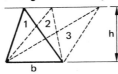 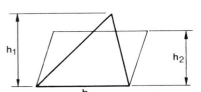

Area 1 = Area 2 = Area 3
Triangles with a common base and between the same parallel lines (i.e. the same vertical height) are equal in area.

Area 1 = Area 2
Triangles with equal bases and between the same parallel lines are equal in area.

Quadrilaterals

 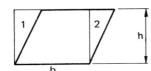  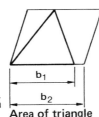

Area of rectangle = bh
Area of triangle $= \frac{1}{2}$ bh.

Area of parallelogram = bh

$$\frac{\text{Area of triangle}}{\text{Area of parallelogram}}$$
$$= \frac{\frac{1}{2} bh}{bh} = \frac{1}{2}$$

$$\frac{\text{Area of triangle}}{\text{Area of parallelogram}}$$
$$= \frac{b_1}{b_2} \times \frac{1}{2}$$

Same vertical height.
Different bases.
Area are in the ratio of the lengths of bases

$$\frac{\text{Area of triangle}}{\text{Area of parallelogram}}$$
$$= \frac{h_1}{h_2} \times \frac{1}{2}$$

Same base.
Different heights.
Areas are in the ratio of the vertical heights.

A parallelogram may be regarded as a rectangle from which a triangle (area 1) has been taken from one side and added to the opposite side (area 2).
Thus the area of a parallelogram = area of rectangle = bh.

EQUIVALENT AREAS

The area of any polygon may be found by dividing the figure into a number of triangles, the separate areas of which may then be added together. In most cases, however, a polygon may be altered in shape so that its area may be found more readily. The following constructions show how this may be achieved.

1.   To draw a triangle equal in area to given figures

a)   a given rectangle

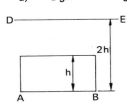

Draw a line DE parallel to the base AB of the given rectangle, at a distance equal to twice the height of the rectangle.

Mark the required apex C of the triangle anywhere along line DE. Join AC and BC to obtain the required triangle.

b)   a given parallelogram

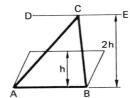

This construction is the same as that for the rectangle.

c)   a given trapezium ABDE

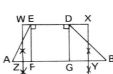 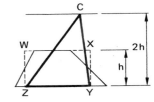

Draw perpendiculars from E and D cutting the base at F and G respectively. Draw perpendicular bisectors of AF and BG to meet ED extended to form a rectangle WXYZ. which is equal in area to the trapezium.

Use the construction shown in 1 a) to obtain the required triangle.

Note: In each case, the apex of the triangle C is chosen arbitrarily, but could be positioned centrally to form an isosceles triangle.

d)   a given irregular quadrilateral ABCD

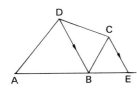 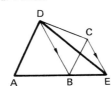

Draw a diagonal BD, and from C draw a line parallel to BD to meet the base line AB extended at E.

Join DE to obtain the required triangle ADE, equal in area to the given quadrilateral ABCD.
Note: Triangle DBE is equal in area to triangle DBC because they have a common base BD and lie between the same parallel lines

e)   a given irregular pentagon ABCDE

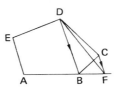 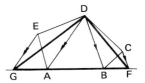

Draw a diagonal BD, and from C draw a line parallel to BD to meet the base line AB extended at F.
Join DF.

Draw a diagonal AD, and from E draw a line parallel to AD to meet the base line AB extended at G.
Join DG to obtain the required triangle DGF.

f) To draw a triangle equal in area to a given triangle ABC but with its vertical height reduced to $\frac{2}{3}$ of its original size i.e. in a given ratio 2:3.

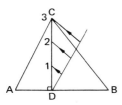

Draw a line CD from C perpendicular to AB. Divide CD into 3 equal parts.

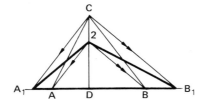

Join 2A and 2B.
Draw lines from C parallel to 2A and 2B to cut AB extended at A_1 and B_1 respectively.
Join $2A_1$ and $2B_1$ to obtain the required triangle A_1B_12.

g) To draw a triangle equal in area to a given triangle ABC but with a base AD of different length.

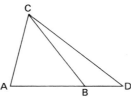

Extend base AB to the required length AD.
Join CD.

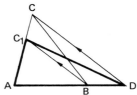

Draw a line from B parallel to DC to cut AC at C_1.
Join DC_1 to obtain the required triangle ADC_1.

h) To draw a triangle equal in area to a given triangle ABC but similar in shape to another given triangle DEF.

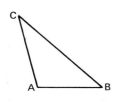

Given Triangles

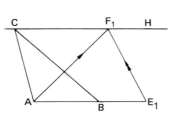

Draw a line CH parallel to AB.
Draw a line from A parallel to DF to cut CH at F_1.
Draw a line from F_1 parallel to FE to cut AB extended at E_1. Triangle AF_1E_1 is similar to given triangle DFE.

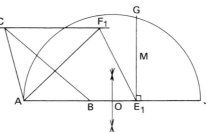

Extend AE_1 to J by a length equal to AB.
Bisect AJ at O.
With O as centre draw a semi-circle on AJ.
Draw a perpendicular from E_1 to cut the semi-circle at G.
E_1G is the mean (M) of AE_1 and E_1J and, therefore, of AE_1 and AB.
($E_1J = AB$)

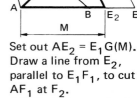

Set out $AE_2 = E_1G(M)$.
Draw a line from E_2, parallel to E_1F_1, to cut AF_1 at F_2.
AE_2F_2 is the required triangle.

2. **To draw a square equal in area to a given figure**

a) a given rectangle

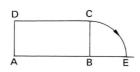

With centre B draw an arc of radius equal to side BC to meet base line AB extended at E.

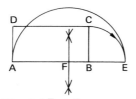

Bisect AE at F.
With centre F and radius FA draw a semi-circle on AE.

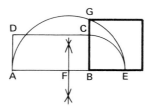

Extend BC to meet the semi-circle at G.
Draw a square on BG.
This square is equal in area to the given rectangle.

b) a given parallelogram

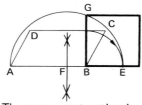

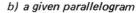

The same construction is used as in *(a)* because the parallelogram has the same base and vertical height as the rectangle in *(a)*.

Note: This construction is based upon the property of the geometric mean which is explained on page 15.

c) a given triangle

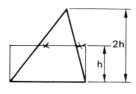

Draw a rectangle equal in area to the given triangle (same base, half vertical height).

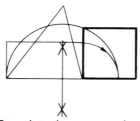

Complete the construction as outlined in *(a)* above.

d) a given quadrilateral ABCD

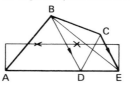

Draw a triangle equal in area to the given quadrilateral, and then draw a rectangle equal in area to the triangle.

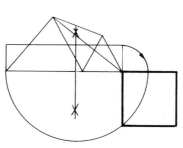

Draw a square equal in area to the rectangle using 2(a) above.

3. **To draw parallelogram equal in area to a given triangle**

i) 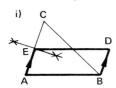 or ii)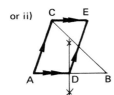

i) Bisect AC and from the mid-point E draw a line parallel to the base AB.
Draw a line from B parallel to AC to complete the required parallelogram ABDE.
Area ABC = Area ABDE.

ii) Bisect AB and from the mid-point D draw a line parallel to side AC.
Draw a line from C parallel to AB to complete the required parallelogram ADEC.
Area ABC = Area ADEC.

4. **To draw a rectangle equal in area to a given figure**
   a) a given parallelogram   *b) a given triangle*

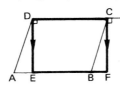

Draw lines DE from D and CF from C perpendicular to AB and AB extended to obtain the required rectangle DEFC.
Area ABCD = Area EFCD.

i)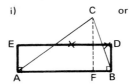

i) Draw perpendiculars at A and B.
Bisect the vertical height of the given triangle CF to intersect the perpendiculars at E and D respectively.
EDBA is the required rectangle.
Area ABC = Area EDBA.

ii) Draw a perpendicular AF and the perpendicular bisector DE of line AB, both equal in length to the vertical height of the given triangle.
Join FE.
Area ABC = Area ADEF.

5. **To draw a rectangle equal in area to a given rectangle ABCD**
   a) with a smaller given base length AE

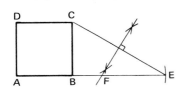

Set out the required base length AE from A on the base AB of the given rectangle ABCD.
Draw a perpendicular at E to cut CD at F.
Draw a diagonal from A through F to cut BC extended at G.

Draw a line from G parallel to AB to cut AD extended at H.
Extend EF to cut GH at J to obtain the required rectangle AEJH.
Area ABCD = Area AEJH.

   b) with a larger given base length AE

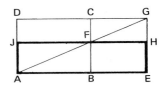

Set out the required base length AE from A on the base AB extended of the given rectangle ABCD.
Draw a perpendicular at E to meet DC extended at G.
Draw a diagonal AG to cut BC at F.

Draw a line through F parallel to AE to meet AD at J and EG at H.
AEHJ is the required rectangle.
Area ABCD = Area AEHJ.

6. **To draw a rectangle equal in area to a given square**
   a) given the length of one side of the rectangle

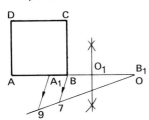

Extend the base of the given square to E with a line BE equal in length to the given side of the rectangle.
Join CE.
Draw the perpendicular bisector of CE to cut BE at F.

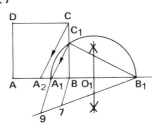

With centre F and radius FE draw a semi-circle, GCE.
Note: By construction, radius FE also equals radius FC.

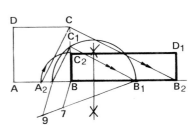

With centre B and radius BG, draw an arc to cut CB extended at H to give the other side of the required rectangle BEJH.

   b) with its sides in a given ratio, say 2:7

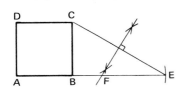

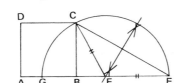

Extend AB by *any* convenient length to B_1.
Set out B_1A_1 on B_1A such that $BA_1 : BB_1 :: 2:7$
Bisect B_1A_1 at O_1.

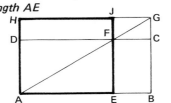

With centre O_1 and radius O_1A_1 draw a semi-circle on A_1B_1 to cut BC at C_1.
Join A_1C_1 and from C draw a line parallel to A_1C_1 to cut AB at A_2.
Join C_1B_1.

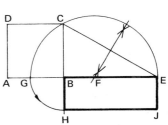

From C draw a line parallel to B_1C_1 to cut AB extended at B_2. BB_2 is one side of the required rectangle.
With centre B and radius BA_2 swing an arc to cut BC at C_2. BC_2 is the second side of the required rectangle.
Draw rectangle $BB_2D_1C_2$.
Note: $BC_2 : BB_2 :: 2:7$.

PLANE FIGURES DIVIDED INTO A NUMBER OF EQUAL AREAS

1. TRIANGLES

a) To divide a triangle ABC into a given number of parts of equal area, say 3, by lines drawn parallel to one side, say AB.

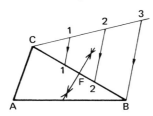 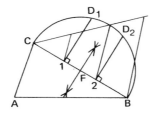 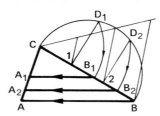

Note: This example once again illustrates the need for care to be taken when a series of constructions are superimposed on one another. Feint lines should be used for all constructions, then the final figure should be outlined as shown.

Divide a side opposite AB into the given number of equal parts, in this case 3. Bisect BC at F.

With centre F and radius FC draw a semi-circle on BC. Draw perpendiculars at 1 and 2 to cut the semi-circle at D_1 and D_2.

With centre C and radii CD_1 and CD_2 swing arcs to cut BC at B_1 and B_2 respectively.
Draw lines from B_1 and B_2, parallel to AB, to cut AC at A_1 and A_2 respectively.

b) To divide a triangle into a given number of parts of equal area, say 3, by lines drawn through a vertex.

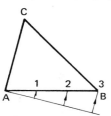 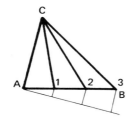

Divide the side opposite the vertex C into 3 equal parts.

Join C1 and C2.
Area C1A = C12 = C2B because they have the same vertical height and equal bases.

c) To divide a triangle into a given number of parts of equal area, say 3, from a point P inside the triangle.

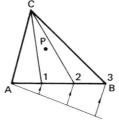 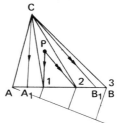 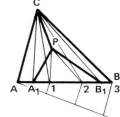

Divide the given triangle into 3 parts of equal area from the vertex C, using the construction 1b).

Join P1 and P2.
Draw lines from C parallel to P1 and P2 to meet AB at A_1 and B_1 respectively.

Join PA_1, PB_1 and PC.
Area $AA_1PC = A_1PB_1$ = BB_1PC.

2. SQUARES

To divide a square into a given number of parts of equal area, say 3, by lines drawn from a corner, D in this case.

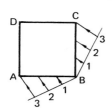 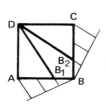

Divide each of the adjacent sides AB and AC, opposite corner D, into 3 equal parts.

Join D to the second division on AB (B_1) and on BC (B_2).
Area AB_1D = DB_1BB_2 = DB_2C.

3. QUADRILATERALS

To divide a quadrilateral ABCD into a given number of parts of equal area, say 5, by lines drawn from a corner, C in this case.

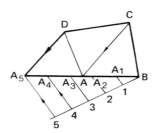 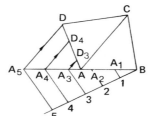 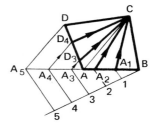

Draw the diagonal CA and from D draw a line parallel to CA to meet BA extended at A_5.
Divide BA_5 into 5 equal parts.
Label A_1 A_2 A_3 and A_4.

From the points which lie on AA_5 (A_3 and A_4 in this case) draw lines parallel to A_5D to meet AD at D_3 and D_4.

Join CA_1, CA_2, CD_3 and CD_4.
Area $CA_1B = CA_1A_2$ = CA_2AD_3 = CD_3D_4 = CD_4D

Note: The accuracy of all constructions shown on this page depends upon the care with which parallel construction lines are drawn. An adjustable set-square is most useful in achieving the accuracy required.

BISECTION OF AREAS

The following constructions show how certain plane figures can be divided into two parts of equal area by one or more lines.

1. TRIANGLES

a) To bisect the area of a triangle through point P, on one of its sides, BC in this case.

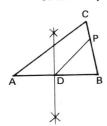 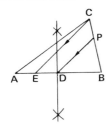 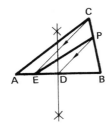

Bisect AB, the side opposite the corner nearer to P. Join PD.

From C draw a line parallel to PD to cut AB at E.

Join PE to divide ABC into two equal areas. Area BPE = Area CAEP.

b) To bisect the area of a given triangle by a line parallel to one of its sides, BC in this case.

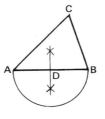 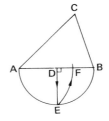 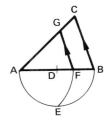

Bisect AB at D. With centre D and radius DA, draw a semi-circle on AB.

Draw a perpendicular from D to cut the semi-circle at E. With centre A and radius AE, draw an arc to cut AB at F.

Draw a line from F parallel to BC to cut AC at G. Area AFG = Area BCGF.

c) To bisect the area of a given triangle by a line perpendicular to one of its sides, AB in this case.

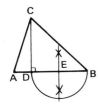 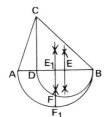 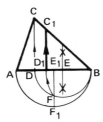

Draw a line CD perpendicular to AB. Bisect DB at E. With centre E and radius ED, draw a semi-circle on DB.

Bisect AB at E_1. With centre E_1 and radius E_1A, draw a semi-circle on AB. Draw a perpendicular from E_1 to cut the two semi-circles at F and F_1.

With centre B and radius BF, draw an arc to cut AB at D_1. Draw a line from D_1 parallel to DC to cut BC at C_1. Area BC_1D_1 = Area AD_1C_1C.

d) To bisect the area of a given triangle through a point P, which lies inside the triangle.

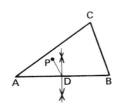 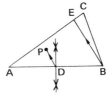 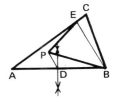

Bisect AB at D. Join PD.

Draw a line from B parallel to PD to cut AC at E.

Join PB and PE. Area ABPE = Area BPEC.

2. RECTANGLE

To bisect the area of a given retangle from any point P, on one of its sides, AB in this case.

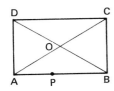 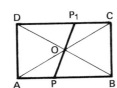

Draw the diagonals AC and BD to intersect at O.

Draw a line from P through O to cut DC at P_1. Area APP_1D = Area BPP_1C.

3. TRAPEZIUM

To bisect the area of a given trapezium by a line drawn from one of its corners, C in this case.

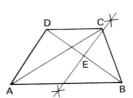 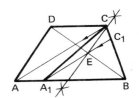

Draw the diagonals AC and BD. Bisect BD at E.

Draw a line through E parallel to AC to meet AB at A_1 and BC at C_1. Join CA_1. Area AA_1CD = Area BA_1C.

ENLARGEMENT AND REDUCTION OF AREAS

A variety of methods may be used to draw a plane figure which is similar in shape to a given figure but which is either enlarged or reduced in area. It is important to distinguish between constructions based on:

A) The ratio of the lengths of sides in which a *focal point* or *pole* is used to draw radial lines from one figure to the other, and
B) The ratio of areas for which the geometric mean is used.

Note: In all cases, the ratios will be expressed in the same way as a scale. If, for example, the area is to be doubled, then the increase in area will be in the ratio 2:1. Similarly, if the area is to be halved, then the reduction in area will be in the ratio 1:2.

A) Ratio of lengths of sides
To enlarge or reduce the area of a given plane figure using a focal point or pole.

a) **Enlarging a given figure by increasing the lengths of sides in the ratio 2:1, with the pole inside the given figure**

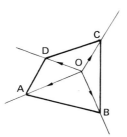
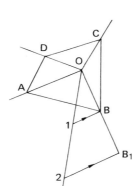
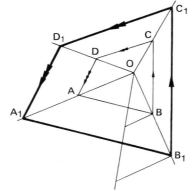

Note: An enlargement ratio of 2:1 means that any *line* in the enlarged figure is twice the length of the original line. However, the enlarged *area* has increased in the ratio 4:1, i.e. the two areas are proportional to the squares of their corresponding sides. It will be noticed that the radial lines form triangles, each of which is enlarged in the same proportion as the whole figure.

Choose any convenient point inside the given figure to be the pole. Label O. Draw radial lines from O to A, B, C and D and extend.

Increase the length of any one of the radial lines in the ratio 2:1. For example $OB_1 : OB :: 2 : 1$

Draw a line from B_1 parallel to BC to cut OC extended at C_1. Draw further parallel lines to obtain the points D_1 and A_1. $A_1B_1C_1D_1$ is the required figure. An adjustable set-square is very useful for drawing parallel lines accurately.

Consider C_1OD_1

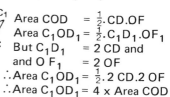

Area $COD = \frac{1}{2}.CD.OF$
Area $C_1OD_1 = \frac{1}{2}.C_1D_1.OF_1$
But $C_1D_1 = 2$ CD and
and $OF_1 = 2$ OF
$\therefore$ Area $C_1OD_1 = \frac{1}{2}.2$ CD.2 OF
$\therefore$ Area $C_1OD_1 = 4 \times$ Area COD

It is often more convenient to make the pole coincide with a corner of the given figure and the following two examples illustrate this. Note that the ratios are expressed in two different ways.

b) **Enlarging a given figure by increasing the lengths of sides in the ratio $1\frac{1}{2}:1$ with the pole coincident with corner A.**

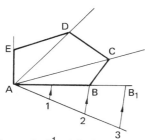
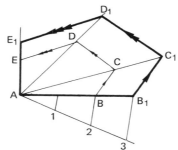

The ratio $1\frac{1}{2}:1$ is the same as 3:2. Extend the sides AB and AE and from A draw radial lines through D and C. Draw AB_1 one and a half times the length of AB, geometrically, i.e. $AB_1 : AB :: 3 : 2$.

Draw a line from B_1 parallel to BC to cut AC extended at C_1. Draw further parallel lines to obtain the points D_1 and E_1. Note that
Area $AB_1C_1D_1E_1$
$= (1\frac{1}{2})^2 \times$ Area ABCDE

c) **Reducing a given figure by decreasing the lengths of sides in the ratio $1:1\frac{1}{4}$ (4:5) with the pole coincident with corner A.**

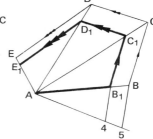

Draw radial lines from A to C and D. Draw AB_1 four-fifths the length of AB, geometrically, i.e. $AB_1 : AB :: 4 : 5$

Draw a line from B_1 parallel to BC to cut AC at C_1. Draw further parallel lines to obtain points, D_1 and E_1. Note that
Area $AB_1C_1D_1E_1$
$= (\frac{4}{5})^2 \times$ Area ABCDE

The fact that two similarly shaped areas are proportional to the squares of their corresponding sides is extremely important in a number of aspects of industrial design for economic reasons. If the linear dimensions of a material are increased without consideration being given to the larger percentage increase in cross-sectional area, then unnecessary expense can be incurred. The design of shafts, welds, concrete foundations and embankments and cuttings for roadworks is influenced in this way.

Note: If any part of the given figure is curved, then extra radial lines would need to be drawn in order to plot extra points for the enlarged free hand curves.

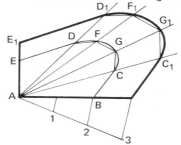

Consider the same construction as in (b) above but with the straight line CD replaced with a curve. Draw any convenient number of radial lines from A (2 in this case) to cut the curve CD at F and G. Join DF, FG and GC and draw lines parallel to these, D_1F_1, F_1G_1 and G_1C_1, to obtain points on the enlarged curve C_1D_1 which can be joined freehand.

d) Enlarging a given figure by increasing the lengths of its sides in the ratio $1\frac{2}{3}:1$ with the pole outside the figure.

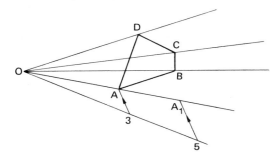

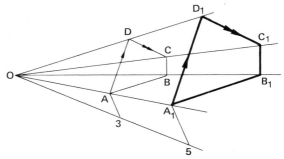

Choose any convenient point outside the given figure to be the pole. Label O. Draw radial lines from O through A, B, C and D. and extend.

Draw OA_1, one and two-thirds the length of OA, geometrically, i.e.
$$OA_1 : OA :: 5 : 3.$$

Draw a line from A_1 parallel to AD to cut OD extended at D_1. Draw further parallel lines to obtain the points C_1 and B_1. Area $A_1B_1C_1D_1 = (\frac{5}{3})^2$ x Area ABCD.

Note: The above construction can be used to explain how a figure $(A_1B_1C_1D_1)$ can be *reduced* in area by decreasing the lengths of sides in the ratio $1:1\frac{2}{3}$ or $3:5$.
1. Draw radial lines from the chosen pole O as in (d).
2. Draw OA, three-fifths the length of OA_1.
3. Draw lines parallel to A_1B_1, B_1C_1, C_1D_1 and A_1D_1 to obtain the reduced figure ABCD. Area ABCD $= (\frac{3}{5})^2$ x Area $A_1B_1C_1D_1$.

B) Ratio of Areas

a) To enlarge the area of a given figure in the ratio 5:3

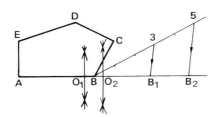

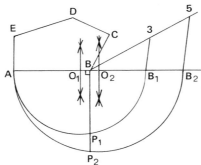

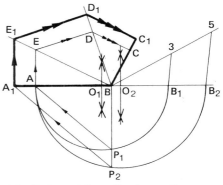

Extend side AB, of the given polygon by any convenient length to B_2. Divide BB_2 in the given ratio 5:3 so that $BB_2 : BB_1 :: 5 : 3$ Bisect AB_1 at O_1 and AB_2 at O_2.

With centre O_1 and radius O_1A draw a semi-circle on AB_1. With centre O_2 and radius O_2A, draw a semi-circle on AB_2. Draw a perpendicular at B to cut the two semi-circles at P_1 and P_2 respectively.

Join P_1A, and from P_2 draw a line parallel to P_1A to cut BA extended at A_1. Join BE and BD. Extend both lines. Draw a line from A_1 parallel to AE cutting BE extended at E_1. Draw further parallel lines to obtain points D_1 and C_1. Area $A_1BC_1D_1E_1 = \frac{5}{3}$ x Area ABCDE

b) To reduce the area of a given figure in the ratio 2 : 5

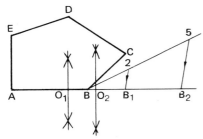

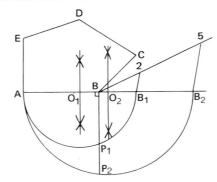

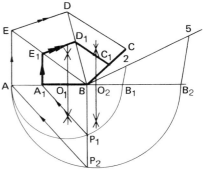

Extend side AB of the given polygon by any convenient length to B_2. Divide BB_2 in the given ratio 2:5 so that $BB_1 : BB_2 :: 2 : 5$ Bisect AB_1 at O_1 and AB_2 at O_2.

With centre O_1 and radius O_1A, draw a semi-circle on AB_1. With centre O_2 and radius O_2A, draw a semi-circle on AB_2. Draw a perpendicular at B to cut the two semi-circles at P_1 and P_2 respectively.

Join P_2A, and from P_1 draw a line parallel to P_2A to cut AB at A_1. Join BE and BD. Draw a line from A_1 parallel to AE cutting BE at E_1. Draw further parallel lines to obtain the points D_1 and C_1. Area $A_1BC_1D_1E_1 = \frac{2}{5}$ x Area ABCDE

COMBINED AREAS

To draw a plane figure which is both similar in shape to two given similar figures and also equal to their combined areas, Pythagoras' Theorem should be utilized, as outlined below:

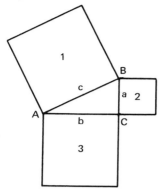

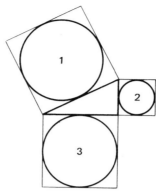

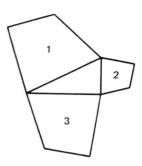

a) ABC is a right-angled triangle and squares are drawn on each of the 3 sides.
From Pythagoras
$$c^2 = a^2 + b^2$$
i.e. Area 1 = Area 2 + Area 3

b) If circles are drawn to fit inside each of the 3 squares then:
Area of circle 1 = Area of circle 2
                              + Area of circle 3.

If similarly shaped irregular quadrilaterals are drawn on each of the 3 sides, then, as in *a)* and *b)*.
Area 1 = Area 2 + Area 3.
Note: This is true for *any* plane figure drawn on the 3 sides of a right-angled triangle.

Note: Pythagoras' theorem can, of course, also be used to draw a plane figure whose area is equal to the DIFFERENCE between the areas of two similar figures, as the following example illustrates.

Problem: To determine, graphically, the length of side of an equilateral triangle whose area is equal to the difference between the areas of two equilateral triangles of given lengths of side. (Assume the given sides are 45 mm and 55 mm.)

Solution:
Draw a horizontal (base) line AB 45 mm long, as shown opposite.
From B, draw a line at 90° to AB.
From A, draw an arc, of radius 55 mm, to cut the vertical line at C.
BC is the required length of side (32 mm).

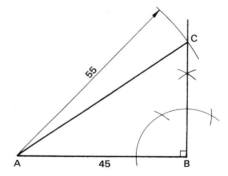

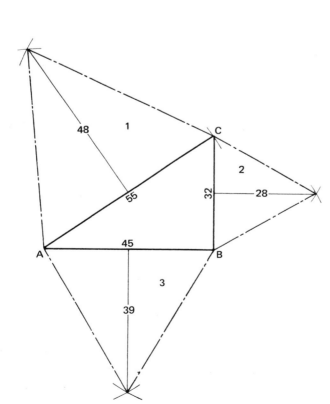

Check:
In the figure on the left,

Area 2   = Area 1 − Area 3

i.e. $\left(\dfrac{32 \times 28}{2}\right) = \left(\dfrac{55 \times 48}{2}\right) - \left(\dfrac{45 \times 39}{2}\right)$

PROPORTIONAL RECTANGLES

Although the rectangle is one of the more simple shapes, it can be used to establish proportional relationships which have had an influence in architecture and, more recently, photographic film and the sizes of paper on which drawings are made.

The internationally recognized 'A' sizes of paper depend initially on an original rectangle of paper (A 0 size) which is one square metre in area. This rectangle is so proportioned that, when it is repeatedly cut into two equal parts, each of the two smaller pieces is exactly the same shape as the original.

This can be illustrated diagrammatically as follows.

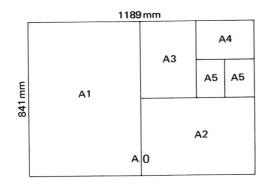

Size (mm)		Area (m²)
A0	1189 × 841	1
A1	841 × 594	$\frac{1}{2}$
A2	594 × 420	$\frac{1}{4}$
A3	420 × 297	$\frac{1}{8}$
A4	297 × 210	$\frac{1}{16}$
A5	210 × 148	$\frac{1}{32}$

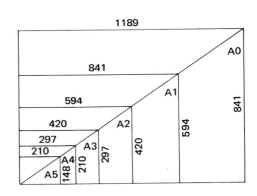

In every case:

The ratio $\dfrac{\text{long side}}{\text{short side}} = \dfrac{\sqrt{2}}{1}$

e.g. $\dfrac{1189}{841} = \dfrac{1.414}{1} = \dfrac{\sqrt{2}}{1}$

Each 'A' size is obtained by dividing the previous size into two equal parts as shown.

A rectangle with proportions which include the square root of a whole number is called a root rectangle.

The 'A' sizes may also be obtained by drawing a diagonal across an A0 rectangle and marking off the lengths of sides as shown above.

Starting with a square with lengths of sides of unity (1), a series of root rectangles can be drawn.

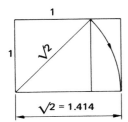

$\sqrt{2} = 1.414$

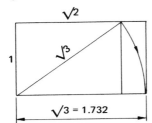

$\sqrt{3} = 1.732$

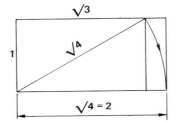

$\sqrt{4} = 2$

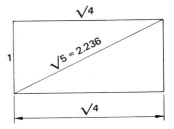

$\sqrt{4}$

Swing the diagonal to the base extended to give a base of rectangle of $\sqrt{2}$.

Draw a rectangle with a base of $\sqrt{2}$. Diagonal is now $\sqrt{3}$. Swing diagonal to base extended.

Draw a rectangle with base of $\sqrt{3}$. Diagonal is now $\sqrt{4} = 2$. Swing diagonal to base extended.

Draw a rectangle with base of $\sqrt{4}$. Diagonal is now $\sqrt{5}$. $(\sqrt{5})^2 = (\sqrt{4})^2 + (1)^2$ i.e. $5 = 4 + 1$

Clearly, this construction may be carried on ad infinitum and it is possible, therefore, to construct any rectangle with an area equal to the square root of a given whole number. Also, any square with an area equal to a given whole number may be drawn on the diagonal of the rectangle.

An alternative method of obtaining the lengths of sides of "root" rectangles is shown below.

One further proportional rectangle is shown below. It is sometimes referred to as the Golden Rectangle.

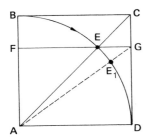

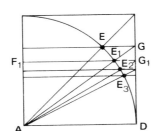

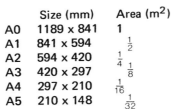

Draw the diagonal of any square to cut arc BD in E. Draw FEG parallel to AD. AG is the diagonal of a $\sqrt{2}$ rectangle ADGF.

Draw $F_1 E_1 G_1$ parallel to AD. AG_1 is the diagonal of a $\sqrt{3}$ rectangle ADG_1F_1. Repeat for E_2 ($\sqrt{4}$) and E_3 ($\sqrt{5}$)

Draw any square ABCD. Bisect AB in E. Join EC. Draw EF = EC and draw rectangle BFGC.

If the side of the square is unity (1), then $EC = \sqrt{1^2 + (0.5)^2} = 1.118$ and $BF = 1.118 - 0.5 = 0.618$ ∴ $AF = 1.618$

$\dfrac{AF}{FG} = \dfrac{1.618}{1} = 1.618$

$\dfrac{FG}{BF} = \dfrac{1}{0.618} = 1.618$

Which means that rectangle BFGC has the same proportions as rectangle AFGD.

Geometrical Constructions for the Ellipse

In the ellipse drawn on the right, the longer, horizontal axis XX is known as the MAJOR axis, the shorter vertical axis YY is known as the MINOR axis. Each of the fixed points F_1 and F_2 is a FOCUS (plural: FOCI). The sum of the distances from the FOCI to any point on the ellipse is equal to the length of the MAJOR axis, e.g. consider point P_1 on the curve.

$$F_1P_1 + F_2P_1 = XX \text{ (length of major axis)}$$

When the point is at the end of the major axis,

$$F_1P_2 + F_2P_2 = XX \text{ (or } F_1F_2 + 2F_2P_2 = XX)$$

This is the basis of the pencil and thread method (below).

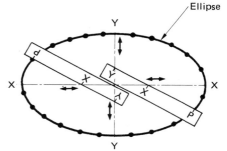

1. **To draw an ellipse using pencil and thread, given the lengths of the major and minor axes**

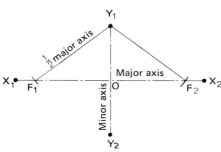

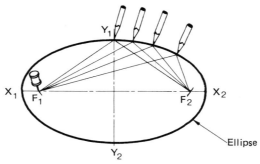

To position the focal points, set out the major and minor axes, X_1X_2 and Y_1Y_2, at right angles to each other. With centre Y_1 and radius equal to $\frac{1}{2}$ major axis, OX_1, draw arcs to cut X_1X_2 at F_1 and F_2. Fix two pins firmly at F_1 and F_2.

Place a loop of thread of length equal to the major axis X_1X_2 *plus* the distance between the focal points, over the pins. With a pencil, keeping the loop taut, trace out a smooth elliptical curve as shown above.

Note Clearly, this is a practical method of drawing an ellipse and would not be used for examination purposes. Mapping pins of the type shown at F_1 provide firm foci. The thread should not stretch, and great care should be taken in forming the loop of thread which has a total length of $F_1Y_1 + F_2Y_1 + F_1F_2$.

2. **To draw an ellipse using a "trammel", given the lengths of the major and minor axes**

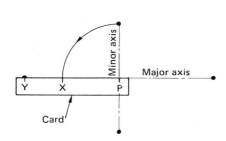

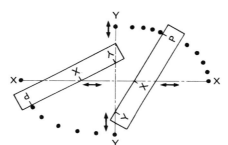

(a) Draw the major and minor axes. On a convenient length of thin card mark out

$YP = \frac{1}{2}$ major axis and

$XP = \frac{1}{2}$ minor axis

This card is called a TRAMMEL and, when marked out as shown above, it is referred to as a SHORT trammel.

Mark out points on the ellipse at P, placing the trammel across the XX and YY axes so that

Y always lies on the YY axis and
X always lies on the XX axis.

Points on the curve in the 1st and 3rd quarters are obtained as shown above.

Points on the curve in the 2nd and 4th quarters are obtained as shown above.
Note This practical method enables a large number of points to be marked out rapidly. It should not be used for examination questions unless specifically requested.

(b) On a convenient length of thin card, mark out

$YP = \frac{1}{2}$ Major axis and

$PX = \frac{1}{2}$ Minor axis

To "plot" the ellipse, the trammel is moved so that X is always on the major axis, or the axis extended and Y is always on the minor axis, or the axis extended. Points are marked at P.

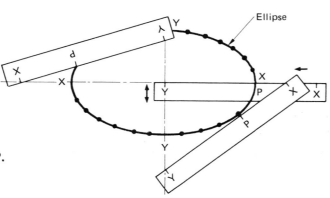

Note When marked out as shown here, the card is referred to as a LONG trammel. A disadvantage of this method is that both major and minor axes need to be extended to complete the ellipse.

3. To draw an ellipse using the focal points and intersecting radii, given the lengths of the major and minor axes

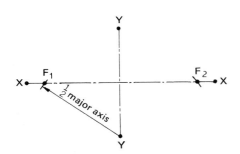

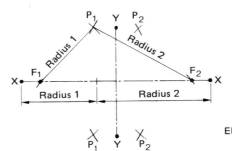

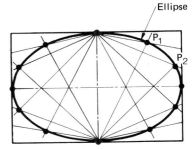

Set out the major and minor axes XX and YY. With centre Y (at either end of the minor axis) and radius equal to $\frac{1}{2}$ major axis, draw radii to cut the major axis at F_1 and F_2.

With centres F_1 and F_2 draw a pair of arcs which intersect at P_1, the sum of the two radii being equal to the length of major axis XX. Obtain 3 other symmetrically placed points using the same pair of radii. Note: The lengths of the radii can be marked off along the major axis, as shown.

Repeat the construction for as many points as may be necessary to obtain an accurate ellipse.
Join the points with a smooth heavy freehand curve.
Remember: The sum of each pair of radii must equal XX.

4. To draw an ellipse using concentric circles, given the lengths of the major and minor axes.

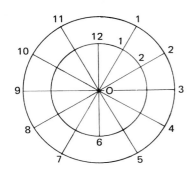

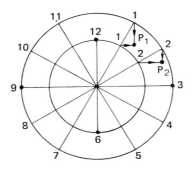

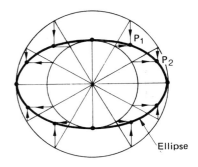

With centre O and radius = $\frac{1}{2}$ minor axis draw a circle.
With centre O and radius = $\frac{1}{2}$ major axis draw a circle *concentric* with the first circle. Divide the circles into a convenient number of equal parts (12 in this case, using 60°/30° set-square) and number as shown.

Points 12, 3, 6 and 9 already lie on the required ellipse.
Draw a vertical line down from 1 on the outer circle to intersect a horizontal line drawn from 1 on the inner circle at P_1.
Repeat from points 2 to position P_2.

Repeat the construction for each quadrant in turn to obtain 12 points on the ellipse which can be joined with a smooth heavy freehand curve.

5. To draw an ellipse inside a rectangle, given either the lengths of sides or the lengths of the major and minor axes

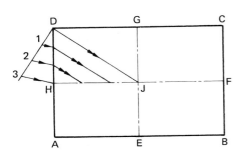

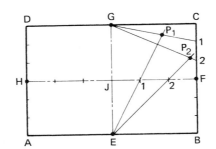

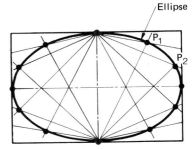

(a) Draw a rectangle ABCD with given lengths of sides (or the given major and minor axes FH, EG).
Draw vertical and horizontal centre lines EG and FH to intersect at J.
Divide DH into any convenient number of equal parts (say 3) and use the divisions on DH to divide HJ into the *same* number of equal parts.

Divide HA, CF, BF and JF into 3 equal parts in a similar manner.
Draw a line from E through 1 on JF to intersect a line from G to 1 on CF at point P_1.
Draw a line from E through 2 on JF to intersect a line from G to 2 on CF at P_2.
G, P_1, P_2 and F are points on the ellipse.

Repeat the constructions for each quarter of the rectangle, in turn, to obtain 12 points on the ellipse which can be joined with a smooth, heavy, freehand curve.
Note: Feint construction lines are essential to avoid confusion.

55

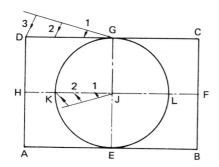

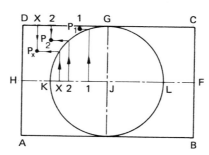

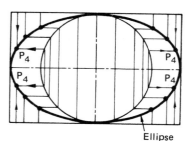

(b) Draw a rectangle ABCD with sides of given length (or equal to the major and minor axes HF and EG).
Draw vertical and horizontal centre lines EG and HF to intersect at J.
With centre J and radius JG, draw a circle cutting HF at K and L.
Divide GD and KJ into the same number of equal parts (say 3).

Draw a perpendicular from 1 on KJ to meet the circle and from this point draw a horizontal to intersect a perpendicular from 1 on GD at P_1.
Repeat from points 2 on KJ and 2 on GD to position P_2.
Note: To provide an additional point (P_x) between P_2 and H divide D_2 and K_2 into 2 equal parts and repeat the construction.

Repeat the construction for each quarter, in turn, to obtain sufficient points for an accurate ellipse.
Join the points with a smooth heavy freehand curve.
Note: Further points (P_4) may be added if required.

6. To draw an ellipse inside a given parallelogram

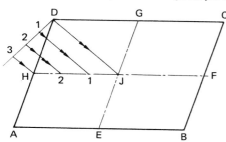

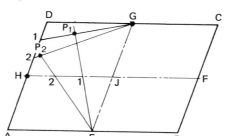

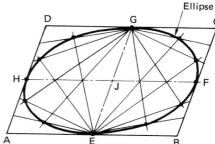

(a) Find the mid-points of the sides, E, F, G and H.
Join EG and FH to intersect at J.
Divide DH into any convenient number of equal parts (say 3) and use the divisions on DH to divide HJ into the *same* number of equal parts.

Draw a line from E through 1 on JH to intersect a line from G to 1 on DH at point P_1.
Draw a line from E through 2 on JH to intersect a line from G to 2 on DH at point P_2. G, P_1, P_2 and H are points on the ellipse.

Divide HA, CF, BF and JF into 3 equal parts. Repeat the construction for each quarter of the parallelogram, in turn, to obtain twelve points on the ellipse. Join the points with a smooth heavy freehand curve.

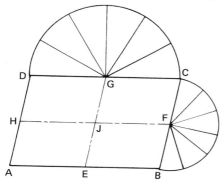

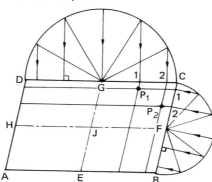

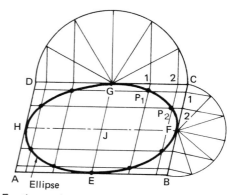

(b) Find the mid-points of the sides, E, F, G and H.
Join EG and FH to intersect at J.
With centres G and F, draw semi-circles on CD and BC.
Divide each semi-circle into the same number of equal parts, say 6.

Draw lines from the points on each semi-circle, perpendicular to its base, and number.
From 1 and 2 on GC, draw lines parallel to BC to intersect lines drawn from 1 and 2 on FC, parallel to DC, to obtain points P_1 and P_2 on the ellipse.

Further points on the ellipse are obtained by completing a grid of construction lines as shown above. The first two points, P_1 and P_2, are "mirrored" in the other three quarters of the parallelogram.

7. Approximate ellipse — used for drawing ellipses quickly.
(not recommended for use in answering examination questions)

Set out the major and minor axes, AC and BD.
Join AB and from B set out BE = AO − BO.
Bisect AE to cut AO at G and, in this case, BD extended at K.
With centres G and K and radii GA and KB, draw arcs which blend at L.
Join DC and repeat the construction to obtain G_1 and K_1 and draw arcs which blend at L_1, L_2 and L_3.

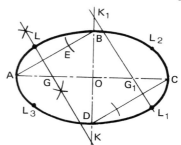

Note: Elliptical curves are commonly encountered in engineering in fabrication and sheet-metal work. They appear quite frequently in engineering drawings, for, when any circle or cylinder is viewed obliquely, i.e. at an angle other than 90°, it is shown as an ellipse. Many examples can be seen in the chapters dealing with Isometric and Oblique drawings.

Tangents to an ELLIPSE

The most commonly used construction for drawing a TANGENT and NORMAL to any point P on an ellipse is presented in the section which deals with the ellipse as a locus (see p. 63). A selection of similar, though less commonly used, constructions are detailed below.

1. To draw a tangent to any point P on a given ellipse.

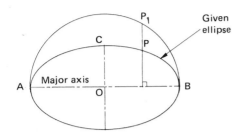

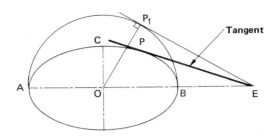

Note: Clearly, this method has limitations. When P is near to C, line PE is too long and, when P is near to B, line PE is too short for convenience of construction.

With centre O draw a semi-circle on the major axis AB.
Draw line perpendicular to AB, through P to touch the semi-circle at P_1.

Join OP_1 and draw a line from P_1, at $90°$ to OP_1, to cut AB extended at E.
Draw a line from E through P to obtain the tangent.

2. To draw a tangent to a given ellipse from any point P, outside the ellipse.

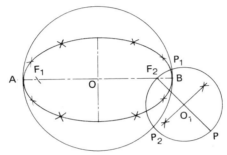

(a) With centre O draw a circle on the major axis AB. Position F_1 and F_2. Join PF_2.

Bisect PF_2 at O_1 and with centre O_1 and radius O_1P draw a circle on PF_2 cutting the first circle (on AB) at P_1 and P_2.

Draw lines from P through P_1 and P_2 to touch ellipse at T_1 and T_2 respectively. PT_1 and PT_2 are tangents to the ellipse.

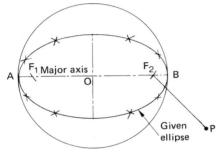

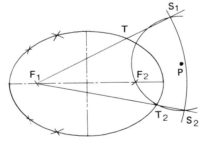

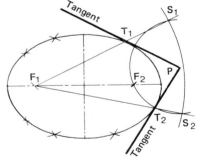

(b) With centre F_1 and radius equal to the major axis AB, draw an arc which passes beyond point P.
With centre P and radius equal to PF_2, draw an arc to cut the first arc at S_1 and S_2.

Join F_1S_1 and F_2S_2 to cut the ellipse at T_1 and T_2 respectively.

Draw lines from P through T_1 and T_2 to obtain the required tangents.

Note: In this example the arc drawn from F_1 is further away from F_1 than is point P.

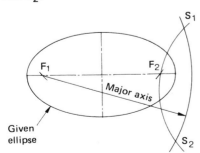

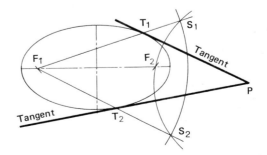

Note: This construction becomes more difficult to accomplish when P is either very near to, or far away from, the ellipse.

(c) With centre F_1 and radius equal to the major axis draw an arc which passes between F_1 and P.
With centre P and radius equal to PF_2 draw an arc to cut the first arc at S_1 and S_2.

Join F_1S_1 and F_1S_2 to cut the ellipse at T_1 and T_2 respectively.
Draw lines from P through T_1 and T_2 to obtain the required tangents.

Geometrical Constructions for the Parabola

The parabolic curve is used extensively for reflectors, vertical curves in road construction and masonry arches. It is also the shape of the bending moment diagram for a simply supported uniformly loaded beam.

To draw a RECTANGULAR parabola given the AXIS and the BASE

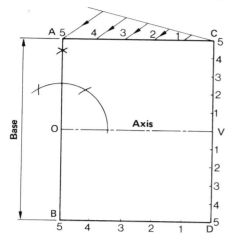

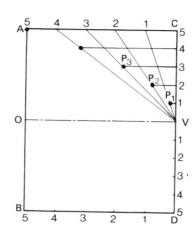

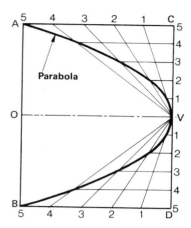

Draw the given axis OV.
Construct a perpendicular at O and step off half the length of the base above and below O.
Complete the rectangle ABCD.
Divide CA, CV, VD and DB into the same number of equal parts — the number being arbitrary — and number as shown.

Join V to point 1 on AC and draw a horizontal line from point 1 on CV to cut V1 at P_1.
Join V2 and V3 and draw horizontal lines from points 2 and 3 on CV to cut V2 and V3 at P_2 and P_3 respectively.
Note: V and A are the extreme points on the parabolic curve.

Obtain the points on the lower half of the curve in a similar manner.
Draw a smooth, heavy curve through the points to obtain the required rectangular PARABOLA.

Note: If a surveyor's steel tape or a flexible chain is allowed to hang freely from two supports at the same level, then the resulting curve, or "catenary" is parabolic in shape. Such a curve can be drawn using the construction outlined above taking L and h as the sides of the rectangle inside which the curve is plotted.

If the two supports are not level, the resulting curve is still parabolic in shape and may be enclosed by a parallelogram. The curve is constructed using a modified version of the one described above and is, literally, a parabola inside a parallelogram.

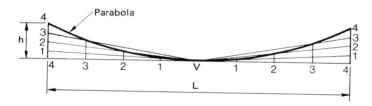

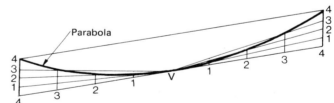

To join two given points with a parabolic curve
(a) Inside a right angle

(b) Inside an angle other than 90°.

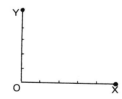

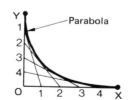

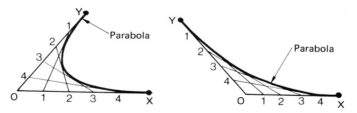

Draw OX and OY to form the required right angle.
Divide OX and OY into the same number of equal parts, say 5.

Number as shown.
Join 1, 2, 3, and 4 on OX to 1, 2, 3 and 4 on OY, respectively.
Sketch a freehand curve which *touches* each line.

In each of the cases shown above, the parabola is drawn using the construction outlined on the left.

Note: The lines joining the pairs of points are tangents of the required parabola and form what is referred to as its "envelope". Curves obtained in this way may be used in the design of components when a parabolic curve is thought to be more pleasing to the eye than the ubiquitous circular arc, e.g. for stonework arches, wrought iron gates, decorative castings, etc.

To draw the tangent to any point P on a given parabola.

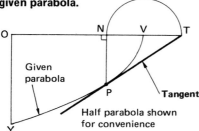

To locate the focus of a given parabola

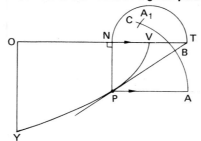

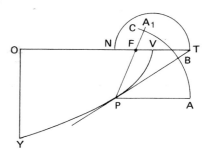

From P draw a line perpendicular to OV to cut OV at N.
With centre V and radius VN draw a semi-circle to meet OV extended at T.
Draw a line from T through P to obtain the required tangent.

Draw a line from P parallel to OT.
With centre P and any convenient radius PA, draw an arc AC to cut PT at B.
With centre B and radius BA, draw an arc to cut arc AC at A_1.

Join PA_1 cutting OT at F, the Focus.
Note: As $\angle BPA_1 = \angle BPA$, F must be the required focus of the parabola.
(Refer to the construction on page 63.)

To draw the tangent to a given parabola from any point P outside the parabola.

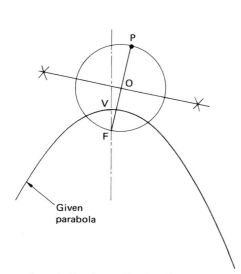

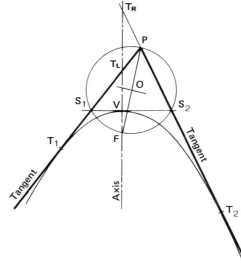

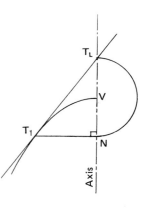

Locate the focus F using the constructions outlined above.
Join PF and bisect PF at O.
With centre O draw a circle on PF.

Draw a line through the vertex V perpendicular to the axis, cutting the circle at S_1 and S_2.
Draw lines from P through S_1 and S_2 to obtain the required tangents.

Note: The actual points of tangency, T_1 and T_2 may be verified. For example, for T_1. With radius VT_L draw a semi-circle to cut the axis at N. Draw a perpendicular from N to cut the parabola at T_1.

To draw a parabola given its tangents and their points of contact T_1 and T_2.

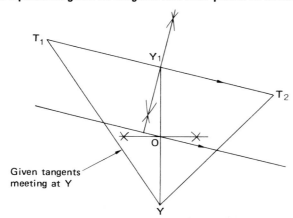

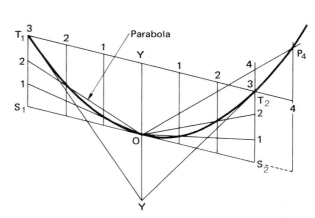

Draw the tangents YT_1 and YT_2.
Join the points of contact T_1 and T_2 and bisect at Y_1.
Join YY_1 and bisect at O.
Draw a line through O parallel to T_1T_2.

Draw lines T_1S_1 and T_2S_2 parallel to YOY_1 to form a parallelogram.
Draw the parabola within the parallelogram using the construction outlined on the previous page.
Additional points, e.g. P_4, may be added as shown.
(A fourth division has been added to the parallelogram both vertically and "horizontally".)

Geometrical Constructions for the Hyperbola

To draw a HYPERBOLA given the TRANSVERSE Axis, the ABSCISSA and the ORDINATE

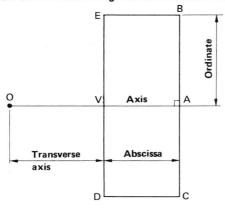

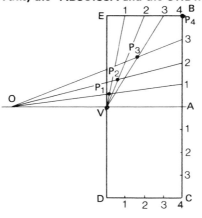

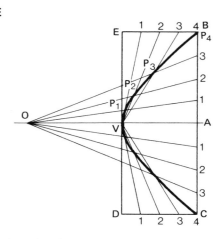

Draw the horizontal axis, any length.
Step off along this axis, the TRANSVERSE axis OV, and the abscissa VA, as shown.
Step off the length of the ORDINATE along a perpendicular drawn through point A, both above and below the axis.
Label the ordinates AB and AC.
Construct the rectangle BCDE.

Divide AB, AC, BE and CD into the same number of equal parts (four being convenient) and number as shown.
Draw feint radial lines from O to points 1, 2 and 3 on AB.
Draw lines from V to 1, 2 and 3 on EB cutting O-1, O-2, O-3 in points P_1, P_2 and P_3 respectively.
Note: V and B are extreme points on the curve.

Obtain the points on the lower half of the curve in a similar manner.
Draw a smooth, heavy curve through the points to obtain the required HYPERBOLA.

Asymptotes

It is advisable to know how lines called *asymptotes* are related to the hyperbolic curves. They are shown in the two figures below and may intersect at any angle. In the figure on the right, they intersect at $90°$, the curve being then referred to as an EQUILATERAL or RECTANGULAR hyperbola.

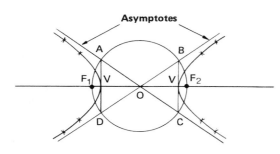

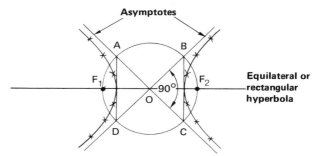

To draw the asymptotes given the double hyperbola and focal points.

From centre O, the mid-point of the transverse axis (VV), draw a circle which passes through the focal points F_1 and F_2.
From the vertex V of each hyperbola, draw a line perpendicular to the transverse axis to cut the circle at A, B, C and D.
Join AC and BD and extend both lines to obtain the required asymptotes.

To draw an EQUILATERAL Hyperbola, given the ASYMPTOTES and a point P on the curve.

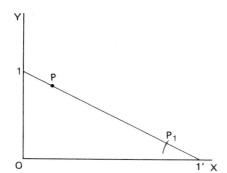

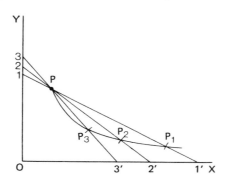

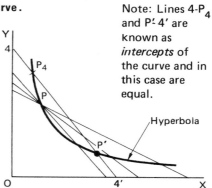

Note: Lines 4-P_4 and P'-4' are known as *intercepts* of the curve and in this case are equal.

(a)   Draw the asymptotes OX and OY at $90°$ to each other, and position the given point P.
Draw a line through P from *any* point 1 on OY to meet OX at 1'.
From 1' on OX set out length equal to 1-P to obtain point P_1.

Draw lines 2-P-2' and 3-P-3' from *any* points 2 and 3 on OY and set out 2'-P_2 and 3'-P_3 equal in length to 2-P and 3-P respectively.
Join points P_1, P_2, etc. with a smooth curve to complete part of the hyperbola.

Draw a line through *any* point P' on the curve to cut OX at 4' and OY at 4.
From 4 on OY set out a length equal to 4'-P' to obtain point P_4.
"Plot" further points if required.
Draw a smooth, heavy curve through the points.

60

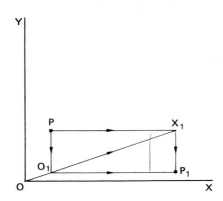

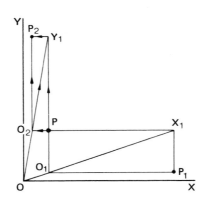

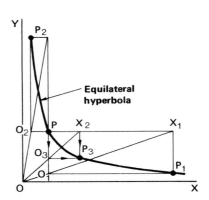

(b)   Draw the asymptotes OX and OY at 90° to each other and position the given point P.

Draw a line PX_1, of any length, parallel to OX.
Join OX_1.
Draw a line from P, parallel to OY, to cut OX_1 at O_1.
Draw a line from O_1, parallel to OX, and a line from X_1, parallel to OY, to intersect at P_1, a second point on the hyperbola.

Draw PY_1, of any length, parallel to OY.
Join OY1.
Draw a line from P, parallel to OX, to cut OY_1 at O_2.
Draw a line from O_2, parallel to OY, and a line from Y_1, parallel to OX, to intersect a P_2, a third point on the hyperbola.

Further points on the hyperbola may be obtained in a similar manner, e.g. P_3. When sufficient points have been "plotted", join them with a smooth, heavy freehand curve.

Note: For an EQUILATERAL hyperbola the asymptotes may be considered as the axes of a graph. Points on the curve may then be referred to by co-ordinates.

To draw a hyperbola given the asymptotes, the angle between them (not 90°) and a point P on the curve.

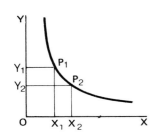

The *product* of the co-ordinates is constant, e.g. in the figure on the left
$$P_1Y_1 \times P_1X_1 = P_2Y_2 \times P_2X_2$$

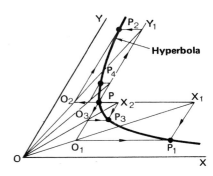

The steps in this construction are very similar to those used to draw the equilateral hyperbola in (b) above.

Note: The resulting curve is *not* an equilateral (rectangular) hyperbola because the angle between the asymptotes is *not* 90°.

Applications
The hyperbola is a less familiar curve than the ellipse or the parabola but is encountered in mathematics and science,
e.g. when a gas is compressed,
    the pressure varies inversely as the volume,
i.e. pressure x volume = a constant
If values obtained from this equation are plotted as a graph, the curve is hyperbolic in shape.

Loci

LOCUS is the name given to a path traced out by a point which moves in a plane (flat surface) according to specified conditions. The plural of locus is LOCI.

Ellipse, Parabola and Hyperbola

A large number of curves may be generated as loci but three in particular — the ellipse, parabola and hyperbola — should be considered as a group.

A point may move so that it is always a prescribed distance from a fixed point and a fixed straight line, and the ratio of these two distances governs whether the resulting curve will be an ellipse, parabola or hyperbola.

The figure on the right shows the three loci drawn relative to the same fixed point (the focus) and the fixed line (the directrix).

Each curve is dealt with in greater detail as follows:

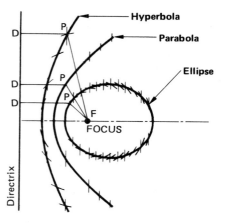

1. THE ELLIPSE The ellipse is the locus of a point which moves in a plane so that the ratio of its distance from a fixed point, the FOCUS, and its perpendicular distance from a fixed straight line, the DIRECTRIX, is always constant and less than unity — i.e. the ratio is always less than 1.

The ratio $\dfrac{\text{distance from focus to point (FP)}}{\text{distance from directrix to point (DP)}}$ is known as the ECCENTRICITY of the curve. (Remember that for the ellipse, eccentricity $\dfrac{FP}{DP} < 1$)

The elliptical path traced out by a moving point P, can be plotted by following the steps outlined below.

(1) Draw the directrix and horizontal axis.

(2) Ascertain the given eccentricity of the curve and position of focus from the directrix (DF). (Assume for this example an eccentricity of $\frac{4}{5}$ and a distance DF of 10 millimetres).

(3) Position focus F 10 mm along the axis as shown opposite.

(4) Draw a right-angled triangle (DPF) with perpendicular sides, in this example, in the ratio 4:5 (eccentricity). Point D *must* be drawn in line with the directrix.
Maximum height (FP_8) is calculated as follows:

$$\frac{FP_{max}}{DP_{max}} = \frac{4}{5} \quad \therefore \quad FP_{max} = \frac{4}{5}DP_{max} \text{ but } DP_{max} = DF + FP_{max}$$

$$\therefore \quad FP_8 \text{ in this example} = \frac{4}{5}(DF + FP_{max})$$
$$= \frac{4}{5}(10mm + FP_{max})$$
$$= 8mm + \frac{4}{5}FP_{max}$$
$$\therefore \quad FP_{max} - \frac{4}{5}FP_{max} = 8mm$$
$$\therefore FP_{max} = 40mm$$

(5) To plot P_1 divide DF , geometrically, in the ratio 4:5. (Note that FP_1 is 4 units and DP_1 5 units).
To obtain successive points on the curve use is made of the 'eccentricity' triangle.

(6) Draw equi-spaced vertical lines, perpendicular to the axis and arbitrarily positioned to the right of point P_1, as shown above, and number 2 to 8.

(7) Project these lines down into the triangle to obtain lines FP_2 to FP_8.

(8) To obtain points P_2 on the ellipse: From point F on the axis draw an arc, length FP_2, from the triangle, to cut vertical line 2 above and below the axis.

(9) Repeat this procedure for points P_3 to P_8, using arc of length FP_3 to cut line 3, arc FP_4 to cut line 4 etc. (Remember that heights FP_2, $FP_3, \ldots, FP_8$, stepped from the triangle, represent distances from the *focus*, F, to respective points $P_2, P_3, \ldots, P_8$.)

(10) Join points P_1 to P_8 with a smooth, heavy curve to obtain the ELLIPSE.

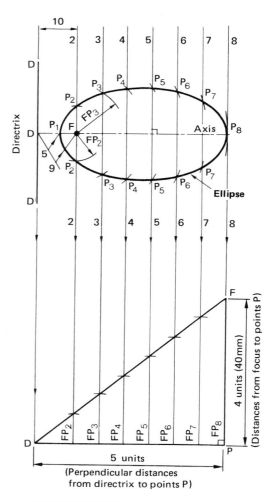

'ECCENTRICITY' TRIANGLE

NORMAL and TANGENT to any point P_T on a given ELLIPSE

(1)   Position P_T on the given curve.

If foci (focal points) are NOT known:

(2)   Draw an arc, length equal to half the major axis (P_1O), from the intersection of the minor axis and the ellipse to cut the major axis in F_1 and F_2, the focal points.

If (when) foci ARE known:

(3)   Draw straight lines from F_1 and F_2 through P_T.

(4)   Bisect angle $F_1P_TF_2$ to obtain the NORMAL to the ellipse.

(5)   Construct a perpendicular to the normal, at P_T, to obtain the TANGENT to the given ellipse.

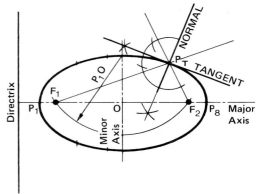

2.   THE PARABOLA.

The parabola is the locus of a point which moves in a plane so that the ratio of its distance from a fixed point, the FOCUS, and its perpendicular distance from a fixed straight line, the DIRECTRIX, is always constant and equal to unity.

i.e. the eccentricity of the parabolic curve, $\dfrac{FP}{DP} = 1$.

The parabolic curve can be plotted as follows:

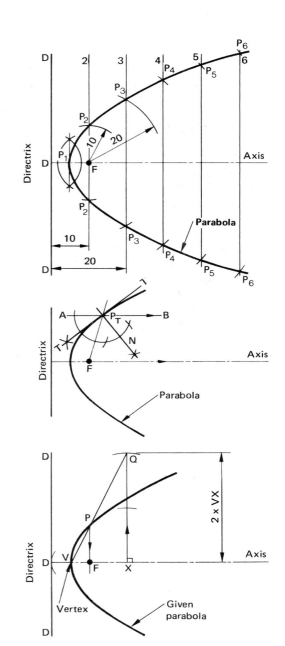

(1)   Draw the directrix DD and the horizontal axis.

(2)   Position the focus F in the correct position relative to DD. (Assume, in this example, that DF = 10 millimetres).

(3)   Locate point P_1 by bisecting DF (i.e. $FP_1/DP_1 = 1$)

(4)   Draw equi-spaced, vertical lines to the right of P_1 and number 2 to 6 as shown.

(5)   To plot P_2: Strike an arc *from focus F,* radius equal to the perpendicular distance of line 2 from the directrix DD (10mm) to cut line 2 above and below the axis.

(6)   To plot P_3: Strike an arc *from focus F,* radius equal to the perpendicular distance of line 3 from DD (20mm) to cut vertical line 3 above and below the axis.

(7)   Repeat this procedure to obtain remaining points P_4, P_5 and P_6.

(8)   Join points P_1 to P_6 with a smooth, *heavy* curve to obtain the required PARABOLA.

Notice that the parabolic curve gets ever larger.

TANGENT and NORMAL to any point P_T on a given PARABOLA.

(1)   Position point P_T anywhere on the given curve.

(2)   Draw a straight line from the known focus F through point P_T, as shown opposite.

(3)   Draw a straight line AB through P_T and parallel to the axis.

(4)   Bisect angle AP_TF to obtain the TANGENT TT.

(5)   Construct a perpendicular to the tangent at point P_T to obtain the NORMAL N. Alternatively bisect angle FP_TB to obtain the normal at P_T.

To locate and draw the FOCUS and DIRECTRIX of a given PARABOLA.

(1)   Label the intersection of the given curve and the horizontal axis, V. This point is called the VERTEX.

(2)   Position a point X anywhere along the axis, but well to the right of V, as shown.

(3)   Draw a straight line from point X, perpendicular to the axis, and equal in length to twice length VX. Label the line XQ.

(4)   Join VQ. Label the point of intersection of line VQ and the parabolic curve, P.

(5)   Draw a line vertically downwards from point P to cut the axis in F. Point F is the required FOCUS of the parabola.

(6)   Step off distance VF along the axis, to the left of V, to position the required DIRECTRIX DD (i.e. VF = VD).

If the eccentricity of the curve and also the relative position of the focus are known, then the construction presented above can be used to draw a parabola. If, however, this information is not given but the lengths of the axis and base are known, then an alternative, geometrical, construction can be used to obtain the curve.

Details of this construction can be found on page 58, where it is more appropriately placed than it would be here in the loci section.

3. THE HYPERBOLA.

The hyperbola is the locus of a point which moves in a plane so that the ratio of its distance from a fixed point, the FOCUS, and its perpendicular distance from a fixed straight line, the DIRECTRIX, is always constant and greater than unity.

i.e. the eccentricity of the hyperbolic curve $\frac{FP}{DP} > 1$.

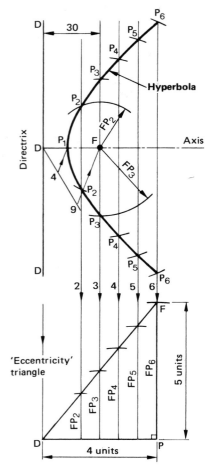

The hyperbolic path traced out by a moving point P may be plotted by following the procedure below.

(1)   Draw the directrix and axis.

(2)   Ascertain the eccentricity of the hyperbolic curve and position of the focus F relative to the directrix DD (Assume an eccentricity of $\frac{5}{4}$ and a distance DF of 30 millimetres in this example).

(3)   Position the focus F.

(4)   To plot P_1, divide DF in the ratio 5 : 4, geometrically.

(Notice that P_1F is *five* units and P_1D *four* units.)

(5)   Draw the 'eccentricity' triangle with perpendicular sides in the ratio 5 : 4 as shown.

Note: Point D is drawn in line with the directrix.

FP is always longer than DP.

The maximum height of the triangle, FP, must be known to enable the curve to be completed. (Assume here that FP_6 is 75mm.)

(6)   Draw equi-spaced vertical lines on the top diagram, starting in any arbitrary position to the right of P_1, and number 2 to 6.

(7)   Project these vertical lines down into the eccentricity triangle to obtain heights FP_2 to FP_6.

(8)   To plot points P_2 on the curve: from the focus F, draw an arc of length FP_2 (from triangle) above and below the axis to cut vertical line 2, as shown.

(9)   Repeat the procedure — arc FP_3 to cut line 3, etc — to obtain successive points P_3 to P_6.

(10)   Join points P_1 to P_6 with a smooth, heavy curve to obtain the HYPERBOLA.

Note: The diagram is drawn half full size to conserve space.

To draw the TANGENT and NORMAL to any point P on a given hyperbolic curve.

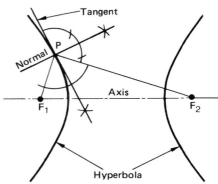

The distance between the foci of 'paired' curves must be known before the tangent can be constructed.

Assuming this to be the case:

(1)   Draw the common axis of the given hyperbolae.

(2)   Position the given foci F_1 and F_2.

(3)   Position point P on one of the curves.

(4)   Join F_1P and F_2P and bisect the angle formed, F_1PF_2, to obtain the TANGENT to the hyperbolic curve at P.

(5)   Construct a perpendicular to the tangent at P to obtain the NORMAL.

Note: Paired hyperbolic curves are obtained by cutting both branches of a double right cone. The diagram opposite shows a typical position of a cutting plane XX, from which a pair of hyperbolic curves — similar to the ones above — could be drawn. (The cutting plane must make a smaller angle with the axis of the cones than do the elements).

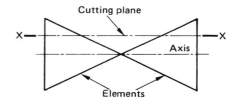

To draw a HYPERBOLA given the position of the FOCI and length of the TRANSVERSE AXIS.

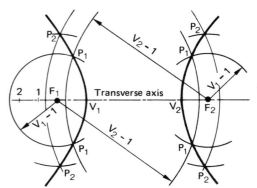

(1)   Draw the given transverse axis V_1-V_2 and extend as shown.

(2)   Position the given foci F_1 and F_2 on the extended axis.

(3)   Mark off any convenient points on the axis, to the left of F_1, and number the points 1, 2 etc.

(4)   With radius V_2-1 draw arcs from F_1 and F_2 respectively.

(5)   With radius V_1-1 draw arcs from F_2 and F_1 respectively, to cut the initial arcs in point P_1 to obtain four points on the hyperbolic curves.

(6)   Further points on the curves P_2, P_3, etc., are plotted by following the same procedure using progressively larger radii.

(7)   Points V_1, P_1, P_2, etc., are joined with a smooth, heavy curve to obtain the HYPERBOLAE.

64

4. THE CYCLOID.

The cycloid is the locus of a point on the circumference of a circular disc as the disc rolls, without slipping, along a straight line. (The straight line need NOT be horizontal.)

The path traced out by the point P as the disc rolls along the line may be plotted by following carefully the steps outlined below.

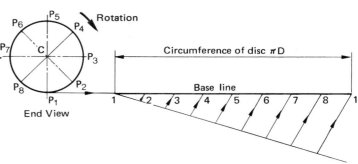

(1) Draw an end view of the disc, diameter D, and divide it into a number of equal divisions (eight being convenient, using a 45° set-square). Label the divisions P_1 to P_8 as shown.

(2) Project a base line from P_1 in the end view, making its length πD (the circumference of the disc). Divide this base line, geometrically, into the same number of divisions as the end view (eight) and number 1 to 8.

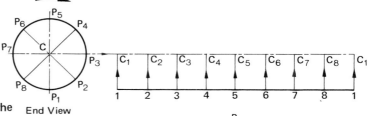

(3) Draw vertical lines up from each of the numbered base divisions to the centre line projected from the end view. Label the intersections C_1, C_2, etc.,

(4) Project horizontal lines from P_1, P_2, etc., in the end view as shown.

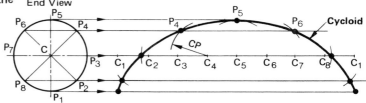

(5) Step off from each of the centre points in turn, C_1, C_2 etc., an arc radius CP (the radius of the disc) to intersect the respective horizontal lines, e.g. arc from centre C_4 intersects horizontal line projected from P_4.

(6) 'Dot' each intersecting point.

(7) Join successive dots with a smooth, heavy curve to obtain the CYCLOID for one revolution of the disc.

TANGENT and NORMAL to the CYCLOID

The tangent and normal to any point P on a given cycloidal curve may be drawn as follows:

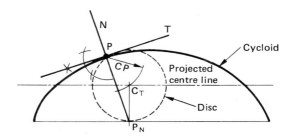

(1) From P draw an arc radius CP, equal in length to the radius of the rolling disc, to cut the projected centre line, to the right of P, in point C_T.

(2) With centre C_T draw the disc (shown with a broken line) to touch the base line in point P_N.

(3) Draw a heavy straight line from P_N through P. This is the NORMAL N to the curve at point P.

(4) Construct a perpendicular to the normal at point P. This is the TANGENT T to the given cycloidal curve at point P.

Note: Radius CP *must* be drawn to the RIGHT of point P, when P is positioned as shown here, otherwise the resulting 'tangent' would cut, not just touch, the cycloidal curve.

Note:

When a circular disc rolls along a straight line and the point for which the locus is plotted is not on the circumference of the *rolling* circle, the resulting locus is *not* cycloidal but of the form shown in the examples below. These loci are called TROCHOIDS.

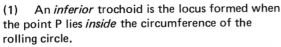

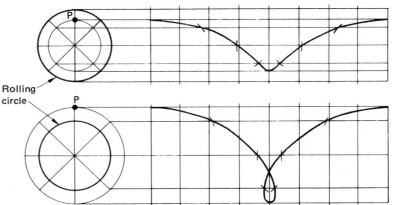

(1) An *inferior* trochoid is the locus formed when the point P lies *inside* the circumference of the rolling circle.

(2) A *superior* trochoid is the locus formed when the point P lies *outside* the circumference of the rolling circle.

5. ARCHIMEDEAN SPIRAL. The Archimedean spiral is the locus of a point which moves uniformly along a straight line as the line rotates at constant speed about a fixed point.

The path traced out by the moving point P may be plotted by following carefully the steps outlined below.

(1)	Draw the centre lines and step off the given maximum radius (OA) and minimum radius (OB) from the pole O.
(2)	With centre O and radius OA draw a circle, feintly,
(3)	Divide the circle into a number of equal sectors (eight or twelve being convenient for division by set-squares) and number radial lines 1 to 8.
(4)	Divide length BA into the same number of equal divisions as there are sectors and number the divisions as shown.

Note: The circle is numbered as shown opposite when 'plotting' an anticlockwise spiral. The numbering is reversed, however, when 'plotting' a clockwise spiral.

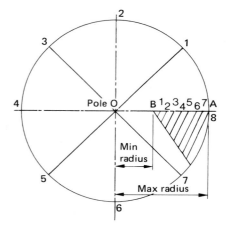

(5)	B is the point from which the spiral starts. Label P_0.
(6)	With centre O and radius 0-1 draw an arc to cut radial line 1. 'Dot' the intersecting point and label P_1. Follow a similar procedure to obtain the remaining points on the curve, P_2 to P_8.
(7)	Join the respective points with a smooth, heavy curve to obtain the anticlockwise ARCHIMEDEAN SPIRAL for one convolution (revolution)

CONVOLUTION is a term used to denote movement through $360°$ when dealing with spirals.

Note: The minimum radius OB may in some questions be given as zero. The spiral then, of course, starts at the pole, O.

If more than one convolution is required then the number of sectors remains the same as above but linear distance AB is divided into the number of divisions appropriate to the required number of convolutions. For example, AB would be divided into sixteen divisions for two convolutions of the spiral shown opposite.

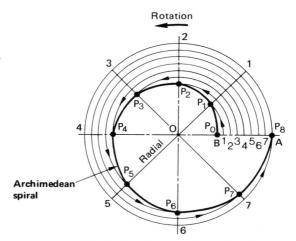

Notice that P moves from B to A at the same rate that AB moves around the circle.

The principle underlying the Archimedean spiral can be used for practical purposes in many different ways. A typical, simple, engineering example is illustrated opposite.

This "heart-shaped" symmetrical cam is used to convert uniform circular motion (the cam revolves about spindle C) into uniform linear motion. (The follower, F, moves vertically upwards at a uniform rate from $0°$ to $180°$, then vertically downwards, uniformly, from $180°$ to $360°$).

The periphery of the cam consists of two "mirror-image" semi-convolutions of an Archimedean spiral. The "lift" — from the starting position to the top position — is merely the difference between the maximum radius and minimum radius of the spiral.

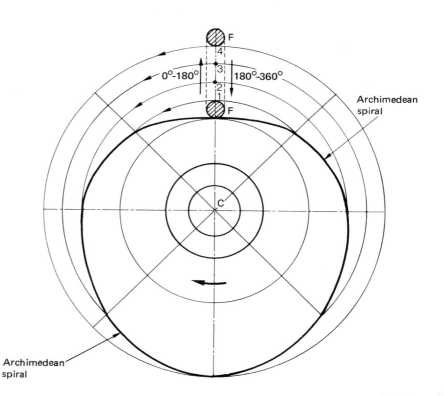

66

6. THE INVOLUTE.

The involute is the locus of a point at the free end of a thread as the thread is unwound, without slipping, from a base shape, e.g. a circular reel.

The path traced out by the end point P as the thread is unwrapped may be obtained by following carefully each of the steps detailed below.

(1)   Draw the base circle (reel), diameter D, and divide it into any number of equal sectors (eight or twelve being convenient). Number the divisions 0 to 7.

(2)   Draw, feintly, tangents from each of the radials. (Notice that the tangents get progressively longer as the thread unwinds).

(3)   Make the length of the tangent from point O equal in length to the circumference of the reel, πD.

(4)   Divide this length, geometrically, into eight equal units (the same number of divisions into which the circle is divided). Number the units 0 to 8.

(5)   The locus starts at point O. Label this point P_0.

(6)   Along the tangent from radial point 1 step off a length of one unit, taken from the base line. Label the end point P_1.

(7)   Along the tangent from radial point 2 step off a length of two units. Label this end point P_2.

(8)   Repeat this procedure to obtain end points P_3 to P_8.

(9)   Join points P_0 to P_8 with a smooth, heavy curve to obtain the INVOLUTE.

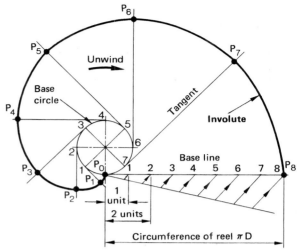

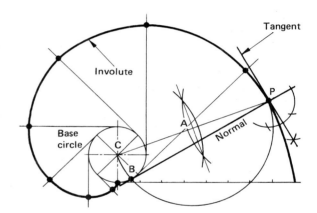

To draw a NORMAL and TANGENT to any point P on the INVOLUTE curve.

(1)   Draw a straight line from given point P to the centre of the base circle, C. Bisect CP, positioning point A.

(2)   Draw a semicircle on CP to cut the base circle in B.

(3)   Draw a *heavy* straight line from P through B (tangential to the base circle).   This is the NORMAL to the involute at P.

(4)   Construct a perpendicular to the normal at P to obtain the TANGENT to the involute at given point P.

Note: The semicircle *must* be drawn 'below' line CP, when P is positioned as shown in this example, to obtain the correct normal and tangent to the curve at point P. If it is drawn 'above' CP then the tangent *cuts*, not *touches*, the involute curve.

The base shape for the Involute does NOT have to be circular, though it more often than not is.

Involutes drawn around an equilateral triangular base shape (length of side L) and a regular hexagonal base (length of side H), for example, are shown here to emphasize the point.

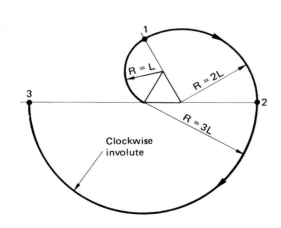

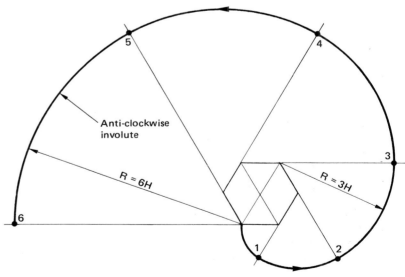

7. THE HELIX.

The helix is the locus of a point which moves around the circumference of a right cylinder with uniform velocity, and simultaneously moves along the cylinder, parallel to the axis, with uniform velocity.

The helical curve traced out by the moving point can be 'plotted' by following the steps outlined in whichever of the two constructions presented below is relevant to the given information.

CONSTRUCTION 1. Diameter of cylinder, pitch and number of turns known.

(1)   A front view and end view of the cylinder on which the helix is to be formed are drawn as shown opposite.

(2)   The PITCH of the helix, P, is drawn on the front view. (The pitch is the distance moved along the cylinder by the moving point, measured parallel to the axis of the cyclinder, in travelling once around the cylinder).

(3)   The end view is divided into a number of equal parts, eight in this example, and numbered 1 to 8.
(Eight or twelve is a convenient number to choose as the division can then easily be carried out using either a 45° or a 60/30° set-square).

(4)   The pitch of the helix is divided, geometrically, into the same number of equal parts (eight) and numbered 1 to 8. Vertical lines are drawn up from each point.

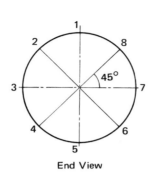
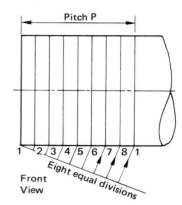

End View — Front View

(5)   A feint horizontal line is drawn from each of the numbered circumferential points in the end view to 'cut' the corresponding numbered vertical line in the front view, as shown opposite, e.g. the horizontal projector from point 2 in the end view intersects vertical line 2 in the front view to position P_2.

(6)   A smooth curve is drawn, relatively heavily, passing through each of the plotted points of intersection to obtain the HELIX.

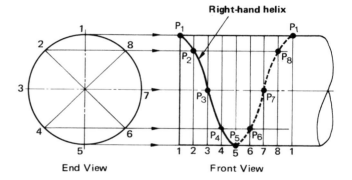

End View — Front View

Note: The second half of the RIGHT-HAND helical curve drawn above is shown with a broken line. This is because it passes behind the solid cylinder and cannot, therefore, be seen.

A LEFT-HAND helix is 'plotted' exactly as detailed above but slopes in the opposite direction, as the photograph and diagram opposite illustrate.

Left-hand thread

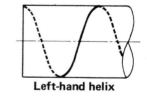

Left-hand helix

There are, in addition to the vee-thread shown above, numerous practical examples of the helix to be seen in engineering workshops. A selection of the more commonly encountered components are shown below.

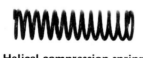

Helical compression spring

Right-hand thread

Square thread   **Helical groove**

Helical tension spring

Worm

Grub screw

CONSTRUCTION 2. Alternative construction: diameter of cylinder, pitch and length of helical curve known.

If a right-angled triangle is drawn, as shown opposite, with its base equal in length to the circumference of the cylinder upon which the helix is to be drawn, and the perpendicular height equal in length to the pitch of the helix then the resulting hypotenuse represents the developed length of the helical curve.

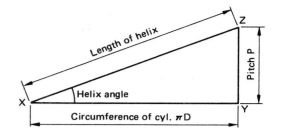

This can be seen to be so if a paper triangle is wrapped once around a right cylinder, of diameter D and length P, as shown below in stages. A RIGHT-hand helix is formed.

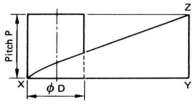 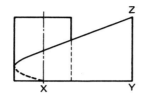

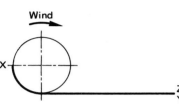 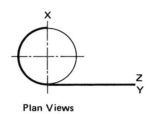

Plan Views

Front View   **Developed Helix**

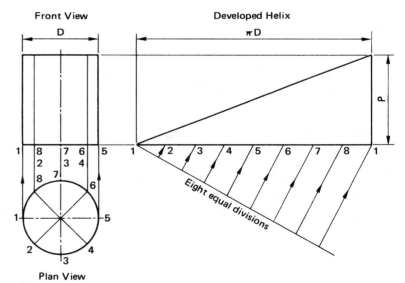

Plan View

CONSTRUCTION:

(1) A right-angled triangle is drawn with base πD and vertical height P. (D is the diameter of the cylinder upon which the helix is to be drawn and P the pitch of the required helix.)

(2) A front view of the cylinder is drawn in line with the triangle.

(3) A plan view of the cylinder is projected below the front view.

(4) The base of the triangle and the plan view are divided into the same number of equal parts (eight in this case) and numbered 1 to 8.

(5) Thin vertical lines are projected from circumferential points in the plan into the front view and numbered 1 to 8.

(6) Vertical lines are drawn up from the base points on the triangle to the hypotenuse and numbered 1 to 8.

(7) A horizontal line is drawn from each of the numbered points on the hypotenuse to 'cut' the correspondingly numbered line on the front view, e.g. horizontal from 2 'cuts' vertical line 2 to obtain point P_2, etc.

(8) A smooth, heavy curve is drawn through progressive intersecting points P_1 to P_8 to trace out the required HELIX onto the surface of the cylinder.

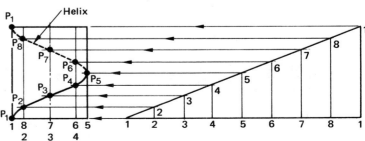

Note: The curve above is a RIGHT-HAND helix.

69

8. MECHANISMS.

A mechanism may be defined as a system of mutually adapted parts working together. For example, the piston, crank arm and connecting rod arrangement on an internal combustion engine is a mechanism.

There are many different types of mechanism. Those detailed in this section are the relatively simple and more commonly encountered ones.

It is often desirable to know precisely the locus of the moving parts of a machine. For example, the design of a guard that is required to cover a connecting rod — crank arrangement would be greatly influenced by the shape of the path traced out by the crank and rod.

The locus of any point on a moving mechanism can be determined by drawing the mechanism in successive positions throughout its movement, plotting the desired point in each of these positions and then joining the series of plotted points with a smooth, distinct curve.

(a) **To draw the locus of a point P on a crank — connecting rod — piston mechanism.**

The crank revolves about centre O. Point C, which is hinged, traces out a circle. Point R, also hinged, reciprocates along the piston axis, as shown.

The locus of point C is a circle. The locus of point R is a straight line. The locus of point P, the mid-point of the connecting rod, may be drawn by following the steps detailed below.

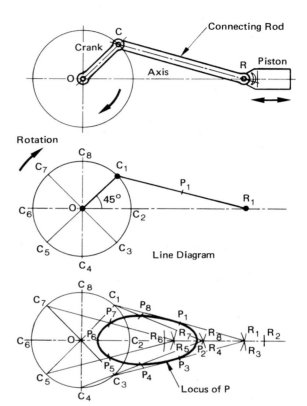

(1)   Draw a scaled line diagram of the mechanism in a convenient starting position (OC_1 at $30°$ or $45°$ being most convenient if using standard set-squares). Position point P_1 mid-way between points C_1 and R_1.

(2)   Draw a circle, radius OC_1, and divide into any number of equal sectors, using crank OC_1 as the first division (8 or 12 most convenient). Number the circumferential points C_1 to C_8, as shown, assuming that the crank rotates clockwise.

To plot P_2 (crank moved clockwise to position OC_2):

(3)   Strike an arc, length $C_1 R_1$, from C_2 to cut the horizontal axis in R_2, as shown opposite. Position P_2 mid-way along $C_2 R_2$.

To plot P_3 (crank moved to position OC_3):

(4)   Strike an arc, length $C_1 R_1$, from C_3 to cut the horizontal axis in R_3, as shown. Position point P_3 mid-way along $C_3 R_3$.

(5)   Repeat the procedure to obtain remaining points P_4 to P_8, as shown opposite.

(6)   Draw a smooth, heavy curve through points P_1 to P_8 to obtain the locus of P, the mid-point of the connecting rod.

Note: The greater the number of positions of the crank that are drawn, the more accurate will be the locus of the moving point P.

(b) **To draw the locus of a point on a slotted-link mechanism (a mechanism similar to that seen on a shaping machine).**

Crank OC revolves about centre O. Slotted link CP slides on the fixed crosshead which pivots about centre H.

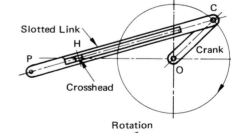

The locus of point P, on the end of the slotted-link, is plotted by following the steps below.

(1)   Draw the scaled line diagram of the mechanism in a suitable starting position (shown heavily in the diagram below). Label the crank OC_1 and the slotted link $C_1 H P_1$.

(2)   Draw a circle, radius OC_1, and divide into eight equal sectors (using a $45°$ square) starting from radial OC_1. Label the circumferential points C_2, C_3, etc.

To plot P_2 (crank rotated from OC_1 to OC_2):

(3)   Strike an arc, length $C_1 P_1$, from C_2 as shown.

(4)   Draw a straight line from C_2, *through pivot H,* to intersect the arc, locating point P_2.

To plot P_3 (crank rotated from OC_2 to OC_3):

(5)   Strike an arc, length $C_1 P_1$, from C_3.

(6)   Draw a line from C_3, *through H,* to intersect this arc, locating point P_3.

(7)   Repeat the procedure for remaining points P_4 to P_8.

(8)   Draw a smooth, heavy curve through successive points P_1 to P_8 to obtain the locus of moving point P.

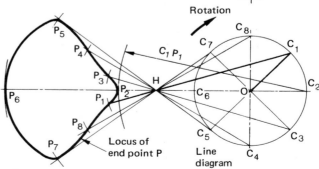

Note: All lines drawn from circumferential points C_1, C_2, etc., to cut successive arcs, radius $C_1 P_1$, MUST pass through fixed point H.

9. MISCELLANEOUS LOC1 . The remaining examples of loci are among those which cannot be categorised under any of the previous headings in this section. (They will, therefore, be classified "miscellaneous").

(a)   To draw the locus of a point which moves so that it is always equidistant from the circumferences of two given circles (in this case circles of unequal diameters).

(1)   Draw the given circles and bisect distance CC_1 to obtain the first point on the locus, P.
(2)   From centre O draw an arc of radius equal to OC + distance d_1 (where distance d_1 is greater than distance CP.)
(3)   From centre O_1 draw an arc, length $O_1C_1 + d_1$, to intersect the arc drawn from centre O, as shown. The points of intersection, above and below the horizontal centre lines, are labelled P_1.
(4)   Repeat the procedure to obtain further points P_2, P_3 etc., gradually increasing distance d for each additional pair of points.
(5)   Draw a smooth, heavy curve through successive points P, P_1 etc., to obtain the required locus, which is equi-distant from the circles.
Note: With circles of unequal diameter the locus is equidistant from the "facing" circumferences only.

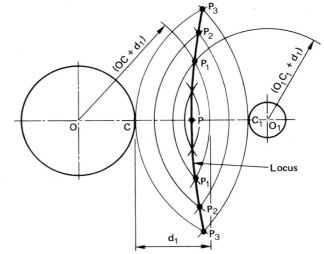

An extended version of the construction detailed above can be used to determine, by using a locus method, the centre of a circle which touches any number of given circles.

(b)   To draw the smallest circle which touches three given circles of unequal diameters.

(1)   Draw the given circles X, Y and Z.
(2)   Construct the locus of a point which moves so that it is always equidistant from circles X and Y by following the steps outlined in (a) above.
(3)   Similarly, construct the locus of a point that is always equidistant from circles X and Z, as shown.
    The point of intersection of the two curves, C, is the centre of the required circle.
(4)   Draw a circle from centre C to touch the circumference of circle X, as shown. It should, providing the loci have been accurately drawn, also touch circles Y and Z.
Note: A similar problem has been solved geometrically earlier in the book. (See page 27.)

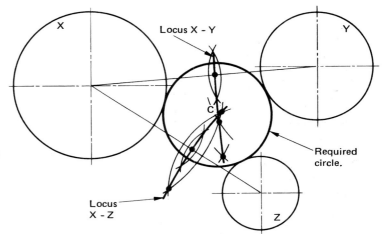

(c)   To draw the locus of a point which moves so that the ratio of its shortest distance from a given straight line and the circumference of a given circle is always constant. (Assume in this example that the ratio is 2:1)

(1)   Draw the given straight line AB and the given circle, centre O.
(2)   Divide distance DC, geometrically, in the given ratio to obtain P, the first point on the locus. (Notice that DP = 2 CP).
(3)   Draw a line A_1B_1 parallel to, and at perpendicular distance d_1 from, line AB. (d_1 must be greater than length DP).
(4)   Draw an arc from centre O, length OC + $\frac{1}{2} d_1$, to cut line A_1B_1 in points P_1.
(5)   Repeat the procedure to obtain further points, increasing gradually the distances from line AB for each pair of points. For example, arc of length OC + $\frac{1}{2} d_2$ cuts line A_2B_2 in points P_2, as shown.
(6)   Join successive points P, P_1, etc., with a smooth, heavy curve to obtain the required locus, as shown opposite.

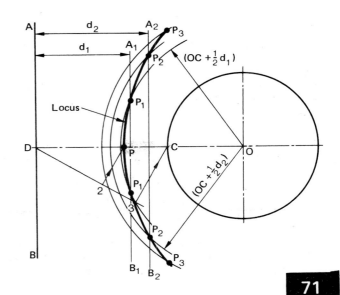

Geometrical Solids

The first part of the book dealt with PLANE geometry. The figures used, as implied by the term "plane", were flat. They had only length and breadth (or width).

In this part of the book, SOLID geometry is dealt with. The objects, or components, used are three-dimensional. They have length, breadth (width) and depth.

The commonly encountered "basic" geometrical shapes are defined and illustrated here at the outset, as a group, rather than individually in the relevant chapters which follow.

1. PRISMS A PRISM is a solid having two end faces which are identical, parallel, plane figures. These end faces are joined to each other by three or more lateral (side) faces which are parallelograms. The lateral faces are parallel to the imaginary axis of the prism.

Prisms are named after the shape of their end faces.

(a) RIGHT prisms A RIGHT prism has its axis and, therefore, lateral faces and lateral edges, perpendicular to its end faces. Each of the solids shown below is a RIGHT prism.

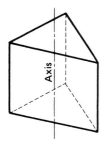

Right triangular prism

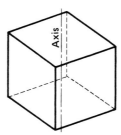

Right square prism (cube)

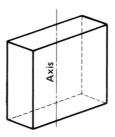

Right rectangular prism

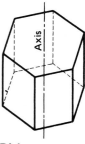

Right hexagonal prism

(b) OBLIQUE prisms An OBLIQUE prism has its axis, lateral faces and lateral edges inclined at an angle, i.e. OBLIQUE, to its end faces. Each solid shown below is an OBLIQUE prism.

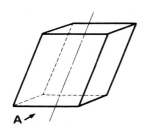

Oblique rectangular prism

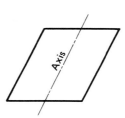

View on A

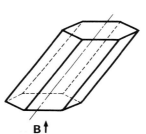

Oblique hexagonal prism

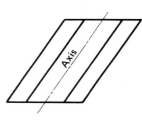

View on B (End-faces are hexagonal)

(c) TRUNCATED prisms If the top of a prism is cut off obliquely, forming an end which is not parallel to the base, then the prism is said to be TRUNCATED.

Each of the solids below is a TRUNCATED prism.

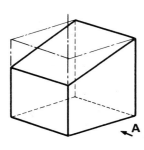

Truncated right square prism

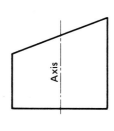

View on A

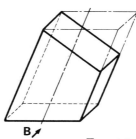

Truncated oblique rectangular prism

View on B

72

2. CYLINDERS

2. CYLINDERS A CYLINDER is a solid with a single-curved surface generated by a straight line called a generatrix, which moves in a fixed curve while remaining parallel to its axis.

(a) RIGHT cylinders. A RIGHT cylinder is one in which all sections taken perpendicular to the axis (centre line) are circular. Each of the solids illustrated below is a RIGHT cylinder.

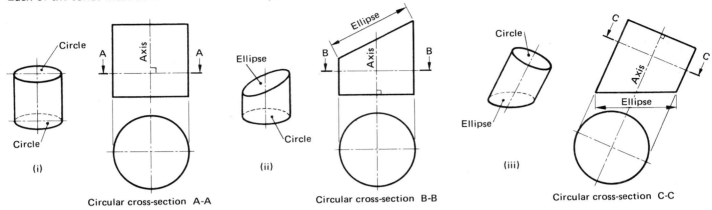

Circular cross-section A-A   Circular cross-section B-B   Circular cross-section C-C

Note: Solids (ii) and (iii) above are commonly referred to as TRUNCATED right cylinders. Such a cylinder, with its top cut off obliquely, can, however, be described as an UNGULA.

(b) OBLIQUE cylinders. An OBLIQUE cylinder is one in which all sections taken perpendicular to the axis are elliptical. Each solid below is an OBLIQUE cylinder.

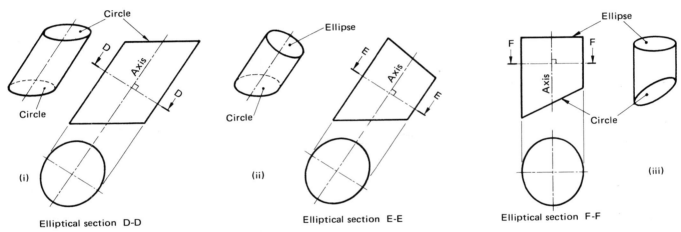

Elliptical section D-D   Elliptical section E-E   Elliptical section F-F

Note: Solids (ii) and (iii) above are TRUNCATED oblique cylinders or UNGULA. A portion of the cylinder has been cut off obliquely relative to the circular base.

3. PYRAMIDS A PYRAMID is a solid that has a polygon for a base and triangular lateral (sloping) faces intersecting at a common point called the VERTEX. A line drawn from the centre point of the base to the vertex is called the AXIS (centre line). A pyramid is named after the shape of its base.

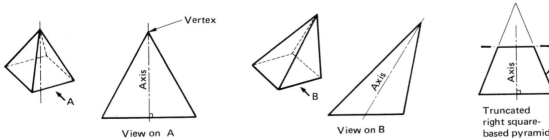

View on A   View on B

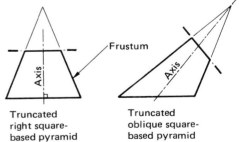

Truncated right square-based pyramid   Truncated oblique square-based pyramid

(a) RIGHT pyramids
A RIGHT pyramid is one in which the axis is perpendicular to the base. The solid above is a RIGHT, square-based pyramid.

(b) OBLIQUE pyramids.
An OBLIQUE pyramid is one in which the axis is inclined at an angle (i.e. is oblique) to the base. The solid above is an OBLIQUE, square-based pyramid.

(c) TRUNCATED pyramids
If the top of a pyramid is cut off, it is said to be TRUNCATED. When the cutting plane is parallel to the base of the pyramid then the portion between the plane and the base is known as the FRUSTUM.

4. CONES

4.   CONES A CONE is a solid with a circular base and a curved surface tapering to a point. The shape is generated by a straight line moving in contact with a curved (circular) line and passing through a fixed point called the VERTEX.
A straight line drawn from the vertex through the centre point of the base is called the axis (centre-line) of the cone.

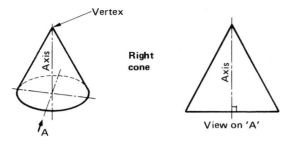

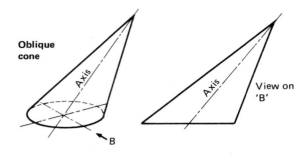

(a)   RIGHT cone. A RIGHT cone is one in which the axis is perpendicular to the base.

(b)   OBLIQUE cone. An OBLIQUE cone is one in which the axis is inclined at an angle (i.e. is oblique) to the base.

TRUNCATED cones.
If the top part of a cone is removed it is said to be TRUNCATED.
When the cutting plane is inclined at an angle to the base, as in figure (i) opposite, that portion of the cone between the plane and the base is known as an UNGULA.
When the cutting plane is parallel to the base of the cone, as in figure (ii), that part of the cone between the plane and the base is known as a FRUSTUM.

SPHERES. A SPHERE is a solid ball. It is generated by a circle revolving about one of its diameters. The diameter about which it revolves is called the axis.

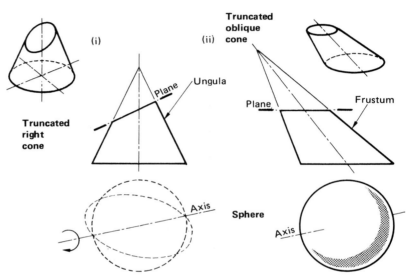

EXERCISE : IDENTIFICATION OF SOLIDS				ARRAY			
Select, from the array opposite, the correct full name for each of the solids shown below. Insert, in the answer column provided, the corresponding number and letter. (Answers on page 137).					A	B	C
				1	Truncated right square cube	Pyramid	Right rectangular prism
Example: 1.	Ans. 3C	6. Ellipse Circle	Ans.	2	Truncated oblique cylinder	Oblique hexagonal prism	Right hexagonal prism
2.		7.		3	Frustum	Oblique cylinder	Right square prism
3. Circle Circle		8.		4	Truncated right cylinder	Wedge	Truncated right octagonal bar
4.		9.		5	Box	Oblique cone	Right square-based pyramid
5.		10.		6	Truncated oblique cone	Right cylindrical rod	Oblique prism
				7	Right triangular prism	Right cone	Rectangular plate

Orthographic Projection

Drawings are the principal medium through which draughtsmen communicate.

Engineering drawings are used to convey ideas and information from the draughtsman to the relevant craftsman and associated technical personnel.

It may well be that for a relatively simple component a pictorial (three-dimensional) sketch or drawing could be used by the draughtsman to transmit the necessary information to enable the component to be manufactured. However, for the majority of engineering components an orthographic drawing is used to convey the shape, sizes, material, finish, etc.

An orthographic drawing portrays a three-dimensional object (component) in two dimensions on a flat surface — the drawing sheet. A minimum of two views, therefore, are necessary to fully represent the component.

Two different systems of orthographic projection may be used to prepare engineering drawings. They are known as FIRST ANGLE orthographic projection (occasionally referred to as EUROPEAN projection) and THIRD ANGLE orthographic projection (known alternatively as AMERICAN projection).

With FIRST ANGLE orthographic projection the object, or component, is imagined to be placed in the FIRST of four right angles formed by the intersection of a horizontal and vertical plane, as shown in figures 1 and 2. With THIRD ANGLE orthographic projection the object is imagined to be situated in the THIRD of the four right-angles.

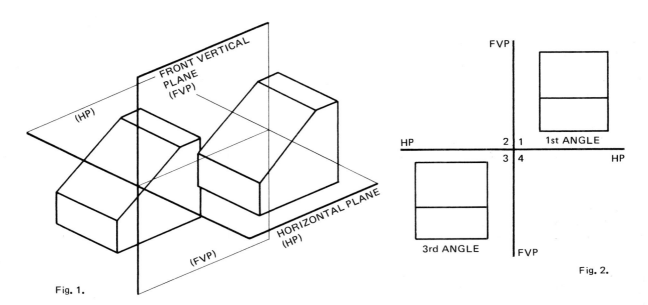

Fig. 1.

Fig. 2.

FIRST ANGLE (EUROPEAN) ORTHOGRAPHIC PROJECTION

It is imagined that the component is positioned in the first quadrant. Its outline is then projected onto the imaginary principal planes, front vertical plane (FVP) and horizontal plane (HP), by drawing lines at 90° from each of its edges, as shown in figure 3.

The view projected onto the FVP is known as the FRONT VIEW or FRONT ELEVATION.

The view projected down onto the HP is known as the PLAN view or, simply, the PLAN.

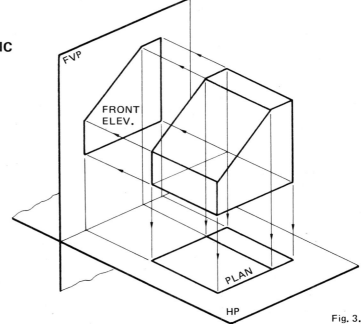

Fig. 3.

75

For relatively simple components, such as the one shown on the previous page, only two orthographic views are necessary to provide the desired information about shape, sizes etc. However, should a third or even fourth view be required, for further information or to assist in dimensioning a more complicated component, then SIDE or END VIEWS are drawn. This is done by projecting the shape of the component onto additional imaginary principal planes known as side vertical planes (SVP), which are at right-angles to both the FVP and HP as shown in figure 4.

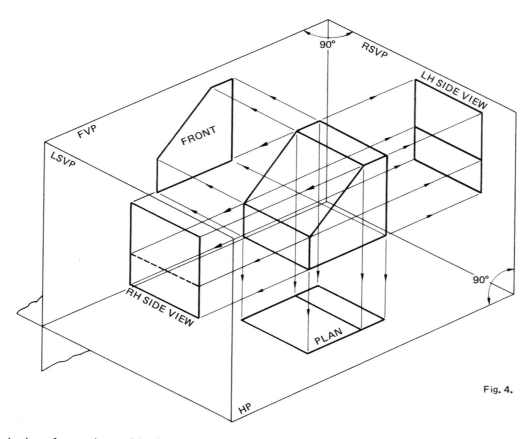

Fig. 4.

To obtain these four orthographic views on a flat surface (the drawing sheet) the principal planes are imagined to be opened out and laid flat as shown below in figure 5.

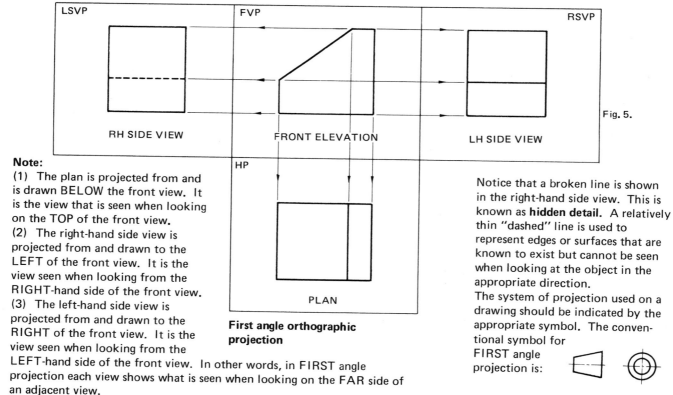

Fig. 5.

Note:

(1) The plan is projected from and is drawn BELOW the front view. It is the view that is seen when looking on the TOP of the front view.

(2) The right-hand side view is projected from and drawn to the LEFT of the front view. It is the view seen when looking from the RIGHT-hand side of the front view.

(3) The left-hand side view is projected from and drawn to the RIGHT of the front view. It is the view seen when looking from the LEFT-hand side of the front view. In other words, in FIRST angle projection each view shows what is seen when looking on the FAR side of an adjacent view.

First angle orthographic projection

Notice that a broken line is shown in the right-hand side view. This is known as **hidden detail.** A relatively thin "dashed" line is used to represent edges or surfaces that are known to exist but cannot be seen when looking at the object in the appropriate direction.

The system of projection used on a drawing should be indicated by the appropriate symbol. The conventional symbol for FIRST angle projection is:

Steps to be followed when drawing a component in FIRST angle orthographic projection.

1 Decide which 'face' of the component is to be drawn as the front view. (The choice is to some extent arbitrary. However, the front view should, ideally, be the one providing most information about the shape of the component.)
2 Draw the front view to scale (use full-size if at all possible). Position the front view carefully so that additional views can be projected from it and positioned correctly.
3 Draw the plan view in projection with, and BELOW, the front view.
4 If the complexity of the component demands a third, or even fourth, view, project this (these) from, and on the appropriate side (sides) of, the front view.

The sequence of drawings shown below should clarify the procedure to be followed.

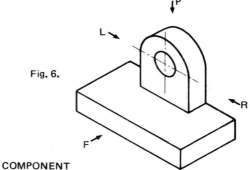

Fig. 6.

COMPONENT

(1) The view on arrow F (Fig. 6) will provide most information about the shape of the component to be drawn. This will, therefore, be taken as the front view.

(2) The front view (F) is drawn centrally at the top of the drawing sheet, as shown, thereby leaving space for a plan view and two side views to be added subsequently. Notice the type of line used to represent a centre line: —————————————— a thin chain!

(3) The plan view (P), looking in the direction of arrow P, is projected directly below, and a reasonable distance from, the front view.
Notice that the hole in plan is represented by two thin 'dashed' lines — it is hidden detail in this view.

Although side views would not normally be required to fully represent this relatively simple component, they will be drawn here to fully illustrate first angle orthographic projection.

(4) The right-hand side view (RHSV), looking in the direction of arrow 'R', is projected from, and in line with, the front view as shown. It is placed on the left of the front view.

(5) The left-hand side view (LHSV), looking in the direction of arrow L, is drawn on the right of the front view.

Special points to note:
(1) All widths for the plan view (e.g. W) are projected from the front view.
(2) All heights for the side views (e.g. H) are projected from the front view.
(3) All depths for the side views (e.g. D) are projected from the plan view. (These depths can be quickly and accurately transferred from plan to side views by projecting onto a suitably placed 45° line, as shown.)

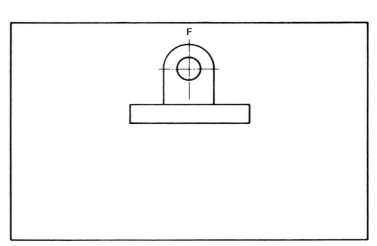

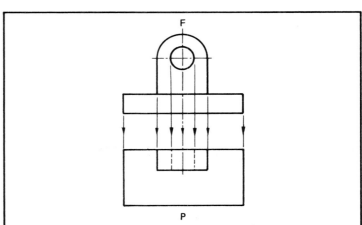

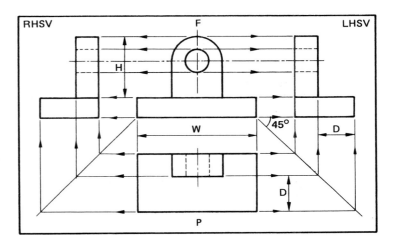

If the principal planes are required to be shown relative to each of the four orthographic views drawn on the previous page, then they are positioned and labelled HP (horizontal plane), FVP (front vertical plane), LSVP (left side vertical plane) and RSVP (right side vertical plane.), as shown in figure 7.

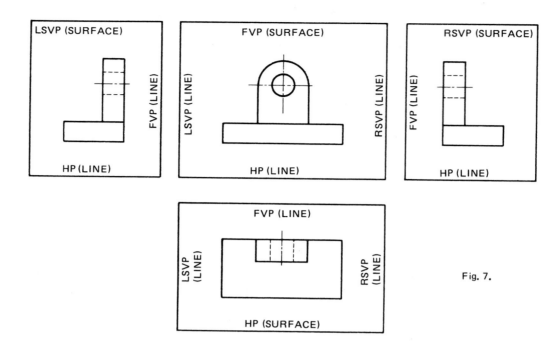

Fig. 7.

Note: The principal planes, particularly the HP and FVP, are sometimes called GROUND LINES.

THIRD ANGLE (AMERICAN) ORTHOGRAPHIC PROJECTION

When using this method of projection it is imagined that the object is placed inside the third (transparent) quadrant and viewed from outside the quadrant. The shape of the component is then projected onto each of the imaginary principal planes by drawing thin projection lines at 90° (i.e. orthographically) from each of its edges, as shown in figure 8 below.

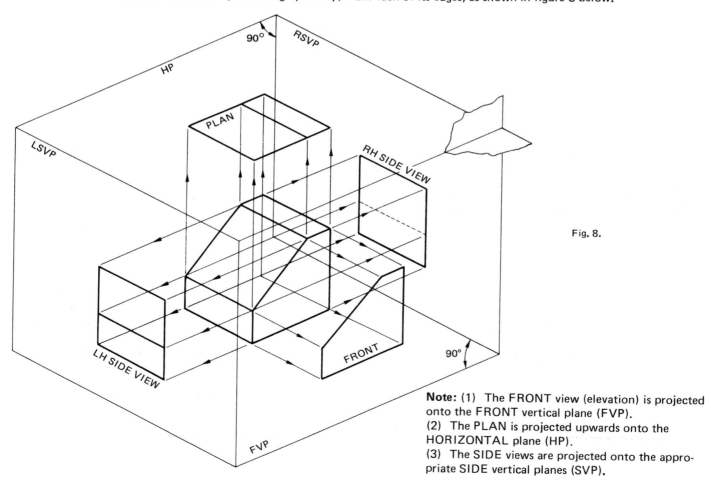

Fig. 8.

Note: (1) The FRONT view (elevation) is projected onto the FRONT vertical plane (FVP).
(2) The PLAN is projected upwards onto the HORIZONTAL plane (HP).
(3) The SIDE views are projected onto the appropriate SIDE vertical planes (SVP).

When the principal planes are imagined to be opened out and laid flat the four orthographic views are positioned as shown below in figure 9.

Third angle orthographic projection

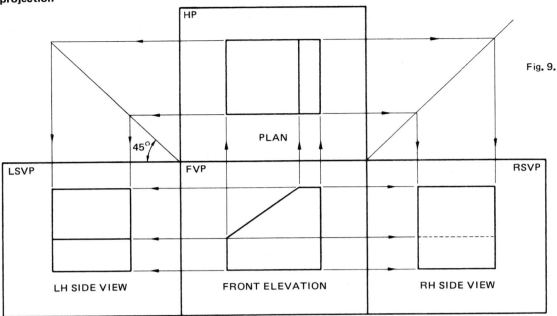

Fig. 9.

Notice that in THIRD angle projection each view shows what is seen when looking on the NEAR side of an adjacent view.

The conventional symbol for THIRD angle orthographic projection is:

It does seem that FIRST angle orthographic projection and THIRD angle orthographic projection are very similar methods of graphic communication. And so they are. However, there are important differences between the two methods of projection which can be clearly seen when figures 5 (page 76.) and 9 (above) are compared closely.
Respective views, whether drawn in first or third angle projection, are identical. However, the plan and side views are drawn in different positions relative to the front view for each of the methods of projection.

Summary

FIRST ANGLE
1 The plan is drawn BELOW the front view.

2 The right-hand side view is drawn on the LEFT of the front view.

3 The left-hand side view is drawn on the RIGHT of the front view.

THIRD ANGLE
1 The plan is drawn ABOVE the front view.

2 The right-hand side view is drawn on the RIGHT of the front view.

3 The left-hand side view is drawn on the LEFT of the front view.

If a component is to be drawn using THIRD angle orthographic projection the procedure is very similar to that outlined for first angle orthographic projection on page 77. The order in which the views are drawn is the same, respective views are identical, but the positions of the views on the drawing sheet are different.

Steps to be followed when drawing the component shown in figure 10, opposite, in THIRD angle orthographic projection.

Fig.10.

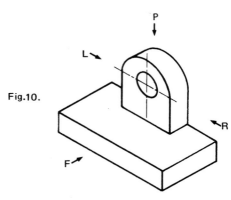

1 The FRONT view (again looking on arrow F) is, in third angle projection, placed centrally at the BOTTOM of the drawing sheet (assuming that two side views are to be drawn).

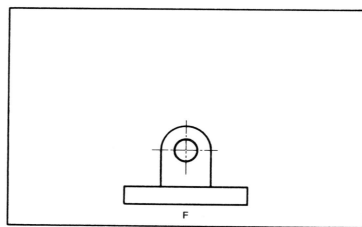

2 The PLAN view, looking in the direction of arrow P, is projected directly ABOVE the front view.

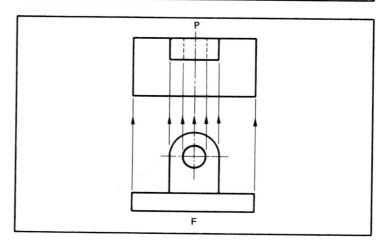

3 The RIGHT-HAND SIDE VIEW, looking in the direction of arrow R, is projected from, and in line with, the front view. It is drawn on the RIGHT of the front view.

4 The LEFT-HAND SIDE VIEW, looking in the direction of arrow L, is projected from, and in line with, the front view. It is drawn on the LEFT of the front view.

Notice that the depths for both side views are obtained by projecting from the plan view onto the conveniently placed 45° line.

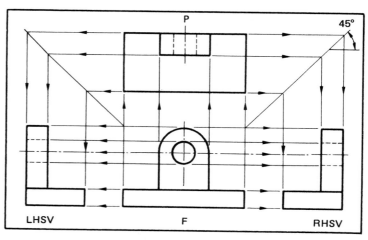

80

EXAMPLES The O-level student is expected to be able to draw simple solids (prisms, pyramids, cones, spheres and their 'composites') in various positions relative to the principal planes using either first or third angle orthographic projection. The following carefully graded, typical examples are used to illustrate how to do this. Explanations are included where it is thought necessary.

1. REGULAR PRISMS. (All drawn in FIRST angle projection)

(a) *Rectangular bar,* parallel to both the horizontal plane (HP) and all vertical planes (VPs).

(b) *Cube,* parallel to the FVP and inclined to both the HP and SVPs.

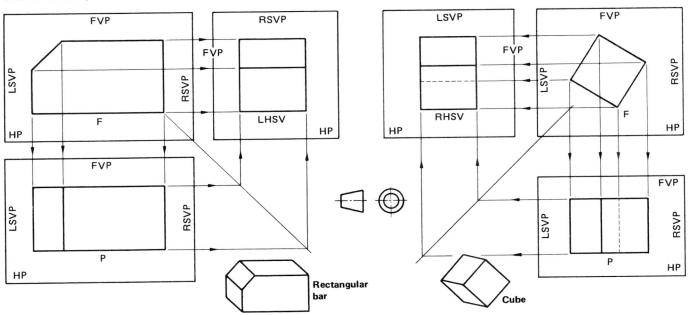

(c) *Hexagonal bar,* parallel to the HP and inclined to both the FVP and the SVPs.

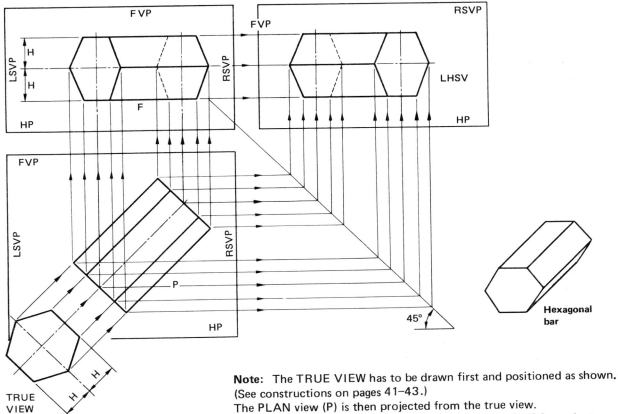

Note: The TRUE VIEW has to be drawn first and positioned as shown. (See constructions on pages 41–43.)
The PLAN view (P) is then projected from the true view.
The heights (H) for the FRONT view (F) are stepped off from the true view as shown.
Heights for the LEFT HAND SIDE VIEW (LHSV) are projected from the front view and depths for the LHSV are projected from the plan view via the 45° line, as shown.

81

2. CYLINDRICAL BAR (SHAFT). Parallel to the SVPs and inclined to both the FVP and the HP.

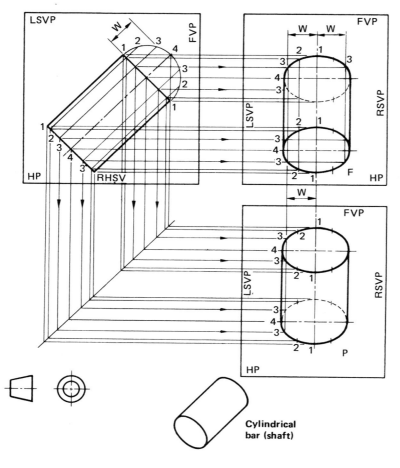

Note: The right hand side view (RHSV) is drawn first, in the position shown. A semi-circle is drawn on top of this view. This is imagined to be a flap which hinges about the centre line of the bar and falls flat onto the top of the bar. The semi-circle is divided into a number of equal divisions (6 being convenient).. Lines parallel to the axis of the bar are drawn from each of the points on the 'flap' to the top and base of the bar, as shown.

Some of the points have been numbered to help identify them in each of the three views and also to illustrate how the widths are transferred from the side view to the front (F) and plan (P). Heights for the front view are projected horizontally from the side view. Widths for each of the numbered points are stepped off from the semi-circular flap in the side view onto the appropriate horizontal projector in front view. For example, the distance of points 3 from the axis in the side view is W; this is stepped off from the axis in the front view along the projectors drawn from points 3 in the side view, as shown. The plan view is drawn by projecting widths from the front view to meet the corresponding projectors from the side view. For example, a projector is drawn from points 3 at the top and bottom of the side view, as shown, to intersect the lines projected from points 3 in front view at a distance W from the axis of the bar.

Cylindrical bar (shaft)

3. RIGHT PYRAMIDS. (All drawn in THIRD angle projection).

(a) *Tetrahedron.* (A solid triangular pyramid. In this example all four faces are identical equilateral triangles.) Base parallel to the HP and axis parallel to both the FVP and the SVPs.

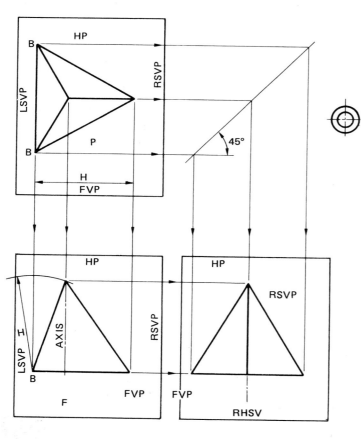

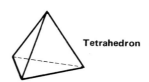

Tetrahedron

Note: The plan view (P) is drawn first and positioned as shown. Two angles or two sides are bisected to obtain the apex.

The widths for the front view (F) are then projected down from the plan. The vertical height of the front view is obtained by striking a radius, equal in length to H from the plan view, from the base edge B to cut the axis of the pyramid, as shown.

A line is drawn from each of the four corners in plan, via the 45° line, to intersect a line drawn from the corresponding corner in the front view, as shown. The corner points are joined to complete the side view (RHSV).

(b) *Square-based pyramid.* Axis parallel to the FVP and inclined at an angle to both the HP and the SVPs.

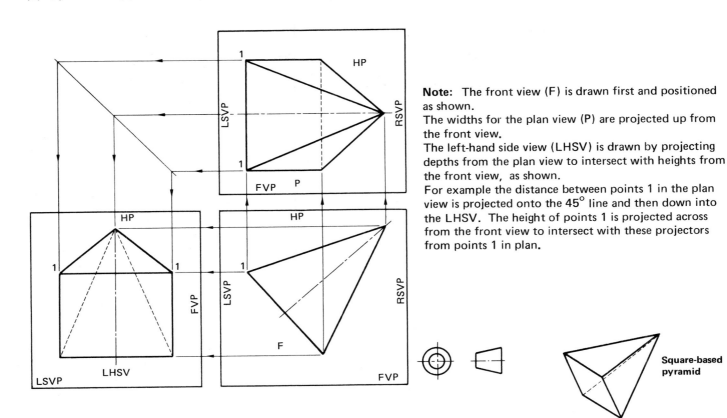

Note: The front view (F) is drawn first and positioned as shown.

The widths for the plan view (P) are projected up from the front view.

The left-hand side view (LHSV) is drawn by projecting depths from the plan view to intersect with heights from the front view, as shown.

For example the distance between points 1 in the plan view is projected onto the 45° line and then down into the LHSV. The height of points 1 is projected across from the front view to intersect with these projectors from points 1 in plan.

Square-based pyramid

(c) *Pentagonal-based pyramid.* Axis parallel to both SVPs and inclined at an angle to both the HP and the FVP.

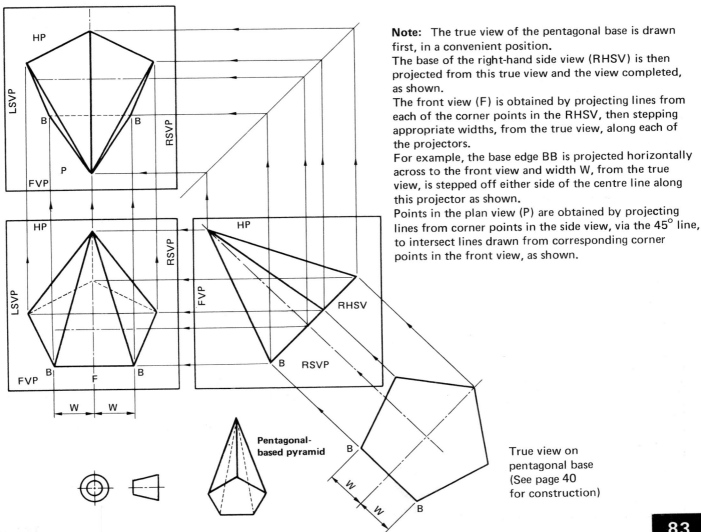

Note: The true view of the pentagonal base is drawn first, in a convenient position.

The base of the right-hand side view (RHSV) is then projected from this true view and the view completed, as shown.

The front view (F) is obtained by projecting lines from each of the corner points in the RHSV, then stepping appropriate widths, from the true view, along each of the projectors.

For example, the base edge BB is projected horizontally across to the front view and width W, from the true view, is stepped off either side of the centre line along this projector as shown.

Points in the plan view (P) are obtained by projecting lines from corner points in the side view, via the 45° line, to intersect lines drawn from corresponding corner points in the front view, as shown.

Pentagonal-based pyramid

True view on pentagonal base
(See page 40 for construction)

83

4. RIGHT CONE. (a) Axis parallel to the FVP and inclined at an angle to both the HP and the SVPs.

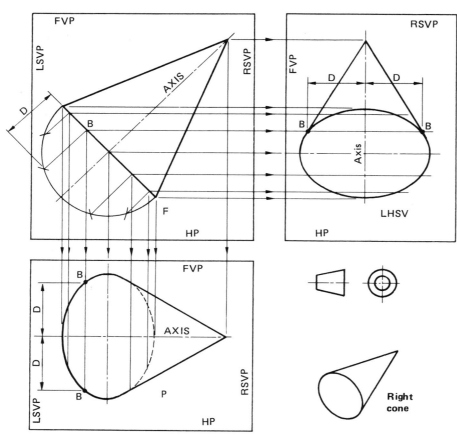

Note: The front view (F) is drawn first and positioned as shown. A semi-circle is drawn on the base and divided into a number of equal divisions (6 being convenient). Lines parallel to the axis are drawn from each of the divisions to touch the base as shown.

The plan view (P) is drawn by projecting widths down from the front view and obtaining depths from the semi-circle on the front view. For example, depth D is stepped off either side of the axis in plan along the projector drawn from points B in the front view.

The left-hand side view (LHSV) is drawn by projecting heights from the front view and obtaining appropriate depths from the semi-circle on the front view. For example, depth D is stepped off, either side of the axis, along the projector from points B in the front view. Depths could, of course, have been projected. from the plan view, via a conveniently placed 45° line.

(b) Right Cone with slant edge lying parallel to the horizontal plane, axis parallel to the SVPs and inclined at an angle to both the HP and the FVP.

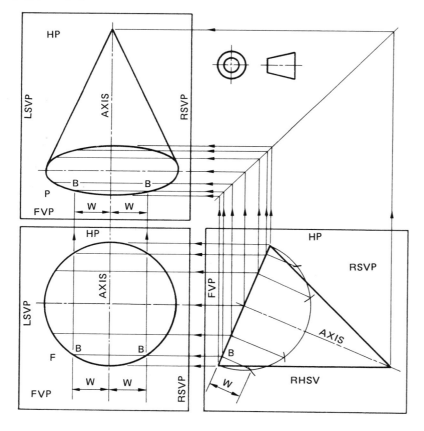

Note: The right-hand side view (RHSV) is drawn first, positioned with slant edge parallel to the HP. A semi-circle is drawn on the base and divided into six equal divisions. Lines, parallel to the axis, are drawn from each of these divisions to touch the base of the cone as shown.

The front view (F) is drawn next by projecting heights across, from the RHSV, then obtaining appropriate widths from the semi-circle. For example, a line is projected from points B on the base of the cone in the RHSV and widths W are stepped off along this projector, either side of the axis, as shown.

The plan view (P) is drawn by projecting depths upwards from the RHSV, via a conveniently placed 45° line, as shown. Corresponding widths are obtained from either the semi-circle in the side view or by projecting them upwards from the front view. For example, points B in plan can be obtained by stepping off width W from the axis along the appropriate projector from the RHSV *or* by projecting from points B in the front view.

Notice that the SPHERE, although a commonly encountered solid, has not been used to exemplify the projection of typical solids. This is because a sphere appears as a circle in front, side and plan views and as such its projection would not prove very informative.

84

Auxiliary Projection

The great majority of technical and engineering drawings are composed of views drawn at 90° to each other. Relatively simple objects are usually represented by means of either a front elevation and an orthographically projected plan view or a front elevation and projected side view, as seen in the previous section.

In order to fully represent more complicated components it is often necessary to draw one or even two side views to augment the conventionally drawn front and plan views.

Occasionally an object or component is shaped such that conventionally drawn orthographic views do not provide an adequately clear and fully informative representation. In such cases a carefully chosen AUXILIARY view can be used to good effect.

The shaped solid drawn below serves to illustrate the point.

(a)   Using conventional orthographic views to represent the component

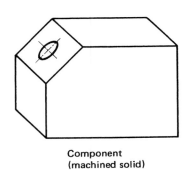

Component
(machined solid)

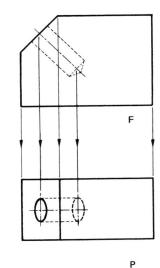

F

P

Notice that the sloping face in the front view (F) is shown fore shortened in the plan view (P)

Notice also that the hole in the plan view has to be "plotted", which is time-consuming. Furthermore, it appears in plan as an ellipse for it is viewed obliquely.

(b)   Using an auxiliary PLAN view in addition to (or alternatively in place of) the conventional plan view.

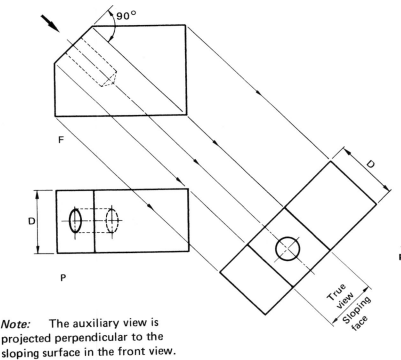

Note: The auxiliary view is projected perpendicular to the sloping surface in the front view.

Notice that a TRUE VIEW of the sloping surface containing the hole is seen, in this example, in an auxiliary PLAN. This enables the hole not only to be viewed without distortion but also to be drawn, relatively quickly, with compasses. In certain cases a carefully chosen auxiliary view enables sloping faces and details contained within these faces (holes, slots, etc.) to be dimensioned much more easily and clearly than does the corresponding conventional view.

Note: The Depth D is taken from the conventional plan view.

Auxiliary plan

The student should be able to draw auxiliary (aiding) views of relatively simple components. Methods commonly used for constructing such views are described and illustrated in some detail in the text which follows.

AUXILIARY PLAN

An auxiliary PLAN is drawn by projecting from a conventional (orthographic) FRONT ELEVATION at an angle other than 90°. Depths for an auxiliary PLAN are obtained from either a given conventional plan view or, less often, a conventional side view. The method used for constructing auxiliary PLANS is illustrated and explained below using, respectively a cylinder, a pyramid and a cone.

1. RIGHT CYLINDER (given the front elevation, plan and "viewing" angle).

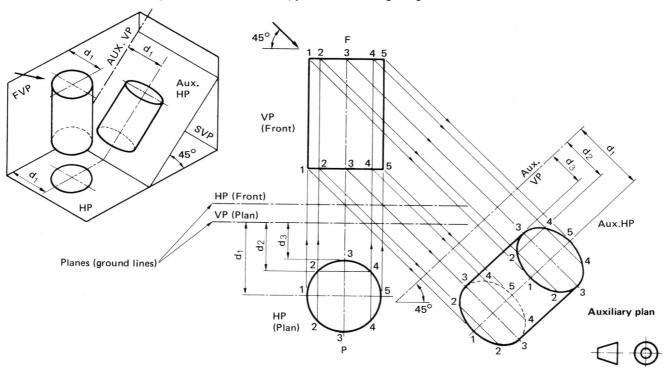

Steps
1. The front elevation (F) and plan (P) are drawn first.
2. The principal planes (or ground lines as they are sometimes called) are positioned and fully labelled. (HP, VP, etc). (The positions of the planes relative to the front and plan are arbitrary unless specifically stated).
3. The plan view is divided into a number of equal divisions (8 being convenient) and numbered 1 to 5, as shown. Lines are projected upwards from each of these numbered points onto the front elevation, to position points 1-5 in that view.
4. The "viewing" arrow is drawn at the given angle (45° in this example)
5. The auxiliary vertical plane (Aux. VP) is positioned at 90° to the "viewing" arrow and clear of the previously drawn view, as shown.
6. Projection lines, parallel to the "viewing" arrow, are drawn from points 1, 2, 3, etc. on the front view.
7. Distance d_1, from the VP to the centre line in plan, is stepped off from the auxiliary VP to position the centre line of the cylinder in the auxiliary plan.
8. Further distances d_2, d_3, etc. from the plan view, are stepped off from the auxiliary VP along appropriate projectors drawn from points 2, 3, etc. in the front view.
9. Finally, respective numbered points on the curves are joined as shown, the outline "heavied-in" and the view appropriately labelled AUXILIARY PLAN.

Important points to note:
(1) *All* distances (depths) stepped off into the AUXILIARY PLAN view above d_1, d_2, d_3 etc., are obtained from the ORTHOGRAPHIC PLAN view. Remember that no matter from what angle the auxiliary plan view is projected, corresponding points on each of the plan views must always be the same distance from the respective VERTICAL planes
(2) The VERTICAL plane is represented by the page itself in the front view and by a line in the plan view and auxiliary plan view.
The HORIZONTAL plan is represented by a line in the front view and the page itself in the plan and auxiliary plan views.
(3) Unlike the example on the previous page there is no PRACTICAL advantage to be gained by drawing either this cylindrical solid or, indeed, any of the solids in the following five examples, as in auxiliary view.
Each has been projected "obliquely" simply as a comprehension and projection exercise.

2. RIGHT SQUARE-BASED PYRAMID (given the front elevation, side elevation and viewing angle)

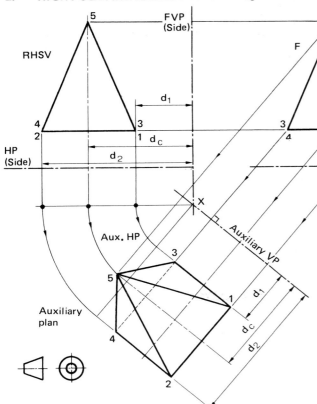

Notice that *all* distances stepped off (or "swung") into the AUXILIARY PLAN view (d_1, d_c and d_2) are, in this example, obtained from the ORTHOGRAPHIC SIDE view.

Steps

1. The front view (F) and right-hand side view (RHSV) are drawn and labelled.
2. Planes are positioned and labelled HP and FVP in the given front and side elevations.
3. The "viewing" arrow is positioned, carefully.
4. The auxiliary vertical plane is suitably positioned at 90° to the "viewing arrow" and labelled.
5. Projection lines, parallel to the "viewing" arrow, are drawn from all numbered points in the front view, as shown.
6. Distances d_1, d_c and d_2, from the front vertical plane to the respective points in the side view, are stepped in front of the auxiliary VP along appropriate projectors from the front view to position points 1 to 5 in the auxiliary plan. (Alternatively, the distances may be "swung" from point X, as indicated).
7. The outline is "heavied-in", hidden detail inserted and the view fully labelled.

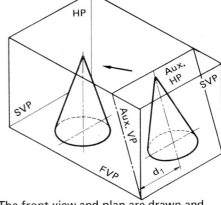

3. RIGHT CONE (given the front elevation, plan and viewing angle)

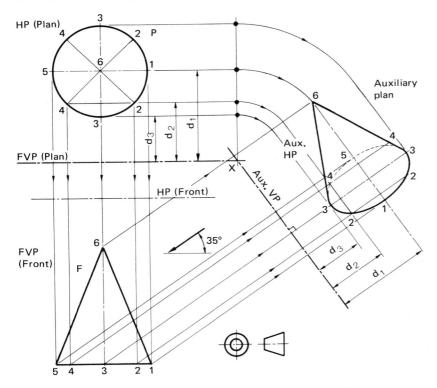

As in example 1, *all* distances used on the AUXILIARY PLAN view above, d_1, d_2, d_3 etc. are obtained from the ORTHOGRAPHIC PLAN view. Corresponding points on each of the plan views are always the same distance from the respective VERTICAL planes.

Steps

1. The front view and plan are drawn and labelled F and P, respectively.
2. Planes in these views are positioned and labelled.
3. The plan is divided into a number of equal divisions.
4. Points 1 to 6 are numbered in the plan and each point is projected downwards into the front view.
5. The "viewing arrow" is positioned, as shown.
6. The auxiliary VP is suitably positioned at 90° to the arrow.
9. Projection lines, parallel to the "viewing" arrow, are drawn from all numbered points in the front view.
8. Distances d_1, d_2, d_3 etc. from the FVP to the respective numbered points in the orthographic plan, are stepped off from the auxiliary VP along appropriate projectors from the front view to position points 1 to 6 in the auxiliary plan view.

AUXILIARY ELEVATION
An auxiliary ELEVATION is drawn by projecting from a conventional (orthographic) PLAN view at an angle other than 90°.

Heights for an auxiliary ELEVATION are obtained from either a given conventional (orthographic) front view or, less often, from a given conventional side view.

The method used for constructing auxiliary ELEVATIONS is illustrated and explained below using first a machined prism, then a composite pyramidal solid, and finally a right cone inclined at an angle to the horizontal plane.

1. MACHINED PRISM (given the front elevation, plan view and viewing angle)

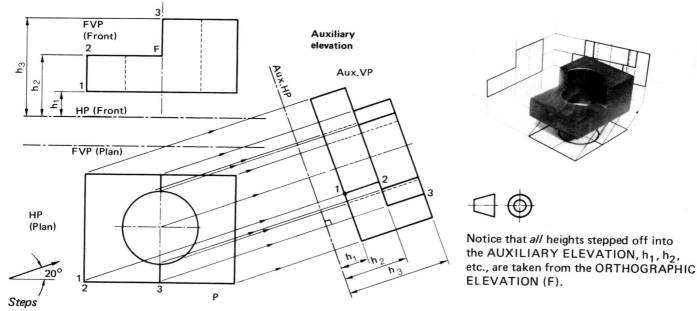

Notice that *all* heights stepped off into the AUXILIARY ELEVATION, h_1, h_2, etc., are taken from the ORTHOGRAPHIC ELEVATION (F).

Steps

1. The front elevation and plan view are drawn and labelled F and P, respectively.
2. The principal planes (ground lines) for both the front view and plan are positioned and labelled.
3. The "viewing" arrow is drawn at the given angle (20° in this example).
4. The auxiliary horizontal plane is drawn at 90° to the "viewing" arrow and positioned so that it is clear of the previously drawn views.
5. Projection lines, parallel to the viewing arrow, are drawn from all edges in the plan view, as shown.
6. Heights h_1, and h_2 and h_3, from the HP in the front view to the respective surfaces in the front view, are stepped off above the auxiliary HP along the appropriate projectors to obtain all necessary points on the auxiliary elevation. For example point 1 in the auxiliary elevation is obtained by stepping off height h_1 from the front view along the projector drawn from point 1 in the plan view, as shown.
7. The auxiliary elevation is completed by joining respective points, "heavying-in" the outline and labelling.

2. COMPOSITE PYRAMIDAL SOLID (given the front elevation, plan view and viewing angle).

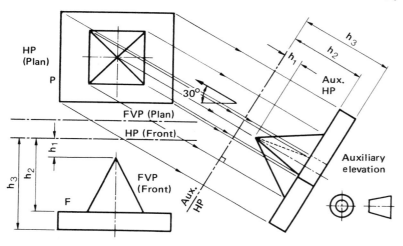

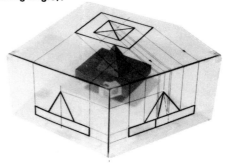

Notice that, as in the previous example, *all* heights stepped off into the AUXILIARY ELEVATION, h_1, h_2, etc, are taken from the ORTHOGRAPHIC ELEVATION (F)

Steps

1. The front elevation (F) and plan view (P) are drawn and their planes positioned and labelled.
2. The "viewing" arrow is drawn at the given angle (30°, here) and the auxiliary HP drawn at 90° to the arrow and positioned clear of the previously drawn views, as shown.
3. Projection lines, parallel to the "viewing" arrow, are drawn from all edges in the plan view.
4. Heights h_1, h_2 and h_3, from the front view F, are stepped off *below* the auxiliary HP along the appropriate projectors from the plan view to position strategic points on the auxiliary elevation.
5. The outline of the auxiliary elevation is "heavied-in" and labelled to complete the drawing.

3. RIGHT CONE, inclined at an angle to the horizontal plane (given the front elevation, plan view and viewing angle).

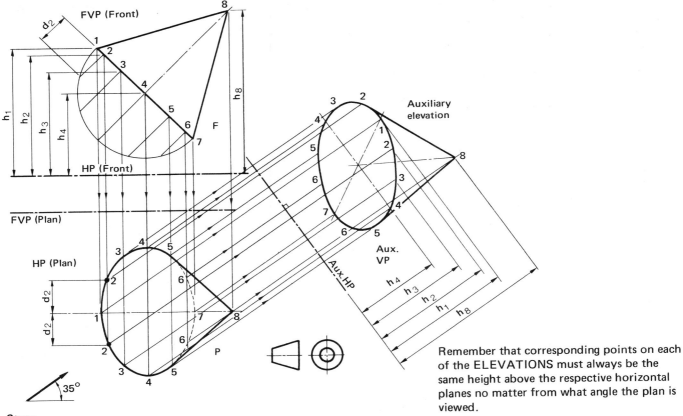

Remember that corresponding points on each of the ELEVATIONS must always be the same height above the respective horizontal planes no matter from what angle the plan is viewed.

Steps
1. The front elevation (F) of the cone is drawn, inclined to the horizontal plane.
2. A semi-circle is drawn on the base, divided into six equal divisions, and points numbered 1 to 7.
3. The plan view (P) is constructed by projecting lines from numbered points 1 – 8 in the front elevation and stepping appropriate distances, from the semi-circle, along these projectors. (for example, distance d_2 is stepped off either side of the centre line along the projector drawn from point 2).
4. The planes for both front elevation and plan are positioned and labelled HP and FVP.
5. The "viewing" arrow is drawn to indicate the direction from which the plan is to be viewed.
6. Projectors are drawn, parallel to the "viewing" arrow, from points 1 to 8 in the plan, as shown.
7. The auxiliary HP is drawn at 90° to these projectors and positioned clear of the previously drawn views.
8. Heights h_1, h_2, h_3 etc., from the front elevation (F), are stepped off above the auxiliary HP along the projectors drawn from points 1, 2, 3 etc., in the plan to position strategic points on the auxiliary elevation.
9. The outline of the auxiliary elevation is "heavied-in" and the view fully labelled to complete the drawing.

SUMMARY
(i) An auxiliary PLAN view is obtained by projecting from an orthographic FRONT view, at any angle other than 90°.

The auxiliary front vertical plane is always drawn perpendicular to the "viewing line".

No matter from what angle the auxiliary PLAN is projected, corresponding points on each of the plan views are always the same distance in front of the respective VERTICAL planes (see points A and B).

(ii) An auxiliary ELEVATION is obtained by projecting from an orthographic PLAN view, at any angle other than 90°.

The auxiliary horizontal plane is always drawn perpendicular to the "viewing line".

Corresponding points on each of the elevations are always the same height above the respective HORIZONTAL planes (see points A and B).

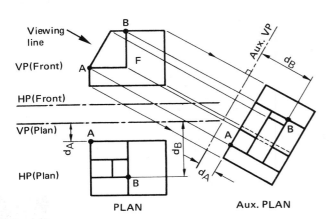

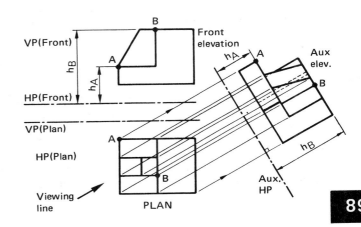

Sections of Solids

A three-dimensional geometrical object is called a SOLID. It is an object (or *component* in engineering terminology) that has length, breadth and depth. Cubes, cylindrical bars, pyramids, cones, spheres, etc., are all solids. (See pages 72-74 for a detailed classification).

A sectional view is an imaginary rather than actual view. The draughtsman imagines the solid to have been sawn through, along a surface known as the CUTTING PLANE. He draws a view of the imagined sliced solid as seen looking in the direction of the arrows placed at the ends of the cutting plane. The resultant view is known variously as a "sectioned solid", "sectional view", "sectional elevation", or just plain "section".

The examples below show "simple" sectional views of a selection of the more commonly encountered solids.

CUBE

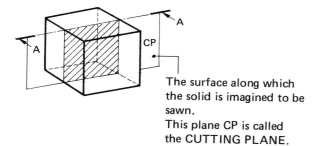

The surface along which the solid is imagined to be sawn.
This plane CP is called the CUTTING PLANE.

SECTION A—A

Note The imagined cut surface is *cross-hatched,* i.e. shaded with relatively thin, equi-spaced lines drawn, usually, at 45° with a set-square.

Note carefully, and REMEMBER, how the cutting plane is designated — with a relatively thin, chain line with its ends "heavied-in". Lettered arrows, placed at the ends of the line, indicate the direction in which the component should be viewed.

RIGHT SQUARE-BASED PYRAMID

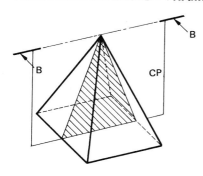

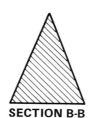

SECTION B-B

Note The spacing of the section ("hatching") lines depends upon the size of the imagined cut surface to be sectioned. The larger the surface, the greater the distance between the hatching lines.
The direction of slope of the section lines is arbitrary.

RIGHT CONE

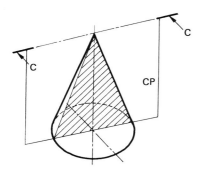

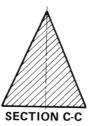

SECTION C-C

Notice the similarity of the sectional view of the pyramid, section B-B, and the sectional view of the right cone when cut along its vertical axis, section C-C.

Note Section C-C is one of five standard CONIC SECTIONS, the others, illustrated later in the text, being the circle, the ellipse, the parabola and the hyperbola.

SPHERE

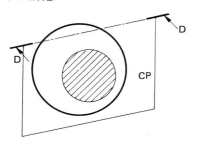

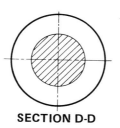

SECTION D-D

Note Part of the sphere behind the cutting plane is shown in this sectional view, even though it has NOT been cut, because it can be seen in the background when looking in the direction of arrows D.

Notice how each of the sectional views above has been labelled, SECTION A-A, SECTION B-B, etc.

The draughtsman draws a sectional view primarily to clarify the internal details of a component. Therefore, sectional views are usually drawn only for those components with relatively complex internal shapes as castings of machine parts, etc. Clearly, geometrical solids do not fall into this category but the student can benefit considerably from drawing sectional views of solids for it means not only practising sectioning and orthographic projection but also developing spatial ability. The student should be able to demonstrate an ability to visualize and construct shapes, in addition to being able to project views orthographically.

Sections of the most commonly encountered solids are illustrated and explained below. The solids are grouped under five headings for clarity: Prisms, Cylinders, Pyramids, Cones and Spheres.

Sectional views whose cutting planes are either parallel to, or perpendicular to, the horizontal and/or vertical planes are dealt with first. Then the more complicated sections, where either the solids themselves, or their cutting planes, are inclined at an angle to the horizontal and/or vertical planes, are explained in greater detail.

Note: All views shown in this Chapter are drawn in FIRST angle orthographic projection.
In all examples the FRONT elevation is designated F
the PLAN view is designated P
the RIGHT-HAND SIDE is designated RS
the LEFT-HAND SIDE is designated LS

(A) CUTTING PLANES (CP) EITHER PARALLEL TO, OR PERPENDICULAR TO, THE HORIZONTAL AND/OR VERTICAL PLANES.

1. PRISMS: Hexagonal bar

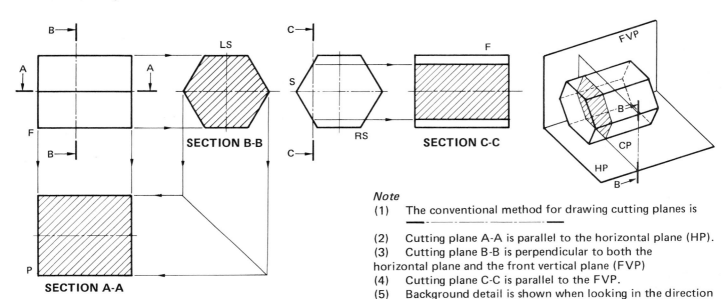

SECTION B-B

SECTION C-C

SECTION A-A

Note
(1) The conventional method for drawing cutting planes is

——— · ——— · ——— · ———

(2) Cutting plane A-A is parallel to the horizontal plane (HP).
(3) Cutting plane B-B is perpendicular to both the horizontal plane and the front vertical plane (FVP)
(4) Cutting plane C-C is parallel to the FVP.
(5) Background detail is shown when looking in the direction of arrows C. However, hidden detail is not shown.

2. CYLINDRICAL bar

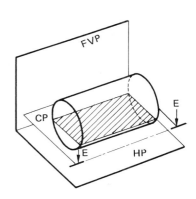

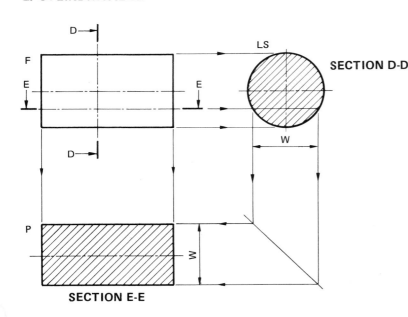

SECTION D-D

SECTION E-E

Note
(1) Cutting plane D-D is perpendicular to both the FVP and the HP.
(2) Cutting plane E-E is parallel to the HP.
(3) Width W, in plan, has been projected from the side elevation (Section D-D)
(4) No background detail is shown in Section E-E because none would be seen when looking in the direction of arrows E.

3. RIGHT PYRAMIDS: regular pentagonal base

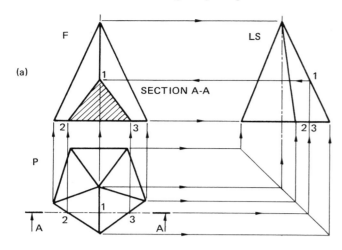

(a)

SECTION A-A

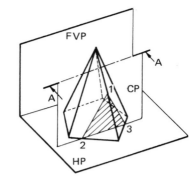

Note
(1) The PLAN view is drawn first.
(2) The height of point 1 in the sectioned view A-A is obtained by projecting from point 1 in the plan (P), into the side view (LS), then across to the front view (F) as shown.
(3) Cutting plane A-A is parallel to the front vertical plane (FVP) and perpendicular to the horizontal plane (HP).
(4) Background detail is shown in Section A-A.
(5) Hidden detail is NOT normally shown on a sectional view. It has, therefore, been omitted in SECTION A-A.

(b)

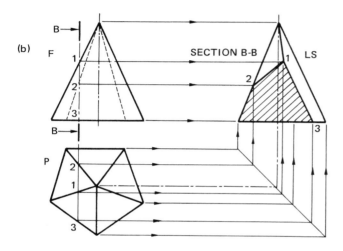

SECTION B-B

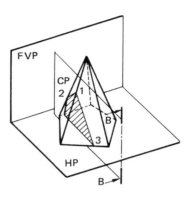

Note
(1) The heights in the sectioned view B-B are projected from the front view. The corresponding "widths" are projected from the plan view as shown.
(2) Cutting plane B-B is perpendicular to both the HP and FVP.

TETRAHEDRON: a triangular pyramid with four identical surfaces. (See page 82 for the construction).

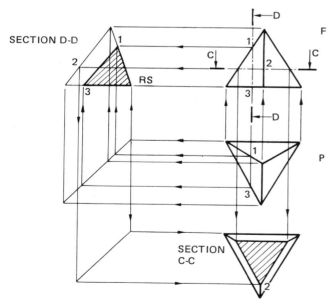

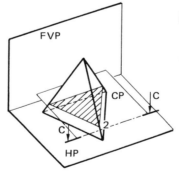

Note
(1) Cutting plane C-C is parallel to the HP and perpendicular to the FVP.
(2) No background detail is shown in Section D-D.

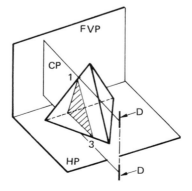

Note
Cutting plane D-D is perpendicular to both the HP and the FVP.

The plan view is drawn first and the elevation projected from this. The height of point 1 in section D-D is projected from the front elevation. The position can be verified by projecting from the plan view, as shown. Point 2 in section CC, drawn separately for clarity, has been projected first from point 2 in the front view to the leading edge in the side view, section D-D, then down to the leading edge in the sectioned plan.

4. RIGHT CONES

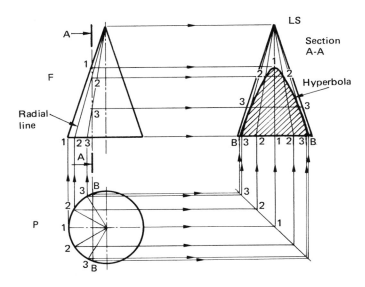

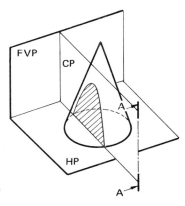

Note
(1) Cutting plane A-A is perpendicular to both the HP and the FVP.
(2) When the cutting plane is parallel to the axis of the cone, as it is here, the resultant curve, B-1-B, is a HYPERBOLA. The cut surface is known as a CONIC section.
(3) These radial lines are construction lines which are drawn on the inclined surface of the cone. They are usually equi-spaced in the plan view.

The heights of points 1, 2 and 3 in sectional view A-A are projected horizontally from the intersection of the radial lines and cutting plane in the front view, as shown. Each of the points in Section A-A is positioned at the intersection of the horizontal projector from the front view and the corresponding radial line, which is projected from the plan view as shown. Points B in Section A-A are projected from the plan.

All sectional views in the examples presented above are TRUE VIEWS because their cutting planes are either parallel to, or perpendicular to, the horizontal plane and/or the front vertical plane.

(B) CUTTING PLANES INCLINED AT AN ANGLE TO THE HORIZONTAL PLANE AND/OR THE FRONT VERTICAL PLANE.

1. PRISMS: Cube

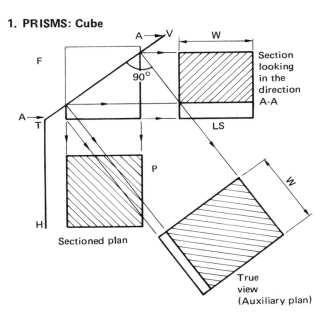

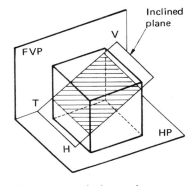

Note
(1) This type of cutting plane is known as an INCLINED plane. In this example it is perpendicular to the FVP and inclined at an angle to the HP.
(2) The lines "traced" onto the horizontal and vertical planes (shown heavily) by the cutting plane are known as TRACES. They are designated H.T. (horizontal trace) and V.T. (vertical trace) respectively, and represented orthographically as shown in the front view and plan view. (See pages 106-7 for further details).
(3) Neither the hatched surface in side elevation nor that in the plan is a true representation of the cut surface. An auxiliary *plan* has to be drawn, at 90° to the vertical trace V.T. to obtain a TRUE view.

PRISMS: rectangular bar

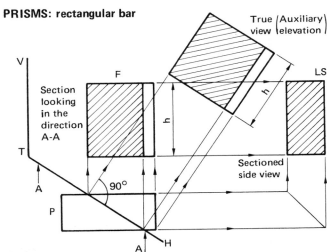

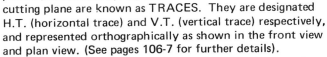

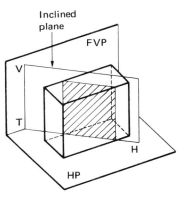

Note
(1) The cutting plane is inclined to the FVP and perpendicular to the HP.
(2) The true view, an auxiliary *elevation,* is always projected at 90° to the cutting plane.
(3) The height of the true view, h, is stepped off from the front view or the side view.
(4) Hatching lines are drawn at 45° to the outline of the component, or at 45° to the centre line for a cylindrical component, wherever possible. These lines may be drawn sloping either to the right or to the left.

93

2. CYLINDRICAL bar (shaft)

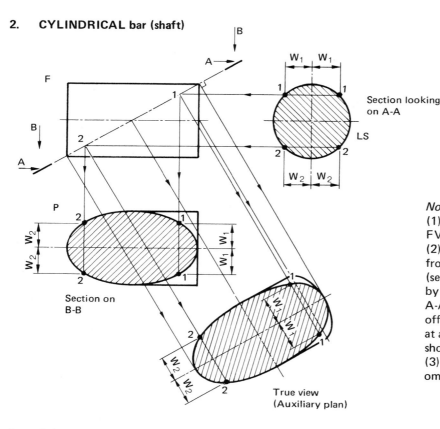

Section looking on A-A

LS

Section on B-B

True view (Auxiliary plan)

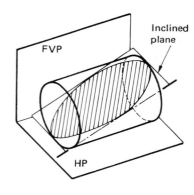

Note
(1)   The cutting plane is perpendicular to the FVP and inclined at an angle to the HP.
(2)   The distance of points on the cut surface from the centre line in both the plan view (section on B-B) and the true view are obtained by stepping them from the side view (section on A-A). For example, points numbered 1 are stepped off along the projector from 1 on the cutting plane at a distance W_1 either side of the centre line, as shown.
(3)   Hidden detail has, quite correctly, been omitted from the true view (auxiliary plan).

3. PYRAMIDS: Hexagonal base.

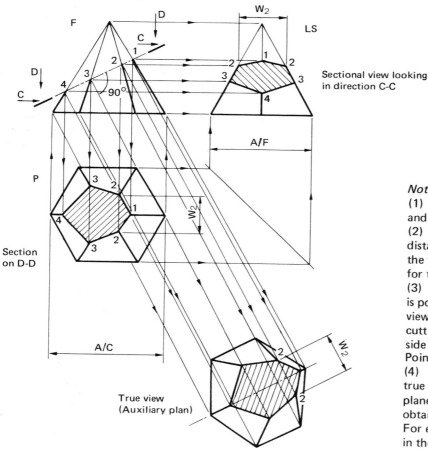

Sectional view looking in direction C-C

LS

A/F

Section on D-D

A/C

True view (Auxiliary plan)

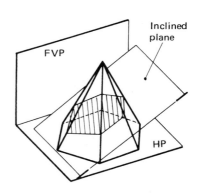

Note
(1)   The cutting plane is perpendicular to the FVP and inclined at an angle to the HP.
(2)   The plan view is drawn first to obtain the distance across the corners of the hexagon (A/C), for the front view, and the distance across the flats (A/F), for the side view.
(3)   Point 1 in both the side view and plan view is positioned by projecting from point 1 in the front view (at the intersection of the slant edge and the cutting plane) to cut the corresponding edge in the side view and plan view, respectively as shown. Points 2, 3, 4 are similarly positioned.
(4)   The projection lines from the front view into the true view are drawn at 90° to the inclined cutting plane. Distances between points on the true view are obtained from either the side view or the plan view. For example, the distance between points numbered 2 in the true view is W_2, as indicated.

When a geometrical solid has had its top removed, as this hexagonal pyramid has, it is said to be TRUNCATED. The remaining, bottom, part of the solid, with cut surface lying *at an angle* to the base, is commonly called a FRUSTUM, but, strictly speaking, this is incorrect. The remaining, lower part of a solid should be called a frustum only when the top surface is cut *parallel* to the base.
(If you have forgotten this turn back to page 73 for details).

PYRAMIDS: square base

Section
looking
in direction
A-A

Sectioned
plan view

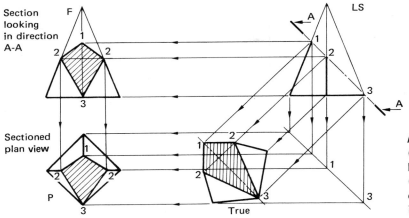

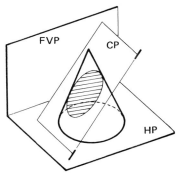

Note
(1)   The cutting plane is inclined at an angle to both the HP and the FVP.
(2)   Points 1 and 3 in the plan view are projected, conventionally, from points 1 and 3, respectively, in the side view, as shown. Point 2, however, has to be projected first from the side view into the front view and then down into the plan.
(3)   Hidden detail is NOT shown in the sectional views.

4. CONES
a) Plane cutting both generators

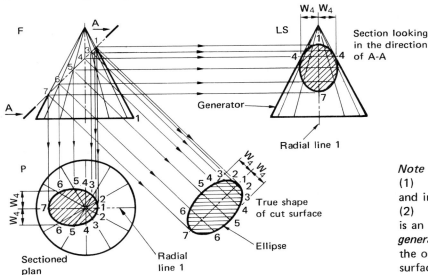

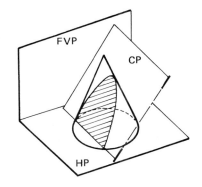

Note
(1)   The cutting plane is perpendicular to the FVP and inclined at an angle to the HP.
(2)   The outline of the *true* shape of the cut surface is an ELLIPSE. If the cutting plane *cuts two opposite generators* of the cone, as it does in this example, then the outline of the section is always elliptical. The cut surface is a "standard" CONIC section.

The shape of the cut surface in all views is obtained by joining up a series of points. Each of the points, e.g. point 1, is "plotted" as follows. A projection line is drawn from point 1 in the front view (i.e. from the intersection of the cutting plane and radial line 1) to cut radial line 1 in the desired view, as shown above.

Width W_4 in plan can be obtained either by projecting conventionally from the side view, using a 45° line, or simply by stepping off W_4 from the side view into the plan view.

b) Cutting plane parallel to a generator

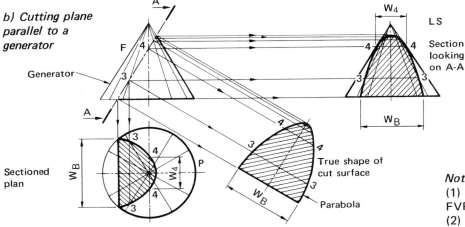

Note
(1)   The cutting plane is perpendicular to the FVP and inclined at an angle to the HP.
(2)   The outline of the *true* shape of the cut surface is a PARABOLA. If the cutting plane is *parallel* to the generator, as it is here, then the true shape, shown opposite, is another "standard" CONIC section.

The distance between points numbered 4 in the plan view, W_4, is either stepped from the side view or projected, conventionally, using a conveniently positioned 45° line. The distance *cannot* be obtained by projecting from the front view. Width W_B in the side and true views is taken from the base of the plan view.

95

5. SPHERES

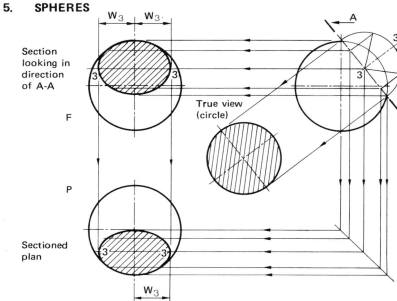

Section looking in direction of A-A

F

P

Sectioned plan

True view (circle)

W_3 W_3

LS

A

W_3

A

Note

(1)   The cutting plane is inclined at an angle to both the FVP and the HP.

(2)   The TRUE view of the cut surface is always a circle.

Distances between paired points on the cut surface of both the front view and plan view are taken from the semi-circle drawn on the cutting plane (imagine it to be a hinged flap). For example, the distance from the centre line of each of the points numbered 3, in both the front view and plan view, is W_3, as shown.

(C)   SECTIONS OF SOLIDS WHICH ARE THEM-SELVES INCLINED AT AN ANGLE TO THE HORIZONTAL PLANE AND/OR THE FRONT VERTICAL PLANE.

1. PRISMS: hexagonal base

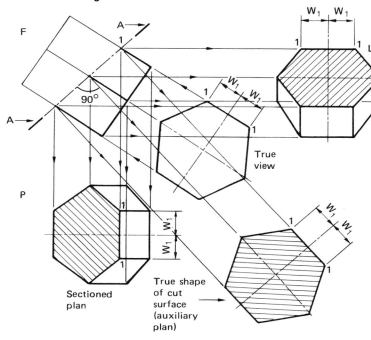

F

90°

A

A

P

Sectioned plan

True shape of cut surface (auxiliary plan)

W_1 W_1

W_1 W_1

LS

Section view looking in direction of A-A

True view

W_1 W_1

Note

(1)   The solid is parallel to the FVP and inclined to the HP.

(2)   The cutting plane is perpendicular to the FVP and inclined at an angle to the HP.

(3)   No hidden detail is shown in the sectional views.

The true view is drawn first, then the front view projected from it, as shown opposite. Distances between paired points in the side view, plan and true shape are taken from the true view. For example, the distance from the centre line of each of the points numbered 1 is W_1, as shown.

2. PYRAMIDS: equilateral triangular base

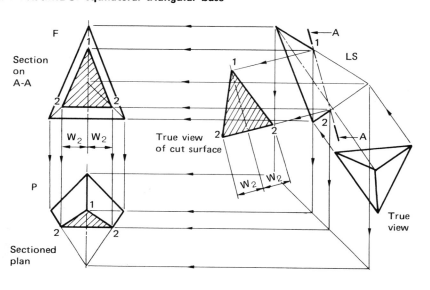

F

Section on A-A

P

Sectioned plan

True view of cut surface

W_2 W_2

W_2 W_2

LS

A

A

True view

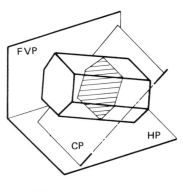

Note

(1)   The solid and the cutting plane are inclined at an angle to both the FVP and the HP.

(2)   The true view is drawn first, then the side view is projected from this, as shown opposite.

3. RIGHT CONES

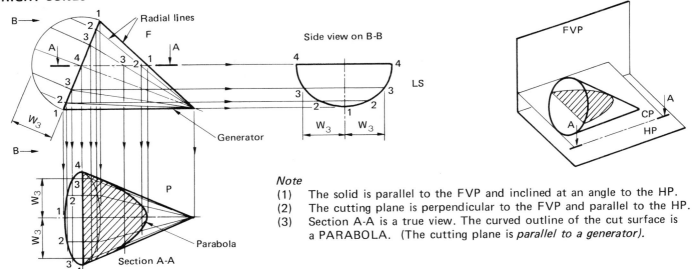

Note
(1) The solid is parallel to the FVP and inclined at an angle to the HP.
(2) The cutting plane is perpendicular to the FVP and parallel to the HP.
(3) Section A-A is a true view. The curved outline of the cut surface is a PARABOLA. (The cutting plane is *parallel to a generator*).

Point 1 on the parabolic curve in Section A-A is positioned at the intersection of the projector drawn from point 1 in the front view (at the intersection of the cutting plane and radial line 1) and radial line 1 in the plan view. Points 2, 3 and 4 on the curve in plan are similarly positioned, as indicated.

The side view is drawn by first projecting horizontally from each of the radial lines at the base of the cone in the front view, as shown above, then stepping off appropriate distances, from the semi-circle drawn on the base of the cone, along the respective projectors. For example, the distance stepped from the centre line along the projector from radial line 3, to position points 3 in the side view, is W_3, as indicated. The side view is *not* a semi-circle because the base of the cone is inclined away from viewing arrows B.

Summary of CONIC sections
An attempt should be made to memorize the position of the plane through which a right cone has to be cut to obtain each of the "standard" conic shapes.

1. TRIANGLE

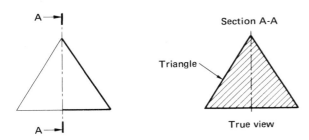

Cutting plane is along the vertical axis of the cone.

2. CIRCLE

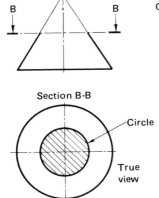

Cutting plane is perpendicular to the axis of the cone.

3. ELLIPSE

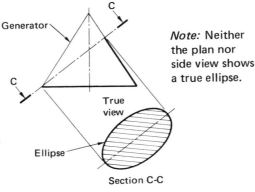

Note: Neither the plan nor side view shows a true ellipse.

Cutting plane lies at a greater angle to the axis than do the generators.

4. PARABOLA

Cutting plane lies at the same angle to the axis as the generators.

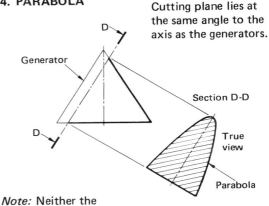

Note: Neither the plan nor side view shows a true parabola.

5. HYPERBOLA

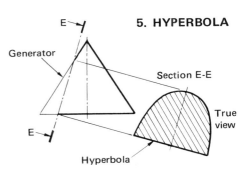

Cutting plane lies at a smaller angle to the axis than do the generators. It is NOT parallel to the generator.
Note: Neither the plan view nor side view shows a true hyperbola.

97

Lines, Laminae and Planes in Space

LINES in space The student should be able to visualize, draw and orthographically project straight lines which lie in any position relative to the principal planes of projection, and should in addition, be able to obtain, geometrically, the true length of any such straight line, its angles of inclination to the principal planes, and also its traces.

In an attempt to assist the student in this task, the following text illustrates the positions of "true" and "non-true" lines relative to the principal planes of projection, explains how to project lines in space to enable the true length to be found, and demonstrates how to find the true angle of inclination of a straight line to each of the principal planes. Finally, the term "trace" is defined and a method presented for determining the positions of the horizontal and vertical traces.

(a) Straight lines parallel to TWO principal planes of projection.

1.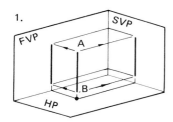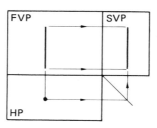

Line AB is parallel to both the front vertical plane (FVP) and the side vertical plane (SVP). The projection of the line onto either of these planes, therefore, produces a line of TRUE length.

2.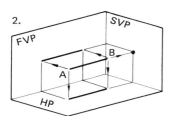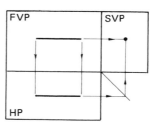

Line AB is parallel to both the front vertical plane and the horizontal plane (HP) in this example.
The projection of line AB onto either of these planes, therefore, produces a TRUE length line.

3.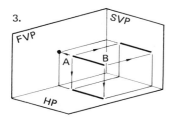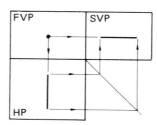

Line AB is parallel to both the side vertical plane and the horizontal plane in this example.
The projection of line AB onto either of these planes produces a TRUE length line.

Remember: Whenever a line is parallel to the plane onto which it is projected, then its projection will be a TRUE LENGTH.

(b) Straight lines parallel to ONE principal plane of projection.

1.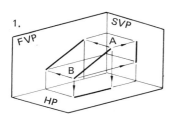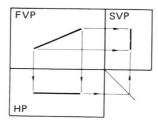

Line AB in this example is parallel to the FVP but inclined at an angle to both the HP and SVP. The projection of the line onto the FVP, therefore, produces a line of TRUE length. The projection of the line onto either the HP or SVP, however, produces a line that is foreshortened, as the diagrams show.

2.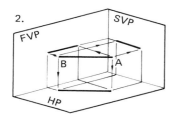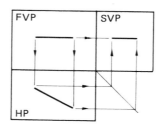

Line AB is parallel to the HP but inclined at an angle to both the FVP and SVP.
The projection of the line onto the HP produces a line of TRUE length. The projection of the line onto either the FVP or SVP, however, produces a line that is foreshortened.

3.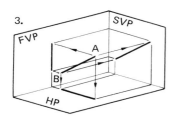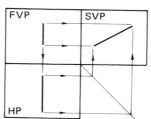

Line AB is parallel to the SVP in this example but inclined to both the FVP and the HP.
The projection of AB onto the SVP, therefore, produces a line of TRUE length. The projection of AB onto either the FVP or the HP produces a line that is foreshortened, i.e. "non-true".

Note: All orthographic views shown on this page, and indeed, throughout this section, are drawn in FIRST angle orthographic projection.

98

(c) Straight lines parallel to NONE of the principal planes of projection.

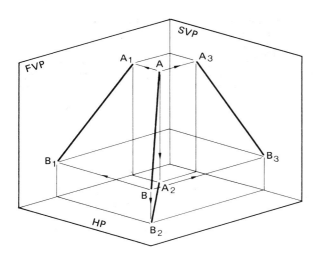

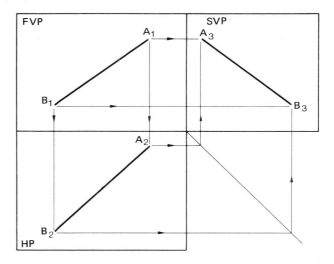

Line AB in this example is inclined at an angle to all three principal planes simultaneously.

Projecting the line onto the FVP, HP and SVP produces, therefore, a foreshortened line in each case as can be seen from the diagrams above.

How then can the TRUE length of the line AB be found in cases such as the one shown here? There are two methods commonly used to obtain the TRUE length of a straight line inclined to all three principal planes of projection. Both are illustrated and explained in detail below.

Method 1 (Line repositioned until it is parallel to one of the principal planes).

1. *AB repositioned until parallel with the horizontal plane (HP).*
The front elevation A_1B_1 is "swung" downwards, from point B_1, until it is horizontal i.e. until it is parallel to the HP (FRONT). The new position of point A_1 (A_h) is projected downwards into the plan view, as shown, to intersect the horizontal projector from point A_2 in plan. A straight line drawn from point B_2 in plan to this point of intersection produces the TRUE length of line AB.

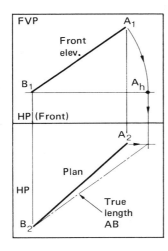

2. *AB repositioned until parallel with the front vertical plane (FVP).*
The plan view A_2B_2 is "swung" downwards, from point B_2, until it is horizontal, i.e. until it is parallel to the FVP (PLAN). The new position of point A_2 (A_v) is projected upwards into the front elevation, as shown, to intersect the horizontal projector from point A_1 in the front elevation. A straight line drawn from point B_1 in front elevation to this point of intersection produces the TRUE length of line AB.

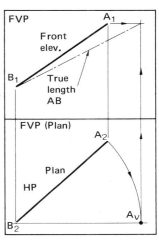

3. *AB repositioned until parallel with the side vertical plane (SVP).*
(a) The front elevation A_1B_1 is "swung" downwards from point A_1 until it is vertical, i.e. until it is parallel to the SVP (FRONT). The new position of point B_1 (B_v) is projected across into the side elevation, as shown, to intersect the vertical projector from point B_3 in the side elevation. A straight line drawn from point A_3 in the side elevation to this point of intersection produces the TRUE length of line AB.

(b) The plan view A_2B_2 is "swung" downwards from point A_2 until it is vertical, i.e. until it is parallel to the SVP (PLAN). The new position of point B_2 (B_{v1}) is projected across, via the 45° line, into the side elevation, as shown, to intersect the horizontal projector from point B_3 in the side elevation. A straight line drawn from point A_3 in the side elevation to this point of intersection produces the TRUE length of line AB.

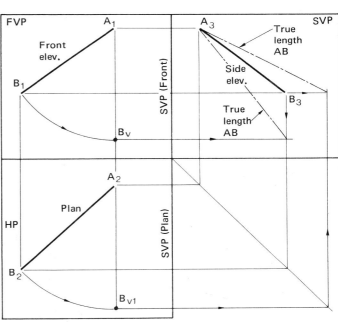

Method 2 (Line projected onto a conveniently placed auxiliary plane)

1. *Line projected onto an auxiliary plane positioned, parallel to the FRONT ELEVATION.*
An auxiliary front vertical plane is drawn PARALLEL to the front elevation A_1B_1, as shown. (The distance from A_1B_1 is arbitrary). Perpendicular projectors are drawn from points A_1 and B_1. The distance of point A in front of the FVP, d_a, is obtained from the plan view. It is then stepped off above the auxiliary FVP, along the perpendicular projector drawn from A_1, to position point A_F. The distance of point B in front of FVP, d_b, is also obtained from the plan view and stepped above the auxiliary FVP, along the perpendicular projector from B_1, to position point B_F. A straight line joining A_F and B_F produces the TRUE length of line AB.

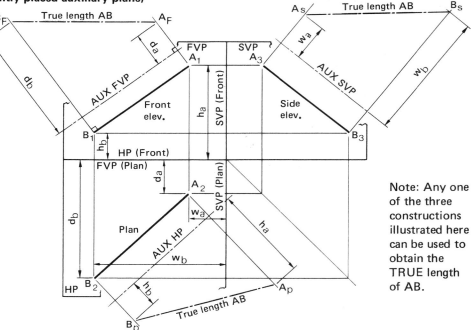

Note: Any one of the three constructions illustrated here can be used to obtain the TRUE length of AB.

2. *Line projected onto an auxiliary plane positioned parallel to the PLAN VIEW.*
An auxiliary horizontal plane is drawn PARALLEL to the plan view A_2B_2, as shown above. Perpendicular projectors are drawn from points A_2 and B_2. The height of point A above the HP, h_a, is obtained from the front elevation and stepped above the auxiliary HP, along the perpendicular projector from point A_2, to position point A_p. The height of point B above the HP, h_b, is also obtained from the front elevation and stepped above the auxiliary HP, along the perpendicular projector from B_2, to position point B_p. The TRUE length of line AB is obtained by joining A_p and B_p.

3. *Line projected onto an auxiliary plane positioned parallel to the SIDE ELEVATION.*
An auxiliary side vertical plane is drawn PARALLEL to the side elevation A_3B_3, as shown above. Perpendicular projectors are drawn from points A_3 and B_3. The distance of point A in front of the SVP, w_a, is obtained from the plan view and stepped off above the auxiliary SVP, along the perpendicular projector from A_3, to position point A_s. The distance of point B in front of the SVP, w_b, is also obtained from the plan view and stepped above the auxiliary SVP, along the perpendicular projector from B_3, to position point B_s. A straight line joining A_s and B_s produces the TRUE length of line AB.

Note: The student will rarely (if ever) have to use construction 3 in either of the two methods outlined above. This is because the the straight line, in exam questions, tends to be shown relative to the FVP and HP only. Constructions 3 have been included here merely to show the obliquely inclined line repositioned parallel to each of the three principal planes of projection in turn.

ANGLES OF INCLINATION of lines to the principal planes of projection.

(a) Straight lines parallel to ONE of the principal planes.

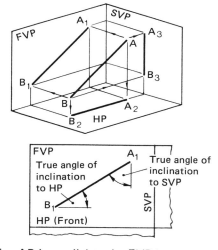

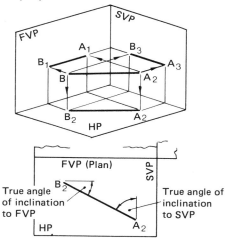

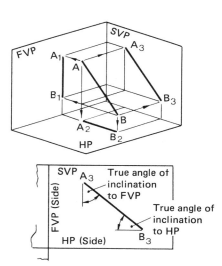

Line AB is parallel to the FVP but inclined at an angle to both the HP and SVP. The TRUE angle of inclination to both the HP and the SVP can be obtained, directly, by first projecting AB onto the FVP then measuring the angles of inclination as shown above.

Line AB is parallel to the HP but inclined to both the FVP and SVP. The TRUE angle of inclination to both the FVP and the SVP can be obtained, directly, by first projecting AB onto the HP then measuring the angles of inclination as shown above.

Line AB in this case is parallel to the SVP but inclined to both the HP and FVP. The TRUE angle of inclination of AB to both the HP and FVP can be obtained, directly, by first projecting AB onto the SVP then measuring the angles of inclination as shown above.

(b) Straight lines parallel to NONE of the principal planes.

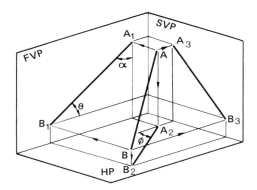

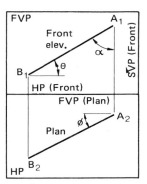

Line AB is, in this case, inclined at an angle to all three principal planes of projection.
The TRUE angles of inclination of AB to these planes cannot, therefore, be found directly by projecting the line onto the respective principal planes. This would produce only *apparent* angles of inclination, as shown right.
To determine the TRUE angle of inclination of the straight line AB to each of the principal planes a true view of AB has to be obtained (using either method 1 or method 2, detailed on pages 99 and 100) and from this the required angle can be measured directly, as shown in the diagrams below.

Note: θ is the APPARENT angle of inclination to the HP, ϕ the APPARENT angle of inclination to the FVP, and α the APPARENT angle of inclination to the SVP.

1.   *Using method 1 (page 99) to find the TRUE angle of inclination of AB to each of the principal planes of projection.*

(a)   Inclination to the horizontal plane (HP).

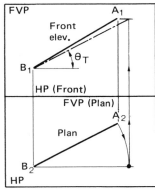

(b)   Inclination to the front vertical plane (FVP).

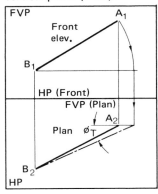

(c)   Inclination to the side vertical plane (SVP).

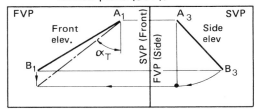

Note: θ_T, in the first diagram, is the TRUE angle of inclination to the HP.
ϕ_T, in the second diagram, is the TRUE angle of inclination to the FVP.
α_T, in the diagram above, is the TRUE angle of inclination to the SVP.

2.   *Using method 2 (page 100) to find the TRUE angle of inclination of AB to each of the principal planes.*

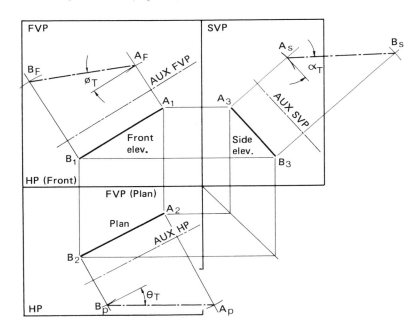

Note: θ_T, in the plan view, is the TRUE angle of inclination of AB to the HP.
ϕ_T, in the front elevation, is the TRUE angle of inclination to the FVP.
α_T, in the side elevation, is the TRUE angle of inclination of AB to the SVP.

It is not often that the student is asked to determine the true angle of inclination of a straight line to the side vertical plane. It is included here primarily for further understanding of the derivation of TRUE angles of inclination to the principal planes.

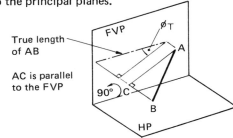

The derivation of both the TRUE length of AB and the TRUE angle at which AB is inclined to each of the principal planes may be more easily understood if line AB is imagined to be the hypotenuse of a set-square which is revolved through $90°$ then projected onto the appropriate plane — the FVP in the pictorial view opposite.

TRACES of straight lines in space

A TRACE is the point where a straight line, or a straight line produced, penetrates a plane (flat surface).

Methods used to obtain the traces of a straight line.
(a)   Line parallel to TWO principal planes.

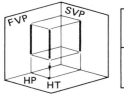 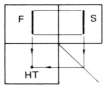 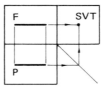 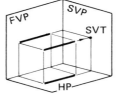 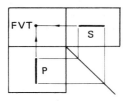

1.   *Horizontal trace (HT)*
A line is projected downwards from the front view (F) to intersect the projector from the side view (S), as shown above right, to position the HT.

2.   *Side vertical trace (SVT)*
A line is projected from the front view (F) to intersect the projector from the plan view (P), as shown above, to position the SVT.

3.   *Front vertical trace (FVT)*
A line is projected upwards from the plan view (P) to intersect the projector from the side view (S), as shown, to obtain the FVT.

Remember that when the line is parallel to two of the principal planes it penetrates, when extended, *one* plane only, i.e. the line has only *one* trace.

(b)   Line parallel to ONE principal plane.

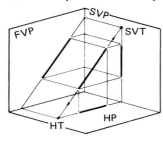 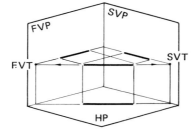 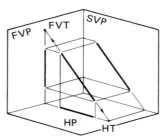

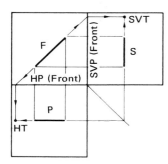 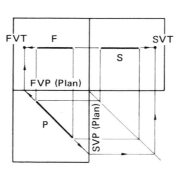 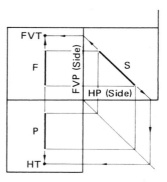

Line parallel to the FVP
1.   *Horizontal trace (HT)*
A line is projected downwards from the front view (F) to the HP in the front view, then vertically into the plan (P) as shown. A line is projected from the plan view to intersect this projector, and in so doing locates the HT.

2.   *Side vertical trace (SVT)*
A line is projected upwards from the front view (F) to the SVP in the front view, then horizontally into the side view(S), as shown. A line is projected up from the side view to intersect this horizontal projector to position the SVT.

Line parallel to the HP
1.   *Front vertical trace (FVT)*
A line is projected from the plan view (P) onto the FVP in the plan, then vertically into the front view (F), as shown. A line is projected from the front view to intersect the projector from the plan to locate the PVT.

2.   *Side vertical trace (SVT)*
A line is projected from the plan onto the SVP in plan, then into the side view, as shown. A line is projected from the side view to intersect this projector from the plan to position the SVT.

Line parallel to the SVP
1.   *Front vertical trace (FVT)*
A line is projected from the side view onto the FVP in the side view, then horizontally into the front view, as shown. A line is projected upwards from the front view to intersect the projector from the side view to locate the FVT.

2.   *Horizontal trace (HT)*
A line is projected downwards from the side view onto the HP in the side view, then around into the plan, as shown. A line is projected down from the plan to intersect this projector from the side view to position the HT.

Remember that, when the straight line lies parallel to only one of the principal planes of projection it penetrates, when produced, *two* planes, i.e. the line has *two* traces.

(c) Line parallel to NONE of the principal planes.

1. Horizontal trace (HT)
A line is projected downwards from the front view (F) onto the HP in the front view, then vertically into the plan (P), as shown in the orthographic drawing opposite. A line is projected from the plan view to intersect the projector from the front view to locate the horizontal trace HT.

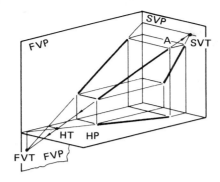

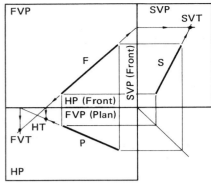

2. Side vertical trace (SVT)
A line is projected upwards from the front view (F) to the SVP in the front view, then horizontally into the side view (S), as shown in the orthographic drawing. A line is projected upwards from the side view to intersect this horizontal projector, positioning the SVT.

3. Front vertical trace FVT.
A line is projected from the plan view (P) onto the FVP in plan, then vertically downwards in this case, as shown in the orthographic drawing. A line is projected from the front view (F) to intersect the projector from the plan view, positioning the FVT. Notice that in this example, the FVT appears in the front vertical plane, as usual, but BELOW the horizontal plane. The line has penetrated the horizontal plane (at the HT) before proceeding to penetrate the front vertical plane (at the FVT), as can be seen in the adjacent pictorial drawing.

Notice that when the straight line lies at an angle to all three principal planes it penetrates, when produced, *three* planes i.e. the line has *three* traces.

Note: It is rarely that a student is asked to determine the position of the side vertical trace (SVT). The constructions showing how its position is determined have been included here for completeness.

In examination questions capital letters may be used to DESCRIBE straight lines. Small (lower case) letters are then used to LABEL views of these lines. In the typical example below, the line is DESCRIBED as AB, whereas in the plan view (Fig. 1) it is LABELLED ab. Line XY in Fig. 1 represents the front vertical plane.

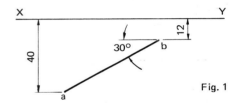

Fig. 1

Example Fig. 1 shows the plan of a line AB. The line is inclined at $30°$ to the horizontal plane (HP) and end A is 15mm above the HP. End B is also above the HP.

a) Draw the plan and front elevation of AB.
b) Determine and state the true length of AB and also the true angle of inclination of AB to the front vertical plane (FVP).
c) Determine and show the position of both the horizontal trace (HT) and the front vertical trace (FVT).

SOLUTION

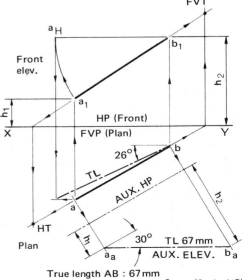

True length AB : 67 mm
Inclination AB to VP: 26° (Scale 1:2)

Steps
The plan view of AB (ab) is drawn, as shown. (It is drawn half full-size here to conserve space).
Point a_1 can be positioned in the front view, 15 mm (h_1) above the HP and vertically above point a in plan. Point b_1 cannot be positioned immediately in the front view because its height above the HP is unknown. However, this height can be obtained from an auxiliary elevation. An auxiliary HP is positioned parallel to ab in plan, point a_a drawn 15mm (h_1) above this auxiliary HP and a line drawn at the given angle (30°) to "set" point b_a. Point b_1 can now be positioned in the front view, vertically above point b in plan, at height h_2 (stepped from the auxiliary elevation) above the HP.
The true length of AB (TL) can be obtained from the auxiliary elevation – it measures 67mm.
The angle of inclination of AB to the FVP is obtained as follows. The front view ($a_1 b_1$) is rotated until horizontal, point a_H is projected down to intersect a horizontal line drawn from point a in plan. A line from this point of intersection to point b in plan produces the true angle of inclination of AB to the FVP (26°). (Notice that the true length can be checked from this line).
The horizontal trace (HT) is found by projecting from the front view $a_1 b_1$ down to the HP (front), projecting vertically downwards into the plan, as shown, to intersect ab produced. The vertical trace (FVT) is positioned by extending ab in plan until it meets the FVP (plan), then projecting vertically upwards to intersect $a_1 b_1$ produced as shown.

LAMINAE in space

Laminae is the plural of lamina. A LAMINA is a thin plate. All laminae illustrated in the following examples will be thin FLAT plates (of various shapes).

A student is expected to be able to draw orthographic views of differently shaped laminae in any position relative to the principal planes of projection, and should, in addition, be able to determine the true shapes of laminae in space and also their true angles of inclination to the principal planes.

Methods to carry out each of these three tasks are illustrated and explained below.

1. Projection of laminae.

(a) Using a 45° set-square as the lamina. (Base edge on the horizontal plane and parallel to the front vertical plane.)

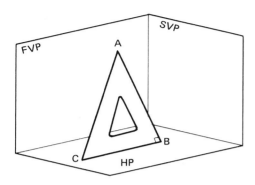

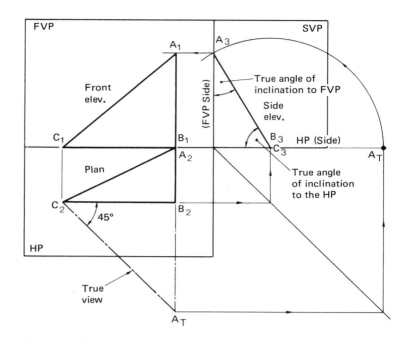

CB is lying on the HP, parallel to, and at a given distance from, the front vertical plane (FVP).
Apex A is touching the FVP.

Base BC can be positioned in the plan view (B_2C_2), front view (B_1C_1) and the side view (B_3C_3). Apex A, however, can be positioned initially in the plan view only (A_2). To enable point A to be positioned in the other two views the true view of the square has to be drawn. Point A_T has to be projected from this true view, via the 45° line, into the side elevation then "swung" from "point" B_3C_3 onto the FVP to position point A_3. Point A_3 is then projected horizontally into the front elevation, as shown, and a line drawn vertically upwards from point A_2, in plan, intersects this horizontal projector to locate point A_1. Notice that the TRUE angles of inclination of the lamina (set-square) to the HP and FVP can be obtained, directly in this example, from the side elevation, as shown.

(b) Using a 60°/30° set-square as the lamina. (Apex on the horizontal plane and hypotenuse parallel to the side vertical plane.)

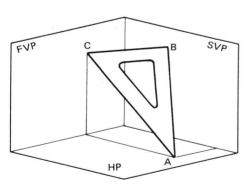

Note: d in the auxiliary view is taken from the front view, as shown.

Apex A is lying on the HP, in a given position. AC is parallel to the SVP. The length and angle of inclination of AC to the HP is given. Point B is touching the SVP. Point C is touching the FVP.

Hypotenuse AC is drawn first in the side elevation (A_3C_3), then projected into the plan (A_2C_2) and front (A_1C_1). Point B cannot, initially, be positioned in any of these views. A true view of the 60°/30° square has to be constructed to determine the point at which B touches the SVP. This is best drawn in the side elevation, as shown. The true height of the lamina (B_TH) is projected from the true view into the auxiliary view, then "swung" to touch the auxiliary SVP, in point B_A, as shown. Point B_A is then projected back to line B_TH in the true view to locate the actual point (B_3) at which point B touches the SVP. Point B_3 in the side view is projected horizontally to cut the SVP in the front view to position point B_1. Finally, point B_3 is projected down from the side view into plan, via the 45° line, to position point B_2. Notice that the TRUE angle of inclination of the lamina (set-square) to the SVP can be obtained from the auxiliary view, as shown.

(c) *Using a scalene triangular lamina* (Lamina inclined to all three principal planes. Base edge lying on the horizontal plane.)

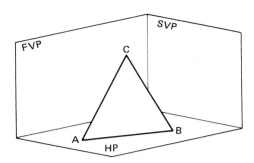

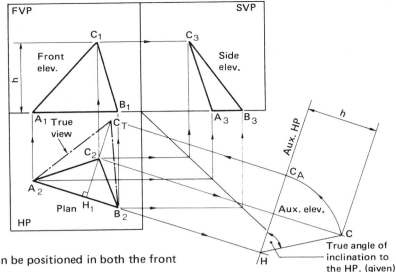

The plan view is given. Base AB is lying on the HP. Corner C is in space. The lamina is inclined to all planes. The true angle at which it is inclined to the HP is given.

The given plan view $A_2B_2C_2$ is drawn first. Base AB can be positioned in both the front elevation (A_1B_1) and side elevation (A_3B_3), as shown.

Corner C cannot, however, be positioned in either front or side views without first ascertaining its height above the HP. This is obtained from an auxiliary elevation, projected from the plan view as shown. (The angle of inclination of the lamina to the HP is given). The height of C above the HP (h) is stepped above the HP in the front view along the projector drawn vertically upwards from C_2 in plan to position point C_1. A horizontal projector is drawn from C_1 into the side view to intersect a projector drawn, via the 45° line, from point C_2 in plan to position point C_3.

The true view of the lamina, $A_2C_TB_2$, can be constructed on the plan view, as shown. The true height of the lamina, $C_T H_1$ is obtained from the auxiliary elevation by "swinging" an arc, length HC, from point H to touch the auxiliary HP at point C_A. Point C_A is then projected into the plan view to intersect line H_1C_2 extended at C_T — the TRUE apex.

Note: The true shape of the lamina could of course, have been drawn by using an alternative, but rather more laborious, construction. The true length of each of the sides could have been determined (using either of the constructions outlined on pages **99** and **100**) and the true shape triangle constructed from these.

(d) *Using a semi-circular protractor as the lamina* (Lamina inclined at an angle to all three principal planes, straight edge lying parallel to and above the horizontal plane).

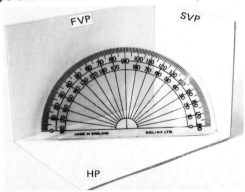

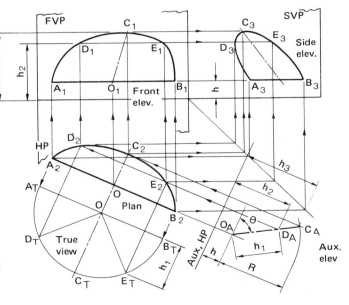

Plan view of the base AB is given. The base is lying parallel to and at a given height h above the HP. The lamina is inclined to all principal planes. The angle at which the lamina is inclined to the HP is given.

The given plan of the base (A_2B_2) is drawn first. This is projected into both the front and side elevations and labelled A_1B_1 and A_3B_3, respectively. (AB is height h above the HP). The true view is drawn next and labelled as shown. An auxiliary elevation is drawn next to enable points C_2, D_2 and E_2, on the curve in plan, to be positioned. This auxiliary view is constructed by swinging an arc, length R (radius of the semi-circle), from point O_A to form an angle θ (true angle of inclination) with the auxiliary HP. Point C_A is projected from the auxiliary view into the plan to position point C_2. Height h_1 from the true view is stepped along $O_A C_A$ in the auxiliary view to position point D_A. D_A is projected into plan to intersect the projectors from D_T and E_T in the true view to position points D_2 and E_2. Vertical projectors are drawn from points D_2 and E_2 in plan into the front elevation to intersect the horizontal projector drawn at height h_2 above the HP to position points D_1 and E_1 (height h_2 is obtained from the auxiliary elevation, as shown). Height h_3 (from aux. elev.) is stepped along a vertical projector from point C_2 in plan to position point C_1 in the front view. Points C_3, D_3, E_3 in side elevation are obtained by drawing horizontal projectors from points C_1, D_1 and E_1 in the front elevation to intersect projectors drawn, via the 45° line, from points C_2, D_2 and E_2, respectively, in the plan view.

105

(e) Triangular lamina completely in space. (None of the edges lying on, or parallel to, any of the principal planes.)

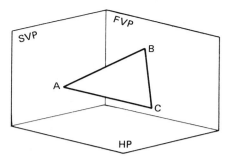

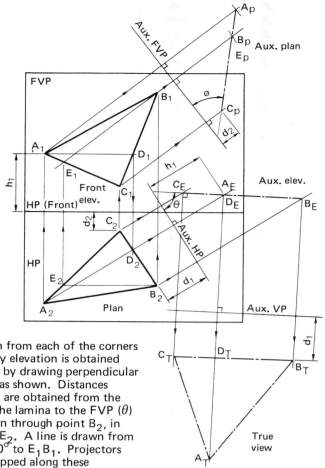

The plan view of the lamina is given. The height of each of the corners above the horizontal plane is given. The lamina is inclined to all principal planes.

The given plan view $A_2B_2C_2$ is drawn first. The front elevation can be drawn by projecting from each of the corners in plan then positioning points A_1, B_1 and C_1 at the given heights above the HP along the respective projectors. An auxiliary elevation is projected from the plan, as shown, to obtain both the angle of inclination of the lamina to the HP (θ) and, from this, the true view. The auxiliary elevation is constructed by drawing a horizontal line through point A_1 in the front view, projecting down from point D_1 to point D_2 in plan. A line is drawn from point A_2, in plan, through point D_2. The auxiliary HP is drawn at 90° to A_2D_2, as shown. Projectors, parallel to A_2D_2, are drawn from each of the corners A_2, B_2 and C_2. The height of each of these corners in the auxiliary elevation is obtained from the front view, for example h_1. The true view is constructed by drawing perpendicular projectors from corners C_E, A_E and B_E in the auxiliary elevation, as shown. Distances stepped along each of these projectors in front on the auxiliary VP are obtained from the auxiliary HP in plan, for example d_1. The angle of inclination of the lamina to the FVP (θ) is obtained by drawing an auxiliary plan. A horizontal line is drawn through point B_2, in plan. A vertical projector is drawn into the front view from point E_2. A line is drawn from E_1 through B_1 in the front view. The auxiliary FVP is drawn at 90° to E_1B_1. Projectors are drawn from corners A_1, B_1 and C_1 as shown. The distances stepped along these projectors, above the auxiliary FVP, taken from the plan view, position the corners in the auxiliary plan. For example, d_2 is stepped above the auxiliary FVP along the projector from point C_1 to position point C_p.

PLANES in space

In this section the student is introduced to both INCLINED and OBLIQUE planes and their traces. It is shown how to project both inclined and oblique planes onto the principal planes of projection and also how to project a point lying in a plane. Constructions are presented which enable not only the true angles of inclination of oblique planes to the principal planes to be found but also the angle between the traces of oblique planes. Finally, a method for determining the unknown position of a trace of an oblique plane is illustrated and explained.

Types of plane
(a)   INCLINED planes and their traces.
A plane which is inclined to two of the principal planes of projection and perpendicular to the other one is known as an INCLINED plane.

The TRACE of a plane is a straight line "traced" onto the adjacent principal plane of projection by the edge of that plane, or the edge produced.

Each of the following pictorial drawings shows an INCLINED plane, and the accompanying orthographic view shows how the traces are represented conventionally.

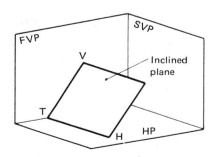

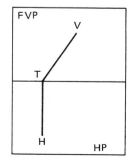

Notice how the traces are represented and labelled in the orthographic view. VT is the vertical trace (i.e. that edge of the inclined plane projected onto the FVP)
HT is the horizontal trace (i.e. that edge projected onto the HP)

1. Inclined to both the HP and SVP and perpendicular to the FVP

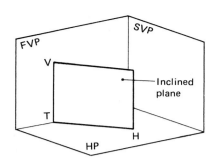

2. *Inclined to both the FVP and the SVP and perpendicular to the HP.*

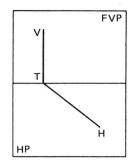

As in the previous example, VT is the vertical trace (i.e. that edge of the inclined plane "traced" onto the FVP).

HT is the horizontal trace (i.e. that edge which is projected onto the HP).

Notice that there are no traces from either of these two inclined planes shown on the side vertical plane (SVP). This is because the student will rarely, if ever, encounter problems in which side vertical planes are involved. Inclined planes and their traces are shown, almost exclusively, relative to the HP and FVP.

(b) OBLIQUE planes and their traces.

A plane which is inclined to all of the principal planes of projection is known as an OBLIQUE plane.
The pictorial drawing below shows an OBLIQUE plane and the orthographic drawing its traces.

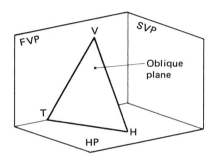

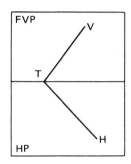

Notice that the traces of this oblique plane are shown on the FVP and HP but NOT on the SVP, as were the traces for the inclined planes shown above.

Inclined to all three principal planes simultaneously.

PROJECTION of PLANES

(a) Inclined planes.

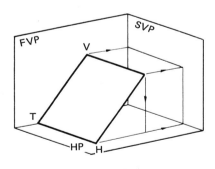

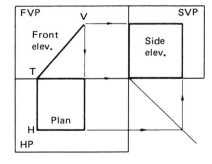

The VT and HT are positioned, as shown.
The VT represents the front elevation of the inclined plane.
A projector is drawn vertically downwards from point V into the plan to intersect a horizontal projector drawn from point H to obtain the plan view. The side elevation of the inclined plane is obtained, conventionally, by projecting heights from the front view and depths from the plan view, via the 45° line, as shown.

Plane inclined to the HP and SVP and perpendicular to the FVP.

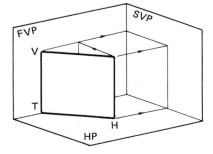

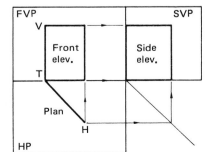

The VT and HT are positioned.
The HT represents the plan view of the inclined plane.
A projector is drawn vertically upwards from point H into the front elevation to intersect a horizontal projector drawn from point V to complete the front elevation, as shown. The side elevation is drawn by projecting hieghts from the front elevation and depths, via the 45° line, from the plan.

Plane inclined to the FVP and SVP and perpendicular to the HP.

(b)   Oblique planes

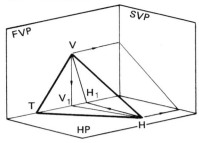

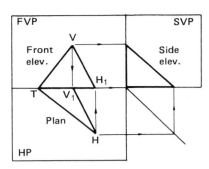

Plane inclined to all three principal planes simultaneously,

The HT and VT are drawn in their inclined positions as shown. A projector is drawn vertically downwards from point V to position the apex V_1 in the plan view. A projector is drawn vertically upwards from point H in plan to position point H_1, thus enabling the front elevation to be completed.

The side elevation is drawn by projecting heights from the front view and depths from the plan, via the 45° line, as shown.

PROJECTION of POINTS in planes
(a)   Inclined planes

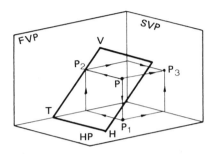

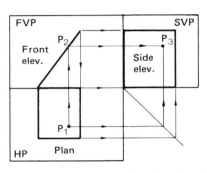

Point in plane inclined to the HP and SVP and perpendicular to the FVP.

The position of point P in the plan view (P_1) is given.

The three views of the inclined plane are drawn, using the procedure outlined on page 107. Given point P is positioned in the plan view (P_1). A projector is drawn vertically upwards from point P_1 to intersect the front elevation of the inclined plane, positioning point P_2. Point P_3 is located by drawing a horizontal line from point P_2 to intersect a line drawn from point P_1, via the 45° line, as shown.

The method outlined above for projecting a POINT which lies in (on) an inclined plane can also be used to project both straight LINES and LAMINAE which lie in an inclined plane. When projecting lines, both end points are drawn in the given view and then projected into the other view(s). They are then joined with a straight line. When projecting laminae lying on an inclined plane, corner points are drawn in the given view, projected into the other view(s), then appropriate points are joined with straight lines.

(b)   Oblique planes

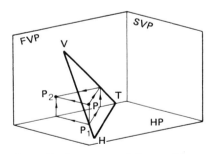

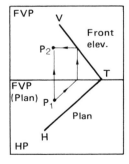

1.   *Both traces and the position of point P in plan (P_1) are given.*

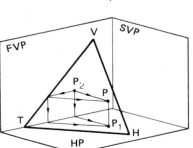

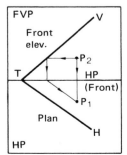

2.   *Both traces and the position of point P in the front view (P_2) are given.*

The method of projection used here is somewhat more complicated than that used to project points lying in inclined planes. It is illustrated with two examples. It is most unlikely that the student would be asked to project points in an oblique plane onto the side vertical plane and these two examples will show points projected onto only the HP and FVP.

The HT and VT are drawn and point P positioned in the plan (P_1) as shown opposite. A projector is drawn from point P_1, parallel to the HT to the line representing the VP in plan. The projector is then drawn vertically upwards to intersect the VT and then projected horizontally as shown. A line drawn upwards from point P_1 intersects this horizontal projector to position point P_2 — the front view of point P.

The HT and VT are drawn and point P positioned in the front elevation (P_2), as shown. A horizontal projector is drawn from point P_2 to VT, then vertically down to the line representing the HP in the front view. It is then projected parallel to HT as shown. A line is drawn vertically downwards from point P_2 to intersect this projector to position P_1 — the plan view of the point P.

Note: This method can also be used to draw both lines and laminae lying in an oblique plane, by projecting end points for lines, corner points for laminae, then joining appropriate points with straight lines.

ANGLES of INCLINATION of PLANES to the horizontal and front vertical planes

(a) Inclined planes

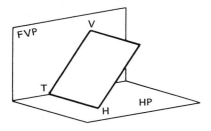

1. *Plane inclined to the horizontal plane (HP)*

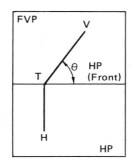

The true angle of inclination of inclined planes to the HP and FVP can easily be obtained. The angles which the respective traces make with the principal planes simply have to be measured.

For example, the angle of inclination of the plane shown opposite to the horizontal plane θ is measured between the VT and the HP (front). (The angle of inclination of this plane to the FVP is, as mentioned previously, $90°$).

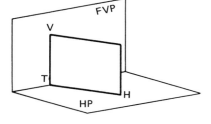

2. *Plane inclined to the front vertical plane (FVP)*

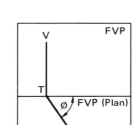

The true angle of inclination of this plane to the front vertical plane ϕ is measured between the HT and the line representing the front vertical plane in the plan view. (The angle of inclination of the plane to the HP is $90°$)

Notice that the angle of inclination of the inclined plane to the side vertical plane has not been shown as it is rarely requested.

(b) Oblique planes

Obtaining the true angle of inclination of an INCLINED plane to each of the principal planes of projection is a relatively simple task, as can be seen above. However, determining these angles for an OBLIQUE plane proves to be somewhat more difficult. The following pair of constructions show how it is done.

1. *Angle of inclination between an oblique plane and the HP.*

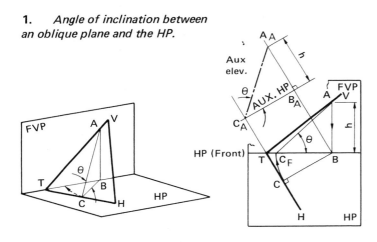

The given traces HT and VT are drawn, as shown. A line is drawn down from any point A on the VT to intersect the line representing the HP in the front elevation at point B. A line BC is drawn from point B, perpendicular to the HT. An arc, length BC, centre B, is drawn to intersect the HP (front) at point C_F, as shown. A line is drawn from point A to point C_F, Angle θ is the true angle of inclination of the oblique plane to the horizontal plane.

The auxiliary elevation (Aux. HP drawn parallel to line CB in plan) has been drawn for two reasons. Firstly, as an aid to understanding how triangle ABC_F in the front view has been obtained, and secondly as an alternative method for determining the required angle θ. Triangles ABC_F and $A_A B_A C_A$ are, in fact, identical.

2. *Angle of inclination between an oblique plane and the FVP.*

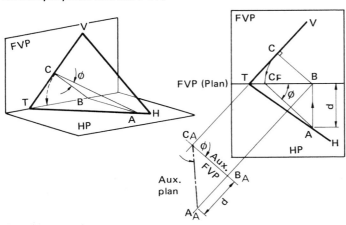

The given traces HT and VT are drawn. A line is drawn vertically upwards from any point A, on the HT to intersect the line representing the FVP in the plan view at point B. A line BC is drawn from point B, perpendicular to the VT. An arc, length BC, is drawn from centre B to intersect the FVP (plan) at point C_F, as shown. A line is drawn from point A to point C_F. Angle ϕ is the true angle of inclination between the oblique plane and the front vertical plane.

The auxiliary plan (Aux FVP drawn parallel to BC) has been included to help the student understand how triangle ABC_F has been obtained. It can also be used as an alternative method for obtaining angle ϕ.

True ANGLE between TRACES of an oblique plane

Whereas no construction is required to determine the true angle between the traces of an INCLINED plane — it can clearly be seen to be 90° — a construction is required to obtain the true angle between the traces of an OBLIQUE plane.
This construction is illustrated and explained below.

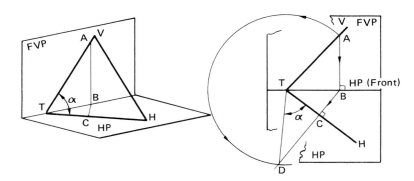

The VT and HT are drawn, as shown. A line is drawn vertically downwards from point A, which can be positioned anywhere along VT, to intersect the HP (Front) in point B. A line, perpendicular to the HT, is drawn from point B to cut the HT in point C. With centre T and radius AT, an arc is drawn to cut BC extended in point D. A line is drawn between points T and D. The true angle between the traces, α, lies between this line TD and line HT.

Note: Triangle TCD is actually the true view of triangle TBC. TC is a true length because it lies on the horizontal plane. TD is the same length as TA, which is the true length of line TB because it lies on the FVP. Line CD is the true length of line CB. As triangle TCD is a TRUE view then angle α is the TRUE angle between HT and VT.

Determination of the position of a "missing" trace of an oblique plane.

1. The position of the "missing" HORIZONTAL trace of an oblique plane can be determined from either of the following constructions provided that the position of the vertical trace and the projections of a point lying in the plane are known.

Method 1.

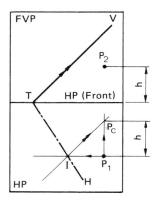

The given vertical trace VT and projections of point P, P_1 and P_2, are positioned as shown. The height of point P above the HP in the front view, h, is stepped along a vertical line drawn from point P_1, in plan, to position P_c. A horizontal line is drawn to the left of point P_1. A line, parallel to the VT is drawn from P_c to intersect this horizontal line in point I. A line from point T drawn through I produces the horizontal trace HT.

Method 2.

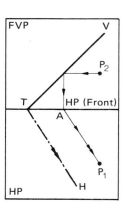

The given vertical trace VT and projections of point P, P_1 and P_2 are positioned. A horizontal line is drawn from point P_2 to the VT as shown. It is then projected down vertically to meet the HP (Front) in point A. A line is drawn joining points A and P_1.
A line, drawn parallel to line AP_1 from point T, produces the "missing" horizontal trace HT.

2. The position of the "missing" VERTICAL trace of an oblique plane can be determined from either of the constructions outlined below provided that the position of the horizontal trace and also the projections of a point lying in the oblique plane are known.

Method 1.

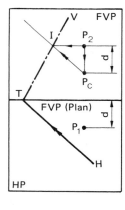

The given horizontal trace HT and projections of point P, P_1 and P_2, are positioned. The distance of point P in front of the FVP in plan, d, is stepped along a vertical line drawn down from point P_2 to position point P_c. A horizontal line is drawn to the left of P_2, as shown. A line, parallel to the HT is drawn from P_c to intersect this horizontal line in point I. A line drawn from point T through point I produces the required vertical trace VT.

Method 2.

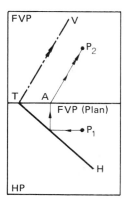

The given horizontal trace and projections of point P are positioned. A horizontal line is drawn from point P_1 to the HT, as shown. It is then projected vertically upwards to intersect the FVP (Plan) in point A. A line is drawn joining points A and P_2. A line drawn parallel to line AP_2 from point T produces the required vertical trace VT.

Developments

A DEVELOPMENT, or PATTERN as it is more often referred to in industry, is the TRUE shape of the surface area of a component laid out flat.

The development (pattern) of a cylindrical tin-can for example, is shown in the figure on the right below.

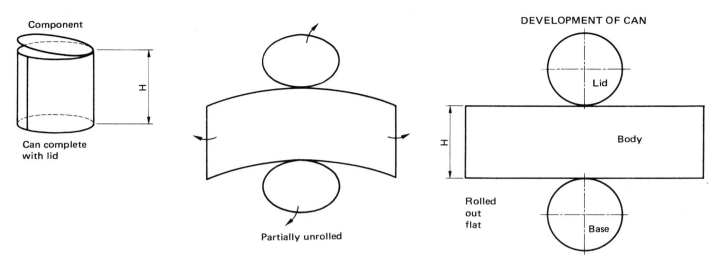

In this chapter methods used for obtaining developments (patterns) of a selection of the 'basic' geometric shapes —prisms, cylinders, pyramids, cones and spheres are illustrated and explained. Constructions used for obtaining the developments of a selection of miscellaneous components, i.e. those components whose shapes cannot readily be classified as one of the above mentioned "basic" shapes, are also presented.

PRISMS and CYLINDERS

The method used to obtain developments of both prisms and cylinders, right and oblique, is known as *PARALLEL LINE development*. It can be used to determine patterns only for those components having a constant cross-section throughout their length.

When developing prisms, existing lateral (side) edges are used as the parallel construction lines. When developing cylinders, lines parallel to the axis are drawn on the curved surface and these are used as construction aids.

1. RIGHT PRISMS
(a) **Cube — shaped box, with lid.**

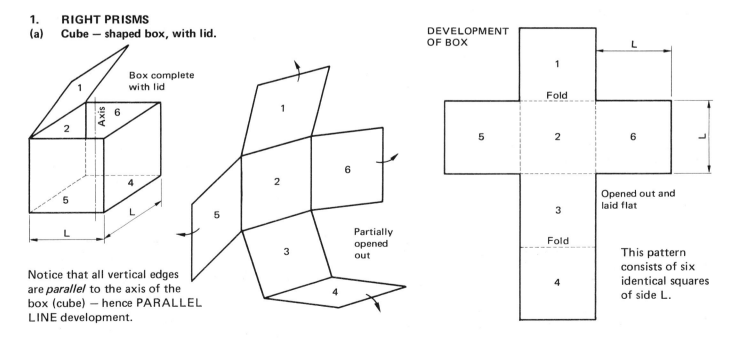

Note: FOLD, or BEND, lines are represented with relatively thin, full lines, chain-dotted lines or broken ("dashed") lines, as used in this example. This is to distinguish between those edges which have to be cut and those which have to be folded.

No fixing flaps, or tabs, will be included in any of the developments presented in this section. Whilst they need to be added to paper and cardboard patterns, which are joined with adhesives, they are less frequently required on sheet metal components, the abutted edges of which may be joined by soldering or brazing.

(b)   Truncated rectangular bunker (box), with lid and base

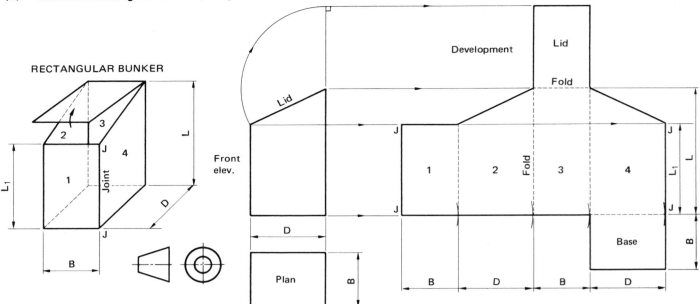

RECTANGULAR BUNKER

Steps

The front and plan views are
drawn, as shown. Feint lines
are projected horizontally from the top, front and base edges
in the front elevation into the development. Joint line JJ is
drawn in a convenient position. (The shortest edge is usually
taken as the joint line so that the component can be joined in
the minimum time, using minimum jointing materials.) Thin
vertical lines are drawn, parallel to line JJ, at distances
B and D, respectively, as shown. (These distances are stepped
off from the plan view.) The Sloping edges are drawn. The

Notice that the lid has been placed above the back
plate (3) to enable it to open as shown in the pictorial
sketch.
Whilst hinging along a fold line might be acceptable for
a cardboard model, it certainly would not be practically
acceptable for a sheet metal container. For a metal
bunker the lid would probably be cut from a separate
sheet, to minimise waste material, and swung about a
pair of metal hinges.

lid is "swung" to the open position in the front view, projected across into the development, and placed above side 3. The base
(B x D) is positioned below side 4 to minimise waste material. Fold lines are shown broken ("dashed") and the outline "heavied-in".

(c)   Truncated hexagonal ducting, with base but no top (lid).

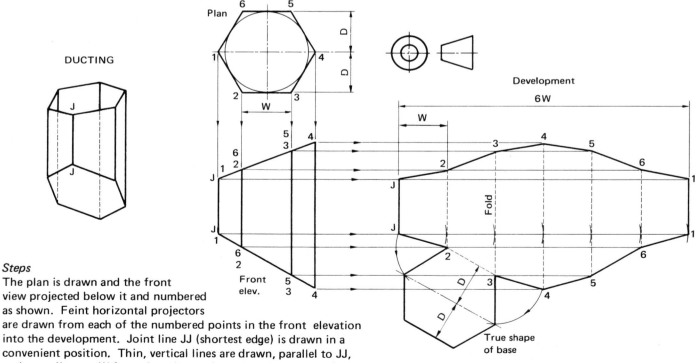

DUCTING

Steps

The plan is drawn and the front
view projected below it and numbered
as shown. Feint horizontal projectors
are drawn from each of the numbered points in the front elevation
into the development. Joint line JJ (shortest edge) is drawn in a
convenient position. Thin, vertical lines are drawn, parallel to JJ,
each at a distance W from the other and numbered as shown. (W is taken from the plan view). The shapes of the top and
bottom outlines of the development are obtained by drawing *straight* lines between successive points of intersection of
correspondingly numbered horizontal and vertical lines, as shown. The true shape of the base is determined by using distance
2D (from plan) for the width and radii 2-J and 3-4 for edge lengths as indicated. The fold lines are added and outline "heavied-in"
to complete the development.

2. RIGHT CYLINDERS

(a) Offset, open-ended, cylindrical connecting pipe.

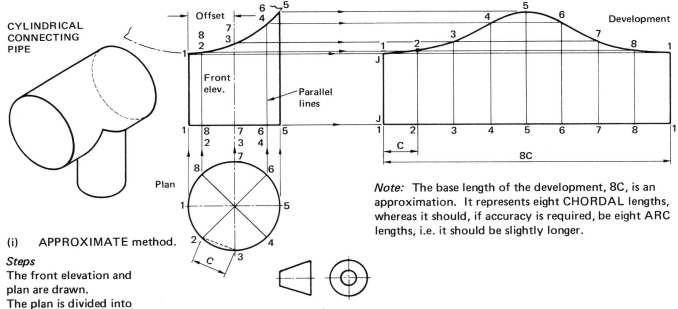

CYLINDRICAL
CONNECTING
PIPE

Offset

Front elev.

Parallel lines

Development

Plan

Note: The base length of the development, 8C, is an approximation. It represents eight CHORDAL lengths, whereas it should, if accuracy is required, be eight ARC lengths, i.e. it should be slightly longer.

(i) APPROXIMATE method.

Steps

The front elevation and plan are drawn.

The plan is divided into a number of equal divisions (eight being convenient as a 45° set-square can be used to achieve the division). The divisions are numbered 1 to 8 as shown. Each of the numbered circumferential points is projected into the front elevation to position the parallel lines. These lines are numbered 1 – 8, as indicated. Joint line JJ is conveniently positioned to start the development. *Chordal* length C is taken from the plan and stepped along the base line of the development eight times as shown. Thin, vertical lines, parallel to JJ, are drawn up from each of the base divisions and numbered. Thin lines are projected horizontally from the point of intersection of the parallel lines and the curve in the front view, as shown. The point of intersection of horizontal line 2, from the front elevation, and vertical line 2, from the base of the development, positions point 2 on the top curve of the development. All other points on the top curve of the development are similarly determined. The outline is "heavied-in" to complete the development.

(ii) Using the ACCURATE method to obtain the development of the offset cylinder above.

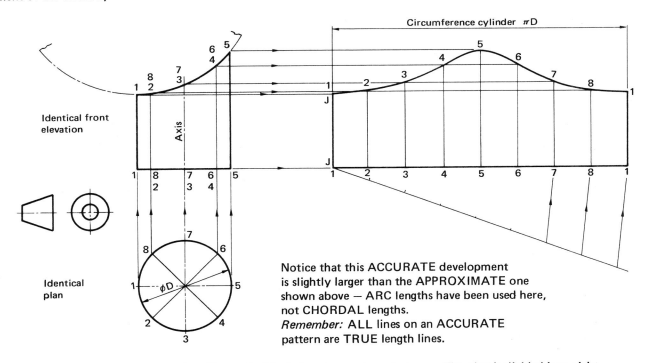

Circumference cylinder πD

Identical front elevation

Axis

Identical plan

φD

Notice that this ACCURATE development is slightly larger than the APPROXIMATE one shown above — ARC lengths have been used here, not CHORDAL lengths.
Remember: ALL lines on an ACCURATE pattern are TRUE length lines.

Steps

The identical front elevation and plan of the offset cylindrical pipe shown above is drawn. The plan is divided into eight divisions and numbered. Lines parallel to the axis are projected from each of the points into the front elevation and suitably numbered. Joint line JJ is positioned in the development. The circumference of the pipe is *calculated* (πD). This distance is stepped along the base line of the development from point J, divided geometrically into eight equal divisions, using the standard construction outlined on page 13, and numbered as shown. Vertical lines are drawn up from each of the numbered base divisions. Points on the curve are "plotted" feintly, using the method detailed above. The outline is "heavied-in" to complete the ACCURATE development of the offset pipe.

(b) Semi-cylindrical bin, with base and lid.

SEMI-CYLINDRICAL BIN

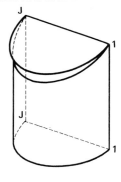

Development

Lid

Front elev.

Fold

Part plan

J

Base

W_3 W_3
W_2 W_2
W_1 W_1

C C

6C

Note:
(i)   Neither the base nor the lid are semi-circles.
(ii) The pattern is an approximate one because CHORDAL lengths have been used.

Steps
The front elevation and part plan are positioned as shown. The part plan is divided, and circumferential points numbered 1-4. Vertical lines are projected from these points to position the parallel lines on the surface of the bin in the front elevation. Joint line JJ is conveniently positioned. (In this example the joint is not taken at the shortest, front, edge but along a practically convenient corner.) The back plate is drawn by projecting the height from the front elevation and stepping the width $(2W_1)$ from the plan. Chordal length C, from plan, is stepped off six times from line 1-1 in the development, and numbered as shown. Vertical lines are drawn up from each of these numbered points. Points on both the top and bottom curves of the body are plotted using the method outlined in the previous example. e.g. point 2 is located at the intersection of horizontal line 2 from the front view and vertical line 2 in development. The true view of the base and lid have to be added to complete the development. Both lid and base in the front view are "swung" from point 1 until vertical. Points 1, 2, 3 and 4 are projected across into the development as shown. Widths W_2 and W_3 are stepped from the plan into the development to "form" the shapes of lid and base as indicated. The fold lines are added and the outline "heavied-in" to complete the development.

3.   OBLIQUE PRISM. Square duct, with base but no top.

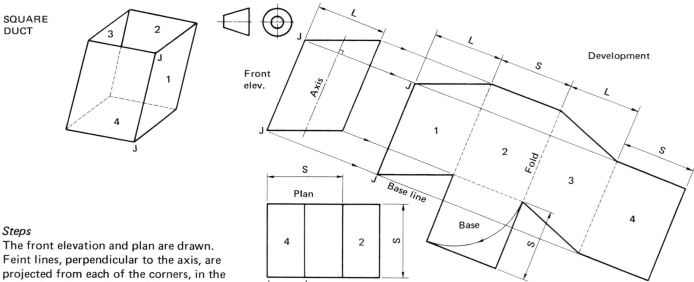

SQUARE DUCT

Front elev.

Axis

Plan

S

Development

L

S

L

S

Base line

Fold

Base

Note: All sides in the development are NOT of equal width, even though the duct is classified "square". This is because the cross-section of the duct, perpendicular to the axis, is rectangular (L x S) not square (S x S)

Steps
The front elevation and plan are drawn. Feint lines, perpendicular to the axis, are projected from each of the corners, in the front elevation as shown. Joint line JJ, *parallel* to the axis of the duct, is conviently positioned. The TRUE widths of each side of the duct, L, S, L and S respectively, are stepped off from JJ along the base line of the development. Feint vertical lines are drawn upwards from each of these base points to intersect the appropriate horizontal projector from the front elevation.

The respective points of intersection are joined with straight lines to obtain the developed shape of the four sides of the bin, as shown. The base, which is a square (S x S) is added. The outline is "heavied-in" and fold lines added to complete the development of the oblique square duct.

4. OBLIQUE CYLINDER. Open-ended, cylindrical pipe.

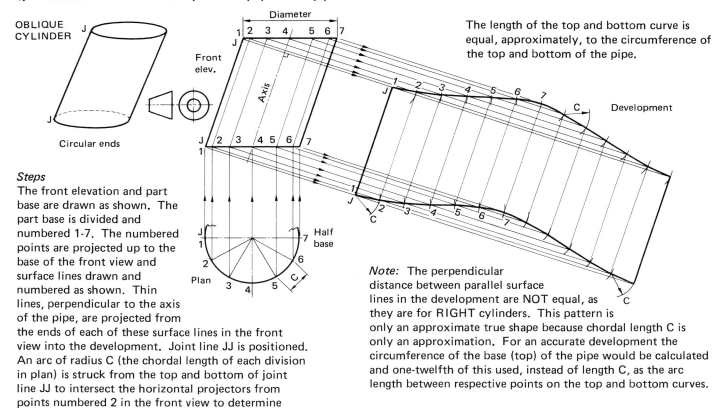

OBLIQUE CYLINDER

Circular ends

Front elev.

Diameter

Axis

The length of the top and bottom curve is equal, approximately, to the circumference of the top and bottom of the pipe.

Development

Half base

Plan

Steps

The front elevation and part base are drawn as shown. The part base is divided and numbered 1-7. The numbered points are projected up to the base of the front view and surface lines drawn and numbered as shown. Thin lines, perpendicular to the axis of the pipe, are projected from the ends of each of these surface lines in the front view into the development. Joint line JJ is positioned. An arc of radius C (the chordal length of each division in plan) is struck from the top and bottom of joint line JJ to intersect the horizontal projectors from points numbered 2 in the front view to determine points 2 in the development, as indicated. Points 3 to 7 are similarly determined. (This is a more tedious procedure than the one used to develop the RIGHT cylinder because the distances between the parallel surface lines in the pattern above are *not* equal.) A smooth curve is drawn through successive points at the top and bottom of the pattern and the outline "heavied-in" to complete the development of the oblique cylindrical pipe.

Note: The perpendicular distance between parallel surface lines in the development are NOT equal, as they are for RIGHT cylinders. This pattern is only an approximate true shape because chordal length C is only an approximation. For an accurate development the circumference of the base (top) of the pipe would be calculated and one-twelfth of this used, instead of length C, as the arc length between respective points on the top and bottom curves.

PYRAMIDS and CONES

The method used to construct developments (patterns) of pyramids and cones, both right and oblique, is known as **RADIAL LINE** development. With pyramids the sloping edges are used as surface (radial) lines to aid the construction. With cones the radial lines are drawn on the surface of the cone from the apex to the base.

5. RIGHT PYRAMIDS
(a) Hexagonal pyramid, complete with base.

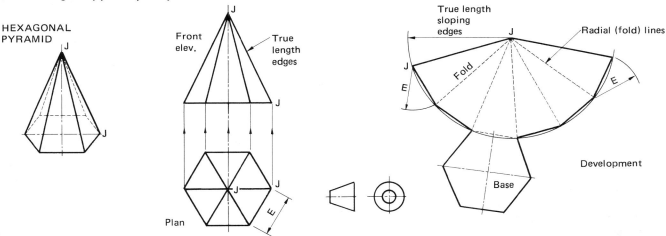

HEXAGONAL PYRAMID

Front elev.

True length edges

Plan

True length sloping edges

Radial (fold) lines

Fold

Base

Development

Steps
The plan is drawn first and the front elevation projected from this, as shown. Line JJ in the front view is a true view of the sloping edge of the pyramid (it is parallel to the front vertical plane). Joint line JJ is conveniently positioned to commence the development. An arc, length JJ (from the front view), is drawn from the top of the joint line in the development, as shown. An arc, radius E, the true length of the base edge of the pyramid in plan, is stepped off six times along the first arc starting from point J at the bottom of the joint line. Radial (fold) lines are drawn from the apex to each of the points of intersection of the large and small arcs, as shown. These points of intersection are joined by straight lines. The true shape of the base, an identical copy of the plan view, is added to the pattern and the outline "heavied-in" to complete the development.

(b)   Square-based hopper (truncated pyramid), with hinged base.

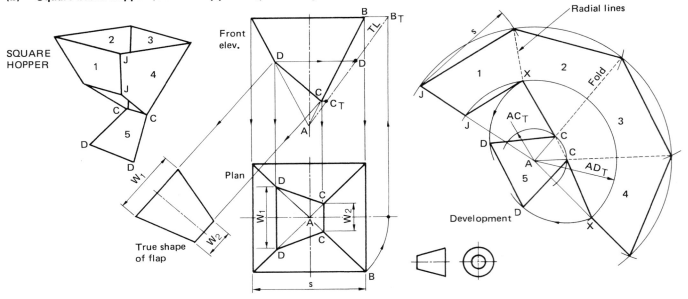

Steps

The front elevation is drawn first and the plan projected below. Sloping edge AB is not a true length in either front or plan view. The true length has, therefore, to be determined. With centre A, in plan, and radius AB, an arc is swung upwards to the horizontal centre line and the point projected to the base line extended, in the front view, to position point B_T as shown. Line AB_T is the true length (TL) of AB. Points C and D in the front view are projected horizontally on to line AB_T to obtain the true lengths of sloping edges AC (AC_T) and AD (AD_T). A true view of the bottom flap is drawn, with the centre line parallel to the flap DC in the front view, as shown. True widths W_1 and W_2 are taken from the plan view. To commence the development an arc, length AB_T from the front view, is drawn. Joint line JJ is conveniently positioned. The *true* length of the base edge, s, taken from the plan, is stepped four times around this arc. Then radial lines are drawn from vertex A to each of these divisions as shown. Arcs of radii AC_T and AD_T, respectively, are drawn from point A in the development. The outline of the sloping edges (body) of the hopper is completed, as shown. The flap at the bottom of the hopper hinges about edge C on side 3. The true shape of the flap is, therefore, added to side 3 as indicated. Fold lines are added and the outline "heavied-in" to complete the pattern of the hopper.

Note: An alternative method could have been used to determine the shape of the hinged flap.
Arcs, length CX from the development, are swung from points C to intersect a line (DD) drawn parallel to line CC. The distance of line DD from CC in the development is equal to the *true* length of the flap in the front view — line CD.

6.   OBLIQUE PYRAMIDS
(a)   Oblique square-based pyramid, complete with base.

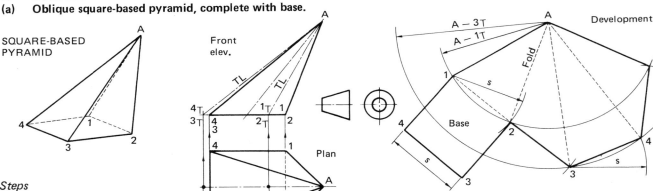

Note: The base has been added to side A-1-2 rather than any of the other three sides to minimise waste material, though, of course, a one-piece pattern tends to be wasteful of material.

Steps

The front elevation and plan are drawn. As none of the sloping edges in these views are of true length, true length lines (TL) have to be constructed. An arc, length A3 in the plan, is "swung" from point A up to the horizontal centre line, then projected into the front view to intersect the baseline extended in point 3_T. Line $A - 3_T$ is the *true* length of edges A3 and A4. An arc, length A2, is "swung" from point A in plan to the horizontal, then projected into the front view to intersect the base in point 2_T. Line $A - 2_T$ is the *true* length of edges A2 and A1. To start the development, arcs of lengths $A - 1_T$ and $A - 3_T$, respectively, from the front view, are drawn from point A, as shown. Joint line A1 is suitably positioned. An arc, length s from plan, is drawn from point 1 to cut the inner arc in point 2; from point 2 to cut the outer arc in point 3; from point 3 to cut the outer arc in point 4; and from point 4 to cut the inner arc in point 1 as shown. The *true* shape of the base of the pyramid, from plan, is drawn on the bottom of side A-1-2, as indicated. Fold lines are added and the outline "heavied-in" to complete the development.

(b)   Truncated, oblique, equilateral traingular pyramid, without base.

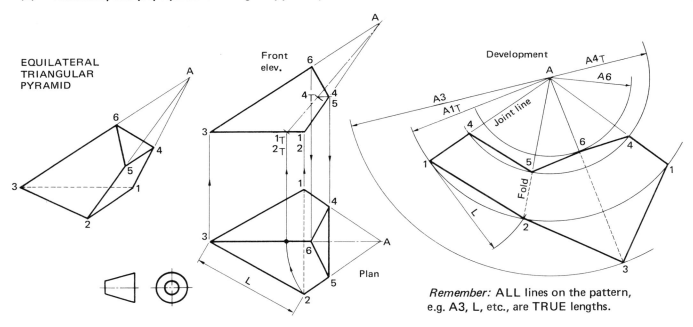

Remember: ALL lines on the pattern,
e.g. A3, L, etc., are TRUE lengths.

Steps

The base, in plan, is constructed first. The front elevation is drawn out and then the plan view completed. Sloping edge A3 in the front elevation is a true view (parallel to the front vertical plane). Sloping edges A1 and A2, however, are not true views in the front elevation. The true length of A1 and A2 is constructed as follows. Line A2 in plan is "swung" to the horizontal and projected up to intersect the base of the pyramid in the front view in point 2_T. Line A-2_T is the true length of sloping edges A1 and A2. Line A6, in the front view, is a true length of that part of edge A3 that is removed in truncating the pyramid. Line A-4_T, in the front view, is the true length of those parts of edges A1 and A2 that are removed. (Notice that is is measured along line A-2_T, NOT along line A2.) Four arcs of radii A3, A-1_T, A-4_T and A6, respectively, are drawn from a conveniently positioned point A to start the development. Joint edge A1 is suitably positioned. Base edge, length L, taken from the plan view, is struck from point 1 in the development to position point 2; from point 2 to position point 3; and from point 3 to position point 1, as shown. Feint lines are drawn from vertex A to points 1, 2 and 3, respectively, to form the development of the complete pyramid. Line 4-5, in the development, is drawn parallel to line 1-2. Point 6 is positioned on arc A6, as shown, and lines 5-6 and 6-4 drawn in. Fold lines are indicated and the outline "heavied-in", as shown, to complete the development of the truncated oblique pyramid.

7.   RIGHT CONES
(a)   Full cone, complete with base.

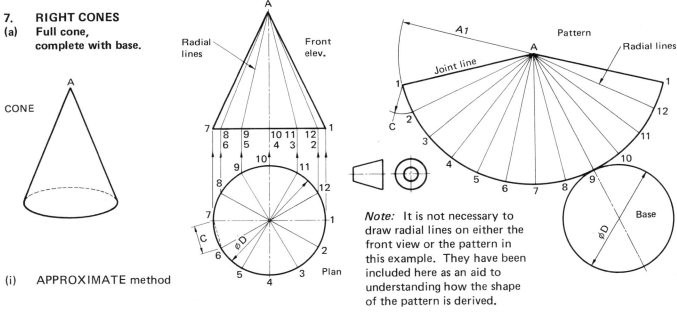

Note: It is not necessary to draw radial lines on either the front view or the pattern in this example. They have been included here as an aid to understanding how the shape of the pattern is derived.

(i)   APPROXIMATE method

Steps

The front and plan views are drawn. The base, in plan, is divided into a convenient number of equal divisions (twelve in this example) and numbered as shown. Radial lines, projected from the plan, are drawn in the front view and numbered. Line A1 in the front view represents the true length of the sloping edge of the cone. (It is the true length of all radial lines.) Joint line A1 is conveniently positioned to start the developoment. An arc radius A1 is drawn from vertex A as indicated. An arc, chordal length C (from plan), is stepped twelve times around the large arc, starting from point 1. Each division is numbered. Radial lines are drawn from apex A to each base division. The true view of the base of the cone (a circle diameter D), from plan, is added, in any position along the large arc, and the outline of the pattern "heavied-in" to complete the development.

(ii)   ACCURATE method

CONE

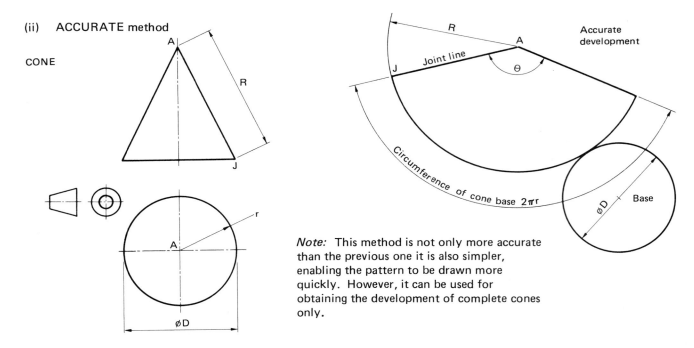

Accurate development

Note: This method is not only more accurate than the previous one it is also simpler, enabling the pattern to be drawn more quickly. However, it can be used for obtaining the development of complete cones only.

Steps

The front and plan views are drawn *accurately.* Angle θ, in the development, is calculated from the formula

$$\theta = \frac{2\pi r}{2\pi R}$$ where r is the radius of the base of the given right cone.
and R is the slant height (true length of the sloping edge of the cone.)

Notice that the formula is merely a ratio of the length of the circumference of the base of the cone, $2\pi r$, and the length of the circumference of a circle of radius, R, the true length of the sloping edge, i.e. θ is to $2\pi r$ as $360°$ is to $2\pi R$.
An arc, length R from the front view, is drawn from a conveniently positioned point A to start the development. Joint line AJ is positioned. The calculated apex angle θ is measured from joint line AJ to obtain the pattern of the curved surface, as shown. The base is added, in any position along the base arc, and the outline "heavied-in" to complete the ACCURATE development of the right cone.

(b)   Truncated right cone, without base.

TRUNCATED CONE (UNGULA)

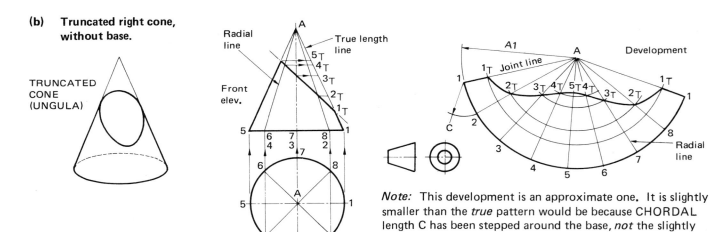

Note: This development is an approximate one. It is slightly smaller than the *true* pattern would be because CHORDAL length C has been stepped around the base, *not* the slightly longer (true) ARC length.
A more accurate pattern can be obtained by dividing the base circle into a greater number of parts.

Steps
The full front and plan views are drawn. The base, in plan, is divided into eight equal divisions and numbered. Radial lines, projected from the plan, are drawn on the front view and appropriately numbered. The cone is truncated in the front elevation. (It is not necessary to show the resultant cut surface in plan.) Horizontal lines are drawn from the intersection of the cutting plane and the radial lines in the front elevation, across to line A1 (a true length line), as shown. Lines $A1_T$, $A2_T$, etc. represent the true lengths of the respective radial lines from apex A to the cut surface. Joint line A1 is conveniently positioned to start the development. Arcs of radii $A5_T$, $A4_T$, $A3_T$, $A2_T$, $A1_T$ and A1, respectively, taken from the front view, are drawn from point A as shown. Chordal length C, from plan, is stepped eight times around the base arc of the development, as shown, commencing from point 1, and each division numbered. Radial lines are drawn from apex A to each of the numbered divisions. The shape of the top of the pattern is determined by "plotting" a series of points at the intersection of each of the radial lines and their respective true length arcs. For example, the top point is located at the intersection of radial line 5 and arc $A5_T$, as shown. The "plotted" points are joined by a smooth curve and the complete outline "heavied-in" to complete the development of the truncated cone.

8. OBLIQUE CONE. Truncated cone, without base.

TRUNCATED
CONE
(UNGULA)

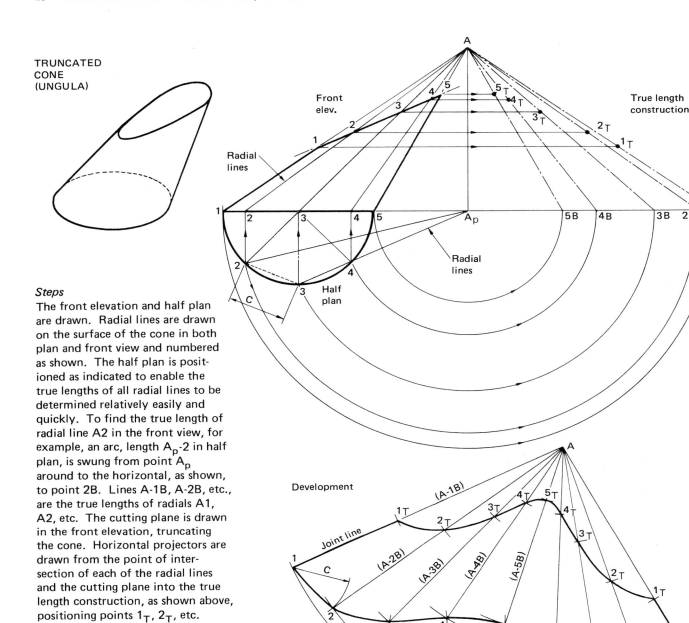

Front
elev.

True length
construction

Radial
lines

Radial
lines

Half
plan

Development

Joint line

Note: This is an approximate method as chordal lengths (C), not arc (true) lengths, have been used to obtain the length of the base of the development.

Steps

The front elevation and half plan are drawn. Radial lines are drawn on the surface of the cone in both plan and front view and numbered as shown. The half plan is positioned as indicated to enable the true lengths of all radial lines to be determined relatively easily and quickly. To find the true length of radial line A2 in the front view, for example, an arc, length A_p-2 in half plan, is swung from point A_p around to the horizontal, as shown, to point 2B. Lines A-1B, A-2B, etc., are the true lengths of radials A1, A2, etc. The cutting plane is drawn in the front elevation, truncating the cone. Horizontal projectors are drawn from the point of intersection of each of the radial lines and the cutting plane into the true length construction, as shown above, positioning points 1_T, 2_T, etc. Joint line A1, true length A-1B, is suitably positioned to start the development. Five arcs, true lengths A-5B, A-4B, A-3B, A-2B and A-1B, respectively, are drawn from vertex A. An arc, radius chordal length C from plan, is drawn from point 1, at the foot of the joint line, to cut the arc of length A-2B in point 2. An arc, length C, is struck from point 2 to cut arc A-3B in point 3. A similar procedure is used to plot the remaining points on the bottom curve. Radial lines are drawn from vertex A to each of these plotted points. Points on the top curve are plotted as follows. An arc, length A-1_T from the true length diagram, is drawn from vertex A, in the development, to cut both radials numbered 1. An arc, length A-2_T, is drawn from A to cut the radials numbered 2, etc. A smooth curve is drawn carefully through both the top and bottom set of plotted points, as shown. The outline is "heavied-in" to complete the development of the truncated oblique cone.

Note: This construction is much more laborious than the approximate one used to develop a similarly truncated RIGHT cone (page 118). This is because the radial lines on an oblique cone are of different true lengths, whereas all of those on a right cone are the same true length. This means that each "sector" on the pattern of an oblique cone, therefore, has to be constructed individually.

9. "MISCELLANEOUS" COMPONENTS. Those methods of development presented so far are used to draw patterns of "standard" components, i.e. prisms, cylinders, pyramids and cones. Constructions used to develop two miscellaneous ("non-standard") components — a hipped roof and a hemi-spherical bowl — are outlined below to conclude the chapter.

(a)   A symmetrical hipped roof.

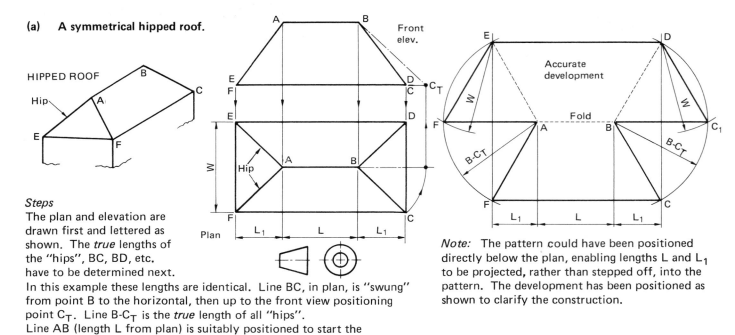

Steps
The plan and elevation are drawn first and lettered as shown. The *true* lengths of the "hips", BC, BD, etc. have to be determined next.

In this example these lengths are identical. Line BC, in plan, is "swung" from point B to the horizontal, then up to the front view positioning point C_T. Line $B\text{-}C_T$ is the *true* length of all "hips".

Line AB (length L from plan) is suitably positioned to start the development. A vertical line is drawn to the left of, and at a distance L_1 from, point A. Another is drawn to the right of, distance L_1 from, point B. (Distance L_1 is taken from the plan view.) An arc, radius $B\text{-}C_T$ from the front view, is drawn from points A and B to cut these vertical lines in points E and F, and C and D, respectively. Arcs, of radius W from the plan view, are drawn from points D and E to cut the initial large arcs in points C_1 and F, respectively. The lettered corner points are joined with straight lines, as shown, fold lines labelled, and the outline drawn in heavily to complete the accurate development of the symmetrical hipped roof.

Note: If the student were asked to draw the development of an ASYMMETRIC (non-symmetrical) hipped roof, which is rarely encountered practically, he would have to determine the true length of each hip separately.

Note: The pattern could have been positioned directly below the plan, enabling lengths L and L_1 to be projected, rather than stepped off, into the pattern. The development has been positioned as shown to clarify the construction.

(b)   Hemi-spherical bowl, without lid.

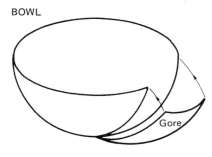

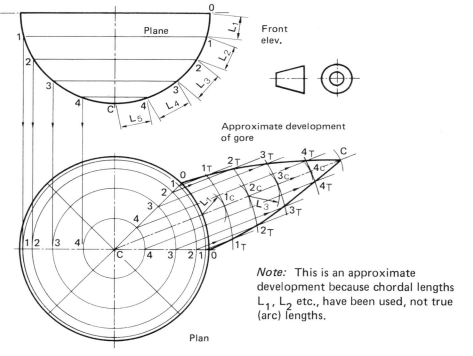

Steps
The front elevation and plan are drawn. The front view is "cut" by a number of arbitrarily spaced horizontal planes, the ends being numbered 1 to 4 as shown. Circles representing each of the planes are drawn in plan and appropriately numbered. The plan is divided into a number of equal divisions (eight being convenient.) Centre line C-C, the bisector of one of the sectors in plan, is drawn. Chordal lengths L_1, L_2, L_3, L_4 and L_5 from the front view, are stepped progressively along line C-C, starting from arc O-O, positioning points 1c, 2c, 3c, 4c, and C, respectively. Arcs are drawn from point C, the centre of the plan, through each of these points as shown. Lines, parallel to centre line C-C, projected from points numbered 1 in plan cut the arc drawn through point 1c to position points 1_T. Lines projected from points numbered 2 cut the arc drawn through point 2c in points 2_T, etc. The pattern shown, called a GORE, represents one-eighth of the complete pattern. An additional seven gores would have to be similarly constructed and all outlines "heavied-in" to complete the development of the hemi-spherical bowl.

Note: This is an approximate development because chordal lengths L_1, L_2 etc., have been used, not true (arc) lengths.

Interpenetration of Right Regular Components

Many engineering components, particularly sheet-metal ones, are fabricated by joining together two or more of the "standard" geometrical shapes, namely prisms, cylinders, pyramids, cones and spheres.

A common joint line is formed where the respective component parts meet or interpenetrate. This joint line is known as the CURVE of INTERPENETRATION or, alternatively, because "interpenetration" and "intersection" tend to be used synonymously, the CURVE of INTERSECTION. The term "curve" is always used, even though in many cases the joint line is not actually a curve but a number of straight lines.

The student should be able to construct "curves" formed by the abutment or interpenetration of right prisms, cylinders, pyramids, cones, spheres and simple "composite" solids as these "curves" are frequently required in both orthographic drawings and pattern developments.

In this section the student is shown how to obtain "curves" formed by the interpenetration of a selection of relatively simple geometric shapes. First angle projection is used throughout.

1. RIGHT PRISMS

(a)   SOLID, square prisms, of indentical cross-section, intersecting centrally, with axes at right angles.

The plan view is drawn first.
The front view is projected from the plan, points 1, 2, 3, and 4 being "plotted" at the intersection of the edges of the squares. Respective points are joined with straight lines to obtain the "curve" of interpenetration.

The side view has been included here to indicate clearly the positions of intersecting points 1, 2, 3 and 4. It would not normally be drawn when the solids intersect centrally.

Note Exactly the same "curve" is obtained if, instead of the two square SOLIDS shown, two identically shaped thin sheet DUCTS intersect.

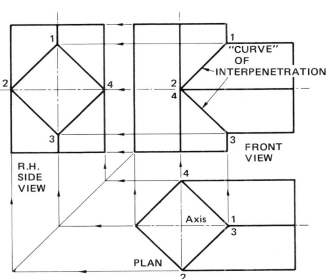

(b)   Square prisms, of different sizes, intersecting off-centre, with axes at right angles.

Greater difficulty is experienced in determining the "curve" in this example because the solids are offset. The procedure is, however, basically the same as used in the previous case — projection of intersecting edge points.

The plan view is drawn first. The side view is projected from the plan and both views numbered to assist in visualizing how edge points 1 – 6 are obtained. The vertical square solid is drawn feintly in the front view. All four horizontal edges of the offset solid are drawn feintly in the front view. Points 1, 2, 3 and 4 on the "curve" in the front view are positioned by projecting from correspondingly numbered edge points in plan, as indicated. Points 5 and 6 on the "curve" are positioned at the intersection of lines projected from points 5 and 6 in the side and plan views. Points 1 to 6 are joined with straight lines to obtain the "curve" of interpenetration, and the front view "heavied-in" to complete the drawing.

Note The far side of the "curve" and the leading edge of the vertical prism have to be shown in hidden detail.

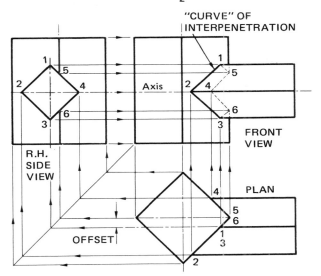

(c)   Square prism and equilateral triangular prism intersecting centrally, with axes inclined at a given angle.

The square solid is drawn first in plan. The front view is drawn next, complete except for the "curve" of intersection. (Height h is stepped from a true end view of the triangular prism.) The plan view is then completed. Point 1 on the "curve" is located at the junction of the top edge of the triangular prism and the front edge of the square prism. A line is drawn from points 2 and 3 in plan to intersect the bottom edge of the pyramid in the front view to position points 2 and 3 on the curve. Points 1 and 2/3 are joined with a straight line, as shown, to complete the "curve" of interpenetration.

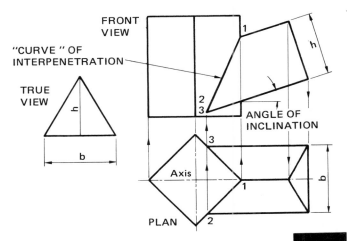

(d) Square prism and equilateral triangular prism intersecting off-centre, with axes inclined at a given angle.

As these prisms are both off-set and inclined to each other, the "curve" of intersection is more difficult to obtain.

The plan view is drawn first, complete except for the triangular end face. The front view is drawn, complete except for the "curve" of interpenetration. (Height h is taken from a true end view of the triangular prism.) The triangular end face is project-ed from the front view to complete the plan. A line from edge point 1 in plan is projected to intersect the top edge of the triangular prism in the front view, locating point 1. Lines from edge points 2, 3 and 5 in plan intersect the base of the triangular solid in the front view positioning points 2, 3 and 5 on the "curve". To obtain point 4 on the "curve" a line is projected horizontally from edge point 4 in plan to the triangular end face, vertically into the front view and then down onto the leading edge of the square solid, as indicated. The curve of interpenetra-tion is completed by joining respective points, once again with straight lines. The triangular prism has purposely been omitted from the side view so that the "curve", obtained by projecting from edge points 1 to 5 in the front view to intersect corresponding projectors from points 1 to 5 in plan, can be seen clearly.

Note Although the common joint line in each of the examples presented above is referred to as the "curve" of INTERPENETRATION, the respective prisms DO NOT actually penetrate each other, they merely abut. The term "interpenetration" should not be taken too literally.

2. RIGHT CYLINDERS (Rods, tubes, ducts, etc.)

(a) Ducts of equal diameters, intersecting centrally, with axes at right angles.

Method 1
The complete plan view is drawn first.
The front view is drawn, complete except for the "curve". A semi-circle is added to the horizontal duct in both front and plan views and divided into a number of equal sectors (six being convenient for division with a set-square). The divisions are numbered carefully, as shown. Horizontal lines are projected from each numbered point in plan to touch the circumference of the vertical duct, then up into the front view. Horizontal lines are projected from each numbered point in the front view to intersect the line from the correspondingly numbered point in plan to form the "curve" of interpenetration.

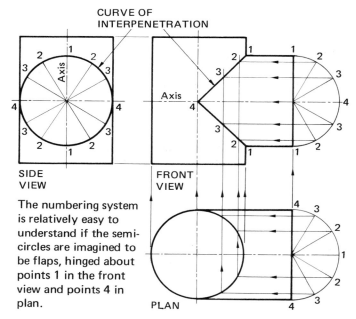

The numbering system is relatively easy to understand if the semi-circles are imagined to be flaps, hinged about points 1 in the front view and points 4 in plan.

Note: Even though the ducts are cylindrical the resulting "curve" appears as straight lines in the front view. This is because the ducts in this example are of equal diameters. The "curve" in the side view is, of course, a circle, as can be seen above.

Method 2
An alternative, much quicker method may be used to obtain the "curve" which is formed when cylinders *of equal diameter* intersect centrally. It is based upon the principle of the Common Central Sphere.

(i) Cylindrical ducts intersecting at right angles
The front view is drawn, complete except for the "curve". A circle of diameter equal to that of the intersecting cylinders is drawn, feintly as shown. It represents a sphere that is both common and central to both ducts. Diagonals of the figure in which the sphere is contained are drawn feintly. The appropriate part of the diagonals is "heavied-in" to obtain the "curve" of interpenetration, as indicated in the two examples opposite. The "curve" in the first example is identical to that shown in the front view immediately above. The "curve" in the second example differs only because it is a corner joint.

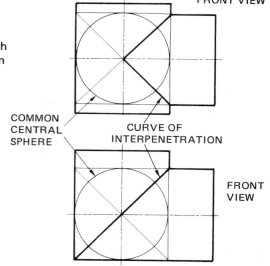

(ii)   Cylindrical ducts with axes inclined at a given angle

Method 1 could be used in this example to determine the shape of the "curve" but as the cylinders interpenetrate centrally and are of equal diameter method 2 will be used as it is both quicker and less complicated.

The front view is drawn, complete except for the "curve". The common central sphere is inserted, feintly. Diagonals of the parallelogram containing the sphere are drawn feintly. The appropriate part of each diagonal is "heavied-in" to obtain the required "curve" of interpenetration. In a case such as this, where the branch duct passes through the vertical duct, the whole of both diagonals has to be "heavied-in".

Notice that, once again, the "curve" of interpenetration consists of straight lines in the front view.

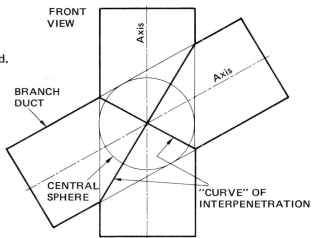

(b)   Cylindrical rods of unequal diameters, intersecting centrally, with axes at right angles.

The complete plan view is drawn first. The front view is drawn next, complete except for the curve. A semi-circle (flap) is drawn on the end of the horizontal rod in each view, divided, and appropriately numbered. A horizontal line is drawn from each numbered point in plan to touch the circumference of the vertical rod, then projected up to intersect the line drawn from the correspondingly numbered point in the front view. The respective points are joined to obtain the curve of interpenetration. The side view has been included merely to show that the curve appears as a circle in that view.

Notice that the curve of interpenetration is, for the first time, an actual curve and not a number of straight lines.

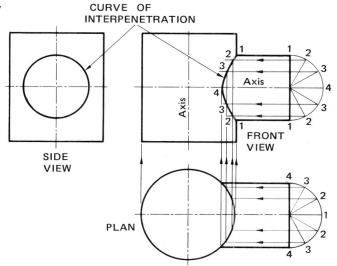

(c)   Cylindrical ducts of unequal diameters, interpenetrating off-centre, with axes at right angles.

The complete plan view is drawn. The front view is drawn feintly, complete except for the required curve. A semi-circle (flap) is drawn on the end of the branch (horizontal) duct in each view, divided, and numbered 1 − 4 as indicated. Additional points 1A and 2A have to be added to the semi-circles to enable limiting points on the curve to be plotted. Width W_1, from the plan, is stepped from point 1 in the front view to obtain the vertical positions of points 1A on the curve. Width W_2, from plan, is stepped from point 1 in the front view to obtain the vertical positions of points 2A on the curve.

A horizontal line is drawn from each numbered point in plan (except lower points 3 and 4 which are redundant in this example) to touch the circumference of the vertical duct, then projected up to intersect the line drawn from the correspondingly numbered point in the front view. The respective points are joined, as indicated, to obtain the curve of interpenetration, and the outline "heavied-in" to complete the view.

The part side view has been included:
(i)   to verify the vertical positions of points 1A and 2A,
(ii)   as an alternative method for obtaining the vertical positions of points 1A and 2A.

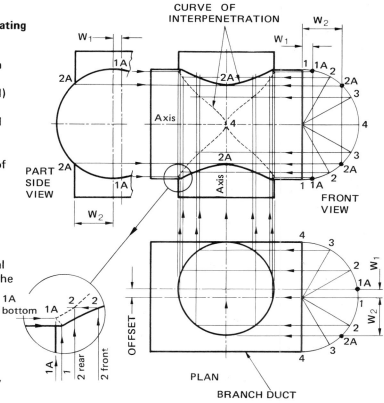

(d) Cylindrical ducts of unequal diameters, intersecting off-centre, with axes inclined at a given angle.

The front view is drawn first, complete except for the required curve. The plan view is drawn, complete except for the elliptical opening on the branch duct. (Inclusion of the ellipse is not necessary for determining the curve of intersection.) A semi-circle is drawn on the end of the branch duct in each view, divided, and numbered 1 – 4 as indicated. Additional points 1A have to be added to the semi circles to enable both points on the leading edge of the vertical duct to be positioned. Width W_1, from the plan, is stepped from point 1 in the front view to position points 1A on the semi-circle in the front view. A horizontal line is drawn from each numbered point in plan to touch the circumference of the vertical duct, then projected up to intersect the line drawn from the correspondingly numbered point in the front view. The respective points are joined to obtain the required curve of interpenetration.

The side view, which can be drawn by projecting conventionally from the front and side views, has been left incomplete so that the curve of interpenetration can be shown clearly. It is NOT a circle in this example.

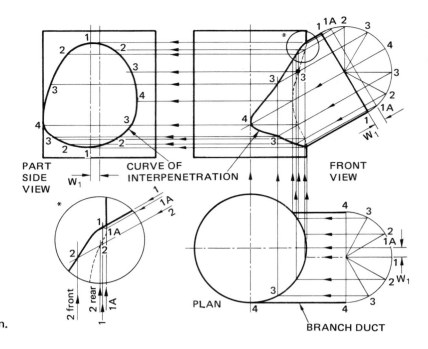

Note Points 1, 1A and 2 must be plotted particularly carefully as their vertical projection lines are very close together. The enlarged inset has been added to clarify the shape of this congested part of the curve.

(e) Cylindrical duct penetrated by a square duct off-centre, with axes at right angles.

The complete side view is drawn first as it contains a true view of the square duct. The front view is drawn next, complete except for the required curve. A complete plan view is then drawn. Strategic points on the circumference of the vertical duct (edge and centre line points) are positioned and numbered 1–4 in plan, as indicated. Corresponding points are numbered in the side view. A vertical line is projected into the front view from each of these numbered points in plan to intersect the horizontal line drawn from the correspondingly numbered point in the side view, as shown, to obtain the curve of interpenetration. The inset has been drawn to clarify the congested part of the curve – in particular the hidden detail around points 2 and 3.

Note Additional points would be needed between points 1 and 2 in both the plan and side views to obtain a more accurate curve in the front view

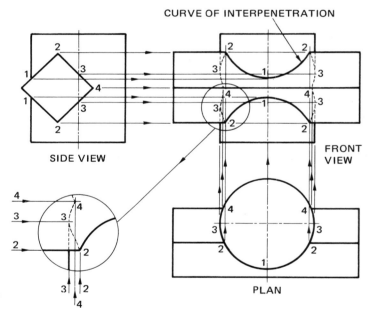

3. RIGHT PYRAMIDS
(a) Square-based pyramid intersected centrally, on a face, by a cylindrical pipe, with axes at right angles.

The complete front view is drawn first. The plan view is drawn next, complete except for the required curve. A semi-circle is drawn on the end of the circular pipe in each of the views, divided into a number of equal sectors, and numbered as indicated. (Only four divisions have been used here to enable the construction of the curve to be shown relatively uncongested).

A horizontal line is drawn from each numbered point in the front view to touch the inclined face of the pyramid, then projected down into plan to intersect the line drawn from the correspondingly numbered point on the semi-circle in plan. The respective points are joined to obtain the required curve of interpenetration.

Note The "curve" would be shown as a circle in a side view.

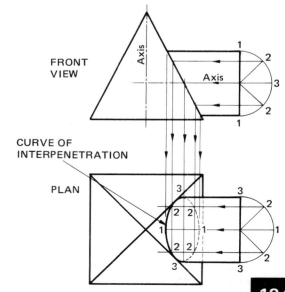

124

(b) Square-based hollow pyramid intersected centrally on an edge, by a cylindrical pipe, with axes at right angles.

The construction outlined in (a) on the previous page is not suitable for use in this example. Points 1 and 5 on the top and bottom of the curve of interpenetration, could easily be positioned — at the intersection of the leading edge of the pyramid and the top and bottom of the pipe. However, intermediate points 2, 3 and 4 could not be positioned using method (a) because they would be projected from the semi-circle onto obliquely inclined faces NOT onto a flat inclined face.
An alternative method is used to obtain the required curve of interpenetration which involves taking horizontal sections, or slices, through the component at appropriate levels.

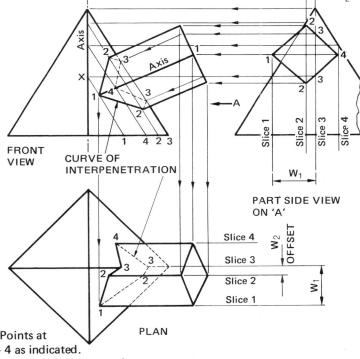

The plan is drawn first, complete except for the curve. The front view is projected from the plan and completed except for the curve. A semi-circle is drawn on the end of the cylindrical pipe, divided into 4 sectors and numbered 1 to 5. Horizontal lines are drawn from each numbered point to touch the leading edge of the pyramid. Points 1 and 5 on the curve lie at the intersection of this edge and the horizontal lines from points 1 and 5, respectively, on the semi-circle. Lines are projected down into plan from the points where the horizontal lines from points 2, 3 and 4 on the semi-circle touch the leading edge of the pyramid. "Slices" are drawn, feintly, from the points in plan where the vertical projectors cut the horizontal axis. Points 1 and 5 on the curve in plan are projected from the front view. Points 2, 3 and 4 have to be "plotted" using the slices. Points 2 and 4 are located at the intersection of lines drawn parallel to and distance W_2 from the axis and slices 2 and 4, respectively. (W_2 is taken from the front view.) Points 3 are "plotted" similarly, the distance from the axis in this case being the radius of the pipe. The points are joined, as indicated, to obtain the curve of interpenetration in plan. Points 2, 3 and 4 on the curve in the front view are obtained by projecting from the respective points in plan to intersect lines drawn from the correspondingly numbered points on the semi-circle.

(c) Square-based pyramid intersected off-centre, on an edge, by a square duct, with axes inclined at a given angle.

Neither of the two preceding constructions are suitable for use in this example. Construction (a) is used with cylindrical ducts whereas in this case the intersecting duct is of square section. Construction (b) could be used to determine the shape of the "curve" but with an inclined duct it would prove somewhat laborious.

A third, quicker method is, therefore, used to determine the shape of this "curve". Suitably spaced VERTICAL sections (slices) are taken through the component at strategic positions to obtain points on the "curve"

The plan view is drawn first, complete except for the "curve" and the end of the square duct. The front view is then drawn, complete except for the required "curve". The part side view is drawn, looking on A, and a number of vertical slices inserted at strategic points through the duct. Points at the intersection of these slices and the duct are numbered 1 — 4 as indicated.
Point 1 on the "curve" of interpenetration in the front view is obtained as follows. A horizontal line is projected from the intersection of slice 1 and the edge of the pyramid in the side view across to the axis in the front view (Point X). A line, parallel to the sloping edge of the pyramid, is drawn to the base (X1). This represents the right-hand side of the section through the pyramid at slice 1. A line is drawn from point 1 in the side view to touch the sloping end face of the inclined duct in the front view then down to intersect line X1 in point 1. Points 2, 3 and 4 on the "curve" in the front view are "plotted" using exactly the same procedure. The respective points are joined, as shown, to obtain the required "curve" of interpenetration. Notice that the far "curve" has to be shown as hidden detail.

Points on the "curve" in plan are obtained by projecting down from each of the numbered "curve" points in the front view to intersect the correspondingly numbered slice in plan (see point 1). The positions of the slices relative to the pyramid, and to each other, are taken from the side view (W_1, W_2, etc). The curve in the side view has been omitted purposely to avoid line congestion. It can be determined quite easily, if required, by drawing a horizontal line from each of the "curve" points in the front view to intersect the correspondingly numbered "slice" in the side view.

4.   RIGHT CONES

(a)   Right cone and cylindrical duct interpenetrating centrally, with axes at right angles.

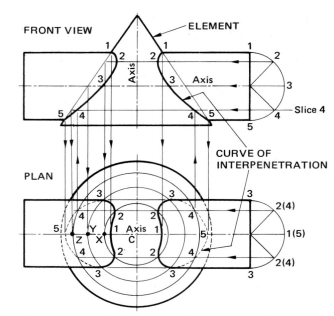

The curve of interpenetration in this and similar examples can be obtained most simply and quickly by taking horizontal sections (slices) through the component at appropriate levels: the greater the number of slices used, the greater the accuracy of the curve.

The front and plan views are drawn, complete except for the curves. A semi-circle is drawn on the end of the cylindrical duct in each view, divided and numbered as indicated. Points 1 and 5 on the curve in the front view are "plotted" at the intersection of the elements (sloping edges) of the cone and the top and bottom of the duct. These points are projected down to the axis in plan to position corresponding points there. Points 2, 3 and 4 are "plotted", first in plan, as follows. Lines are drawn from points 2, 3 and 4 on the semi-circle in the front view to touch the element of the cone, then projected down into plan to cut the axis in points X, Y and Z, respectively. Circles are drawn of radii CX, CY and CZ.

Note In order to avoid line congestion only one point on the curve in plan (point 4) has been shown projected up to the front view to "form" the curve there.

Horizontal lines are drawn from points 2 on the semi-circle in plan to cut the smallest circle (slice) in points 2 on the curve; from points 3 to cut the "intermediate" circle in points 3; and from points 4 to cut the largest circle in points 4. Successive points are joined, as shown, to form the required curve of interpenetration.

Points 2, 3 and 4 on the curve in the front view are obtained by drawing a line from each of these points in plan to intersect the correspondingly numbered slice in the front view. For example, a vertical line is drawn up from points 4 in plan to cut slice 4 in the front view in points 4.

The curve in the side view would be represented with a circle.

In cases where the penetrating cylinder is so large that it lies outside the elements (slant edges) of the cone in the side view, as shown opposite, the "horizontal slices" method can still be used to determine the shape of the curve of interpenetration. The slices, however, are taken only between planes A and B, and C and D.

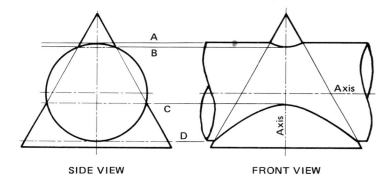

SIDE VIEW   FRONT VIEW

Should the cylindrical duct happen to be of such a diameter and be so positioned that it penetrates the cone at 90° to its axis and also tangential to its elements, as shown opposite, then an easier and much quicker construction can be used to obtain the required "curve" of interpenetration. It is based upon the principle of the Common Central Sphere mentioned earlier.

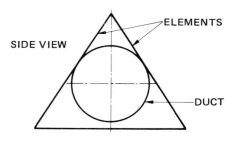

The front view is drawn. A circle of diameter equal to that of the penetrating cylinder is drawn tangential to the elements of the cone. The branch duct is drawn tangential to the circle. (This circle represents an imaginary sphere that is common, i.e. tangential, to both the cone and cylindrical duct). Diagonals are drawn feintly on the trapezium, which circumscribes the sphere. The outlines of the component are then "heavied-in", as shown, to complete the front view.

Notice once again, that the "curve" consists of straight lines. Verify the shape of this "curve" by using construction (a), above, as a check.

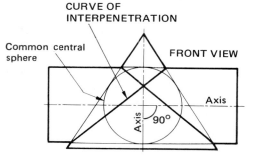

(b)   Right cone and rectangular duct intersecting off-centre, with axes at right angles.

The front view and plan are drawn, complete except for the required curve of interpenetration. Equi-spaced slices (cutting planes) are inserted on the duct in the front view and numbered 1 to 5. A line is projected down from the point of intersection of each of the slices and the slant edge of the cone to touch the axis in plan. The points are numbered C_1 to C_5, as indicated. Circles of radii OC_1, OC_2, ... , OC_5, are drawn feintly from centre O in plan. Points on the "curve" of interpenetration in plan occur at the intersection of the duct sides and each of these circles. The curve of interpenetration in the front view is obtained by projecting a line up from each of the numbered "curve" points in plan to intersect the correspondingly numbered "slice" in the front view. For example, lines are projected from points 3 in plan to cut slice 3, locating curve points 3. (The remaining projection lines have been omitted to minimise line congestion.) Successive points are joined, with a curve to complete the front view.
The part side view has been included (i) to illustrate the shape of the intersecting duct, (ii) to emphasize the offset, and (iii) to demonstrate that the "curve" in the side view appears as a rectangle. The side view is NOT actually required for determining the shape of the curve of interpenetration in either the front view or plan view.

Note The "horizontal slices" method can be used to determine the shape of the curve of interpenetration for a branch duct of any shape, whether penetrating the cone centrally or off-centre, provided that the horizontal axis of the duct is perpendicular to the vertical axis of the cone.

5.   SPHERES

(a)   Solid sphere intersected centrally by a square-sectioned rod, with axes at right-angles.

In examples of this type either the "vertical slice" construction or the "horizontal slice" construction can be used to obtain the shapes of the curves of intersection in the respective views. The latter method will be used here to demonstrate that the shape of the curve in the front view is identical to that in the plan view.

The part side view is drawn first to obtain the diagonal of the square and duct widths. The front and plan views are drawn next, complete except for the required curve. Points 1 on the curve in the front view are positioned at the intersection of the sphere outline and the top and bottom edges of the duct. A line is projected from points 1 in the front view to cut the axis in plan in point 1. Three equi-spaced horizontal slices are drawn in the front and part side view, as indicated. A line is projected down into plan from the point of intersection of each of the three slices and the circumference of the sphere in the front view to cut the horizontal axis in plan. The points of intersection on the axis are labelled X, Y and Z. Circles (slices) of radii OX, OY and OZ are drawn feintly in plan. Intermediate points 2, 3 and 4 on the curve in plan are "plotted" as follows. Lines are drawn, parallel to and distance W_2 either side of the axis, to cut the smallest circle in points 2; distance W_3 to cut the intermediate circle in points 3; distance W_4 to cut the largest slice in points 4. (W_4, etc., are taken from the part side view.) A line is projected from points 2 in plan to intersect slice 2 in the front view to position points 2 on the curve in the front view. Points 3 and 4 are similarly positioned.
As can be seen the curves of interpenetration are identical — because the component itself is identical in both the front view and plan view.

127

(b) Semi-spherical container intersected off-centre by a square-sectioned duct, with axes inclined at a given angle.

The "vertical slices" construction has to be used in this case to obtain the curve of intersection. The curve cannot be determined by using the alternative "horizontal slices" method because the duct is inclined.

The part front view is drawn first, complete except for the required curve. The part side view is drawn next and slices 1 to 5 positioned. (The spacing is arbitrary, but the positioning needs to be considered carefully.) The points of intersection of the respective slices and the end of the duct are numbered 1-5, as shown. Point 1 on the curve in the front view is obtained as follows.

A horizontal line is drawn from point S1 in the side view, the intersection of slice 1 and the circumference of the sphere, to the axis in the front view (S1). An arc, radius O-S1, is drawn from point O in the front view. A line is projected from point 1 in the side view to the end of the duct in the front view, then down, parallel to the inclined axis, to intersect arc O-S1 in point 1.

Points 2 to 5 on the curve of interpenetration in the

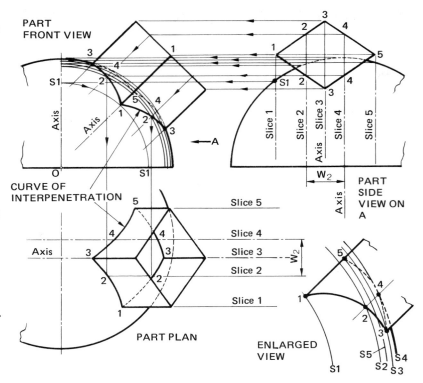

front view are similarly "plotted", as illustrated. An enlarged view of the lower part of the curve in the front view has been included to clarify the shape and, in particular, the hidden detail in that area.

Points on the curve in plan are obtained by projecting down from each of the numbered points on the curve in the front view to intersect the correspondingly numbered slice in plan (see points 2). The relative positions of the slices in plan are obtained from the side view. For example, slice 2 is positioned at W_2 from the axis of the hemisphere.

Note This construction can be used to obtain the curve of interpenetration for an inclined duct of any shape, intersecting either on or off centre.

6.   COMPOSITE SOLIDS

A composite solid is a solid made up from two or more basic geometric shapes. The component parts are usually joined with a radius.

The student may be asked to determine the shape of the curve of intersection, or alternatively complete a partially drawn curve, for a composite solid. Both tasks can be achieved by using one of the "slices" methods outlined previously.

In the following typical example, a right cylindrical rod intersecting a shaped rectangular plate — suitably positioned sections (slices) are drawn through the composite solid to obtain points of intersection of the component solids from which the curve can be formed.

The complete plan view is drawn first. The front view is then drawn, complete except for the required curves. Slices 1 to 4 are suitably positioned through the radius in the front view, as shown opposite. A line is drawn down from the point of intersection of each slice and the radius to position points A, B, C and D in plan. Circles of radii OA, OB, OC and OD are drawn feintly from centre O in plan to cut the rear outline of the solid in points 1, 2, 3 and 4, respectively. A line is drawn up from point 1 in plan to cut slice 1 in the front view positioning point 1 on the rear curve (hidden). Remaining points 2, 3 and 4 on the rear curve in the front view are similarly positioned.

Only two of the four initially drawn circles in plan cut the front outline of the solid — in points 3 and 4. These points on the front curve in the front view are "plotted" as outlined above.

Additional points have to be obtained to complete the shape of the front curve.

A circle, radius OF, is drawn from centre O in plan. A line is drawn up from the point of intersection of this circle and the axis in plan to cut the radius in the front view, positioning slice F. Lines are projected from points F in plan to cut slice F in the front view, positioning points F on the front curve. Further points on the curve, X, are similarly positioned.

The respective points are joined, as shown, to complete the required curve of interpenetration.

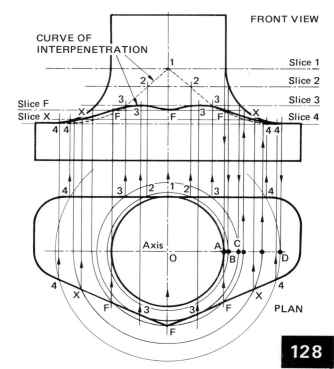

Isometric Drawing of Simple Solids

A pictorial drawing is one which shows three faces of a component simultaneously. It is a three-dimensional drawing showing length, breadth and depth in one view — a "picture".

Each of the five drawings below is a pictorial view of a cube.

PICTORIAL DRAWINGS

An ISOMETRIC drawing is a pictorial drawing. It is, however, a particular type of pictorial drawing. Receding edges of the solid are drawn at a specific angle, i.e. 30° to the horizontal. Other edges are drawn vertically and all edge lengths are usually drawn full size.

Both views of the rectangular solid, shown opposite, have been drawn ISOMETRICALLY. The one on the left has been drawn looking from above, the one on the right from below.

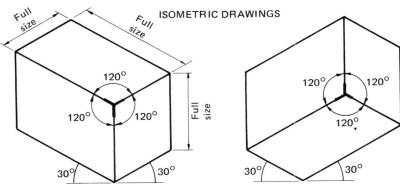

ISOMETRIC DRAWINGS

Notice that although the views look different — they have been viewed from different positions — the isometric axes in each case are spaced at 120° and corresponding edges in each view are parallel to each other.

Note Perspective is ignored in isometric drawing, i.e. the edges do not converge towards a distant point.

Isometric drawings are used primarily to indicate the shape rather than the sizes of a component. They are, therefore, seldom used in the engineering industry where communication of sizes is of major importance. Isometric views tend to be used in catalogues, assembly instructions, etc. Non-technical personnel may find isometric drawings of a relatively complicated component a useful aid when attempting to interpret associated orthographic views.

A distinction needs to be made at this point between an isometric DRAWING, as shown above and an isometric PROJECTION.

An isometric DRAWING is one in which the axes are drawn at 120° to each other and all edges parallel to these axes are drawn full (actual) size. It is an *approximate* representation — in fact a slightly enlarged view of the component.

An isometric PROJECTION is one in which the axes are drawn at 120° to each other and all edges parallel to these axes are shown fore-shortened. Receding edges are, in fact, drawn at 0.816 full size, the dimensions being taken from a specially constructed scale known as an ISOMETRIC SCALE. (Details of the scale are not included here). Isometric PROJECTION, the more laborious of the two methods, produces a true, smaller, similarly proportioned representation of the component.

Isometric DRAWING is merely a simplified and approximate version of isometric PROJECTION.

The difference between these two forms of isometric representation is clearly illustrated below. The cube on the left has been DRAWN isometrically. The identical cube on the right has been PROJECTED isometrically.

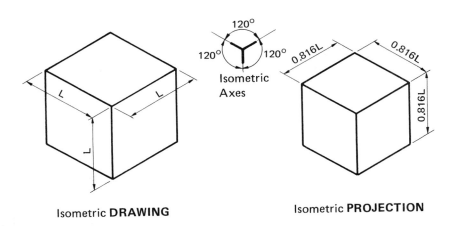

Isometric **DRAWING**

Isometric **PROJECTION**

Remember — Isometric drawing produces an approximate, slightly "oversized" view.

Isometric projection produces a true view. It is less commonly used however, because having to construct a special scale to enable the view to be drawn makes it a relatively time-consuming method of representation.

Note Hidden detail is usually omitted in isometric views unless specifically requested.

Methods commonly used for producing isometric drawings of simple solids, becoming progressively more complicated in shape, are outlined below.

1. RECTILINEAR SOLIDS WITH ALL EDGES PARALLEL TO THE ISOMETRIC AXES.

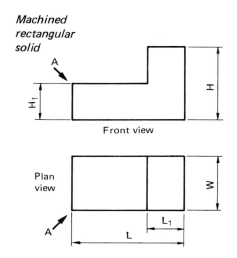

Machined rectangular solid

Front view

Plan view

Steps

A feint, full size isometric "crate", measuring L x H x W, is drawn using a 30° set-square. Sizes are taken from the orthographic views. Length L_1 is stepped along the top edge of the crate to position the top face of the back of the solid. Height H_1 is stepped from the bottom of the crate to form the base. The edges are "heavied-in" as shown, to complete the isometric drawing.

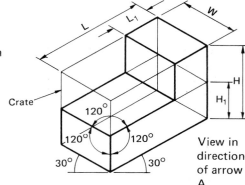

Crate

View in direction of arrow A

Note The crate should always be drawn feintly, usually full size, and with receding edges at 30° to the horizontal (axes at 120°). Visible edges must be shown with heavy, continuous lines.

2. RECTILINEAR SOLIDS WITH INCLINED FACES AND/OR EDGES

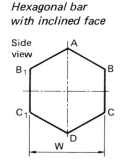

Hexagonal bar with inclined face

Side view

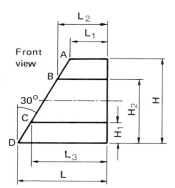

Front view

Note Lengths L_1, L_2, etc., from the front view are used to position edge points A, B, etc., on the inclined face. The 30° angle from the front view is NOT used to position the incline. NEVER transfer angles from orthographic views to isometric drawings.

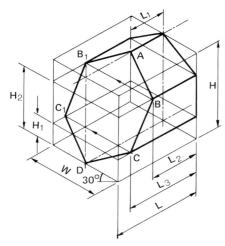

Steps

A feint isometric crate is drawn full size, measuring L x H x W, with all receding lines at 30°. Four centre lines are inserted, as shown, Heights H_1 and H_2 are stepped up from the bottom of the crate and peripheral lines drawn around the crate at these heights. Length L_1, from the front view, is stepped from the rear face of the crate along the top centre line to position point A. Length L_2 is stepped off along the upper peripheral line from the back of the crate to position point B. L_3 is stepped along the lower peripheral line to position point C. Feint lines are drawn at 30° from points B and C to position points B_1 and C_1, respectively. The outline is "heavied-in", as shown, to complete the isometric drawing of the bar.

3. CIRCULAR FEATURES (BARS, TUBES, HOLES, ETC).

Circular bar

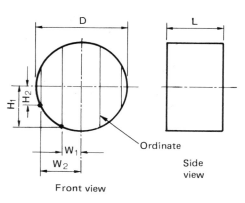

Front view

Side view

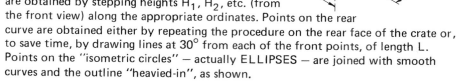

Steps

The isometric crate is drawn feintly, full size, D x D x L. Centre lines are positioned on the front face — carefully.
Ordinates are drawn on the given front view (The more ordinates drawn the more accurate the plotted "isometric circle".) The ordinates are transferred to the front face of the crate, as shown. Points on the front curve are obtained by stepping heights H_1, H_2, etc. (from the front view) along the appropriate ordinates. Points on the rear curve are obtained either by repeating the procedure on the rear face of the crate or, to save time, by drawing lines at 30° from each of the front points, of length L. Points on the "isometric circles" — actually ELLIPSES — are joined with smooth curves and the outline "heavied-in", as shown.

Compare the orthographic views and the isometric view. It can be seen that Isometric DRAWING produces an "enlarged" component.

The Multiple-Ordinate construction, used in the previous example to plot the "isometric circle" (ellipse), is a relatively accurate but laborious construction, especially when using a large number of ordinates.

There are several alternative methods used to draw circular features isometrically which are much quicker, but, unfortunately, less accurate than the ordinate method.

Two of the more commonly used ones are presented below.

(i) The four-centre method

Steps

The relevant face of the isometric crate is drawn feintly with sides equal in length to the diameter D of the circular feature for which an isometric view is required. Centre lines are positioned accurately. The longer diagonal is inserted feintly. Feint lines are drawn from the points of intersection of the centre lines and the crate edges, at 90° to the crate edges. The intersections of the lines drawn from the vertical centre line and the diagonal position points S.

The intersections of the lines drawn from the horizontal centre line and the crate edges position points L. (In isometric views these centres coincide with the corners of the crate.) Small arcs are drawn from centres S, tangential to the crate. Large arcs are drawn from centres L, tangential to the crate, to blend smoothly with the smaller arcs to complete the isometric circle (an approximate ellipse).

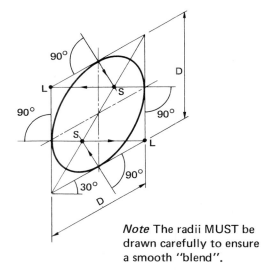

Note The radii MUST be drawn carefully to ensure a smooth "blend".

(ii) The four-point ordinate method

Steps

An orthographic side view of the circular feature is drawn full size. 'Diagonals' are drawn at 45° and vertical ordinates positioned through the points of intersection of the "diagonals" and the circumference. The relevant face of the isometric crate is drawn, full size, measuring D x D. Centre lines and "diagonals" are drawn on the face of the crate. Vertical ordinates are stepped off either side of the vertical centre line, at distance W (from the side view). The intersections of these ordinates and the "diagonals" positions four points on the required curve. A smooth, heavy curve is drawn carefully through all points to complete the ellipse.

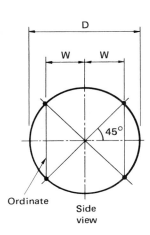

Side view

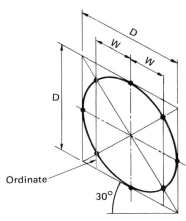

The curve can be drawn either freehand or with curve templates.

Note Both constructions shown above are quicker but less accurate than the Multiple-Ordinate construction.

4. CURVED FEATURES

A modified version of any one of the three constructions for drawing isometric circles, outlined above, can be used to draw radiused curves, provided that the radii are sufficiently large.

The relatively accurate Multiple-Ordinate construction is used below to illustrate how a 90° curve is drawn isometrically.

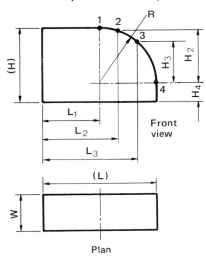

Front view

Plan

Steps

The front view and plan of the curved plate are drawn, full-size. (Only the radius need be drawn when answering an examination question.) Equi-spaced, vertical ordinates are inserted on the quadrant in the front view.

The isometric crate is drawn feintly, measuring L x H x W.

The quadrant centre lines are positioned on the front face of the crate, distances L_4 and H_4 being taken from the front view.

Vertical ordinates are stepped from the front view onto the crate, as shown. Heights H_2, H_3, etc., are stepped from the front view along the respective crate ordinates to position points 2, 3 etc. Corresponding points on the rear curve are obtained by drawing lines, each of length W, at 30° from each of the plotted points on the front curve.

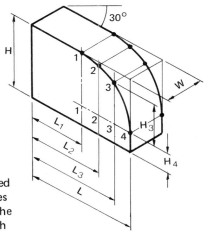

5. CIRCULAR SOLIDS CUT OBLIQUELY

Cylindrical bar with inclined face

A cylindrical bar machined as shown in the orthographic front view is drawn isometrically by following carefully the steps detailed below.

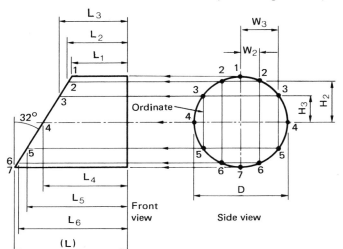

Front view

Side view

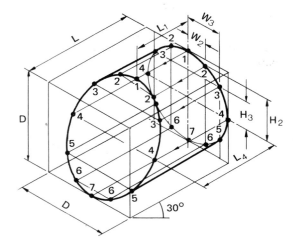

Note Dimension (L) above and (H) and (L) in the previous example, would not normally be included in the orthographic views because they are redundant dimensions. They have been inserted here only to help illustrate crate sizes.

Ordinate sizes could have been obtained from a half side view. The full side view has been shown here for clarity.

Steps

The front view and side view are drawn full size and a suitable number of equi-spaced vertical ordinates inserted in the side view. (The greater the number of ordinates used the greater will be the accuracy of the "plotted" curve).

Lines are projected into the front view from points 1 to 7 in the side view.

The isometric crate is drawn feintly, measuring L x D x D.

The "isometric circle" is plotted on the rear face – FEINTLY – following the steps outlined in Example 3 on page 130.

Feint lines are drawn from each of the numbered points on the rear curve, at 30°.

Length L_1, from the front view, is stepped along the line drawn from point 1, length L_2 is stepped along the lines from points 2, etc. to position points on the front curve.

Points 1 to 7 on the inclined face are joined with a smooth curve and the outline "heavied-in", as shown, to complete the isometric drawing.

Note: In constructions containing curved features, small curves (radii less than 5 mm) are difficult to draw isometrically and it is better to sketch them freehand.

Points which should be memorized

(1) Receding lines on isometric views are drawn at 30° to the horizontal, i.e. isometric axes are at 120° to each other.

(2) Receding lines on isometric DRAWINGS are drawn full size.

(3) Angles should never be transferred from orthographic views to isometric views. Points on inclined faces (surfaces cut obliquely) have to be "plotted".

(4) The more ordinates that are drawn, the more accurate the "plotted" isometric circle.
    However, only a small number of ordinates should be used when answering an examination question to conserve time.

(5) Construction lines, including the isometric crate, should always be drawn feintly. They should NOT be erased in examination solutions – marks are awarded for correct construction lines.

Oblique Drawing of Simple Solids

An oblique drawing, or projection (the terms are used synonymously here) is a pictorial drawing. It is a pictorial drawing of a particular type. One face of the component is drawn full size and parallel to the plane of projection. It is in fact an orthographic front view. This means that two of the three oblique axes are drawn perpendicular to each other. The third, receding, axis may be drawn at any angle. It is, however, usually drawn at 45° to the horizontal or, alternatively, though less often, at 30°. Lengths of receding edges on an oblique view are usually drawn either full size or half full size, though other scales are occasionally used to minimise distortion of the solid.

All four views below, although different, are oblique drawings (projections) of the same solid — in this case a cube. The two on the left are viewed from above, the two on the right have been drawn looking from below the cube.

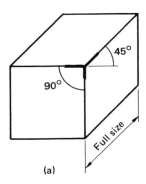
(a)

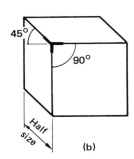
(b)

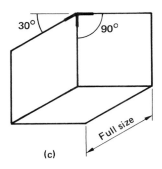
(c)

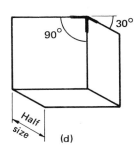
(d)

When receding edges are drawn FULL size and at 45°, the method of projection is known as CAVALIER.

Notice how this method produces a distorted view of the solid, in this case an "elongated" cube.

When receding edges are drawn HALF full size, at ANY angle (though usually 45° or 30°), the method of projection is known as CABINET.

Notice how reducing the receding edges to half size minimises distortion. This view looks "right".

This view with all edges again drawn full size but with receding edges at 30° illustrates a further commonly used method of oblique projection.

It can be seen that this method also produces a rather distorted cube.

This view has been drawn using Cabinet projection with the receding lines drawn in this example at 30°.

It seems, from looking at views (b) and (d) that Cabinet projection produces a reasonably good pictorial representation of the cube.

Oblique drawings, which convey information about shapes of components rather than sizes, are rarely used in industry. When they are used it is usually to augment and clarify the more complicated corresponding orthographic drawings when communicating with non-technical personnel.

The student should be able to produce drawings of relatively simple solids with receding axes at either 45° or 30°, and edges drawn either half or full size.

A selection of such oblique drawings are presented below, together with explanations where necessary.

1. RECTILINEAR SOLIDS WITH ALL EDGES PARALLEL WITH THE OBLIQUE AXES

(a)   Machined rectangular solid with receding axis at 45° and all edges drawn FULL size — CAVALIER projection.

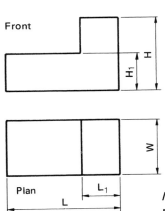

ORTHOGRAPHIC
VIEWS
(Full size)

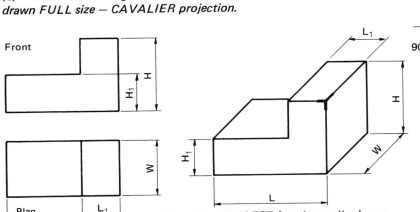

Note The LONGEST face is usually drawn parallel to the plane of projection (at the front), as shown in the view above, to minimise distortion. However, as can be seen from the orthographic views, this oblique view, with *all* edges drawn full size, does not look "right". It appears to be a little too wide.

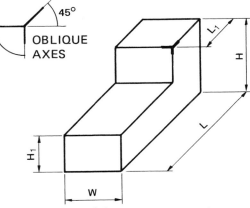

This view, of the same component, illustrates quite clearly that the solid looks much more distorted — far too long — when drawn with the SHORTEST face at the front. *Remember*: draw the LONGEST face of simple rectilinear solids at the FRONT to minimise distortion.

(b) *Machined rectangular solid with receding axis at 45° and receding edges drawn HALF size – CABINET projection.*

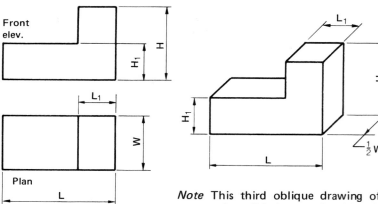

Front
elev.

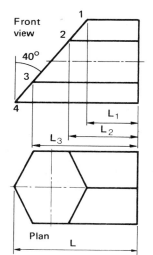

ORTHOGRAPHIC
VIEWS
(Full size)

OBLIQUE
AXES

Note This third oblique drawing of the rectangular solid, drawn using CABINET projection, with the longest face at the front is a good pictorial representation of the component. It looks "right".
Distortion in this view is minimal.

This final view of the solid, again drawn in CABINET projection, but this time with the shortest face at the front, appears to be too short when compared with the orthographic views.
Remember An oblique view with minimal distortion can be obtained by using CABINET projection with the LONGEST face at the front.

2. RECTILINEAR SOLIDS WITH FACES AND/OR EDGES INCLINED AT AN ANGLE TO THE OBLIQUE AXES

(a) *Machined hexagonal bar with receding axis at 30° and all edges drawn FULL size*

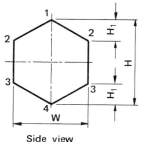

Front
view

Side view

Plan

(i) *With the LONGEST face drawn parallel to the plane of projection*

OBLIQUE
AXES

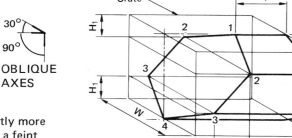

Crate

It is advisable to draw this slightly more complicated component within a feint oblique crate, the overall sizes of which are taken from the orthographic views

Notice that this view looks too wide. It also appears distorted at the right-hand end.

Steps

The oblique crate is drawn FULL SIZE (L x W x H) with the longest face at the front and receding lines at 30°.
The centre line is positioned on the left-hand end face, top and bottom of the crate.
Height H_1 is stepped off from the side view onto the front and back faces as shown, to position the flats of the hexagon.
Length L_1 is stepped off from the front view along the centre line on the top face of the crate to position point 1.
Length L_2 is stepped off along the upper edge of the hexagonal flat on the front and rear faces of the crate to position points 2.
Length L_3 is stepped off along the lower edge of the flat on the front and rear faces to position points 3.
Edge points are joined, as shown, and all edges "heavied-in" to complete the oblique drawing.

Note The 40° angle in the orthographic front view has NOT been used to draw the inclined face of the hexagonal bar in the oblique view. The face has been positioned by plotting, and then joining edge points. NEVER transfer angles from an orthographic view onto the receding faces of its corresponding oblique view.

(ii) *With the SHORTEST face drawn parallel to the plane of projection*

The component is again drawn within a feint, full-size oblique crate but this time the SHORTEST face is positioned at the front.
The view is completed by following, exactly, the steps outlined above.

Notice that in this oblique view the hexagonal bar looks too long. The inclined face in particular appears rather elongated when receding edges are drawn full size.

However, the right-hand end does not appear to be distorted in this view, as it did in the drawing above.

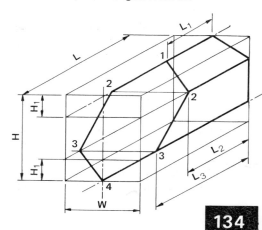

(b)   Machined hexagonal bar with receding axis at 30° and receding edges drawn HALF size.

(i)   With the LONGEST face drawn parallel to the plane of projection

(ii)   With the SHORTEST face drawn parallel to the plane of projection.

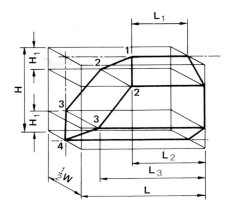

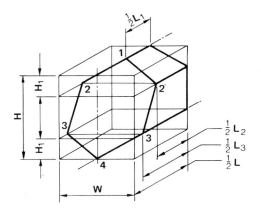

This view, with all receding edges drawn *half*-size, is better proportioned and less distorted than view a(i) on the previous page in which all edges are drawn *full* size.

Drawing the bar in this position produces a reasonably good representation. Neither the overall length nor the inclined inclined face appear to be elongated, as they do in view a(ii) on the previous page.

3.   CIRCULAR FEATURES (BARS, TUBES, HOLES, SLOTS, ETC.

(i)   Accurate, relatively easy and quick method

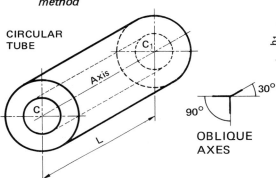

(ii)   Reasonably accurate, laborious and slow method

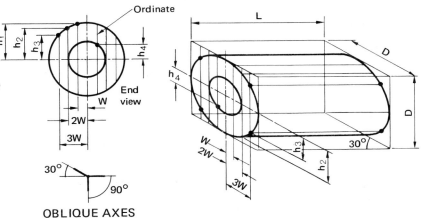

All circles in this view are drawn parallel to the plane of projection (i.e. parallel to the FVP) WITH COMPASSES.

The circles at the front are drawn full size. The correctly scaled length of the tube (full size in this example) is stepped off from centre point C along the receding centre line (axis) to position centre point C_1. The rear circles are then drawn full size from centre C_1.

Notice that hidden detail is shown in the view directly above, as it can be included relatively easily and quickly.

It has been omitted from view (ii) however, because it would have taken so much extra time and effort to include it.

The circles in this view have to be PLOTTED — a time-consuming process. A crate is drawn L x D x D (D being the tube diameter).

An orthographic end view is drawn, full size, and equi-spaced vertical ordinates suitably positioned.

These ordinates are transferred to the end face of the crate. The spacings are identical to those in the end view because receding distances are drawn full size in this example.

Points on the circles are plotted by transferring heights from the end view onto the respective ordinates in the oblique view. For example, height h_3 is stepped above and below the horizontal centre line along ordinates spaced 3W from the vertical centre line, as shown.

Points on the rear curve are positioned at distance L from corresponding points on the front curve.

Successive plotted points are joined with smooth curves and the outline "heavied-in" to complete the oblique drawing.

Think very carefully BEFORE starting to draw oblique views of components with circular features. Use method (i) above rather then method (ii) wherever possible. It is much easier, quicker and more accurate to draw circular features with compasses than it is to plot them.
Remember All circular and/or part circular features should always be drawn parallel to the plane of projection with compasses, if the shape of the component permits.

Note Hidden detail is not usually shown in oblique views, especially for the more complicated components, as it can tend to confuse. It has been included in the view above to demonstrate the advantages of using method (i) rather than method (ii).

It is not always possible, unfortunately, to draw all circular features with compasses, thereby avoiding having to use a more time-consuming method, as the following example shows.

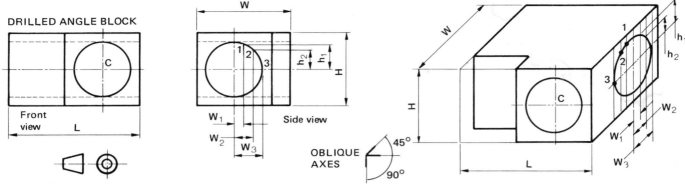

One of the holes in this right-angled component can be drawn with compasses.
The other however HAS to be "plotted" — using in this case, the Multiple-Ordinate construction
It takes more time PLOTTING one hole than drawing out the remainder of the view and would have taken even longer had receding lines been drawn half size instead of full size, and hidden detail included.

There are, in addition to the Multiple-Ordinate construction detailed above, other methods used to draw "oblique circles", or part "circles", on the receding face of an oblique crate where this is found to be necessary.

Two alternative, less accurate, but much quicker constructions are illustrated below.

(i) The four-centre method

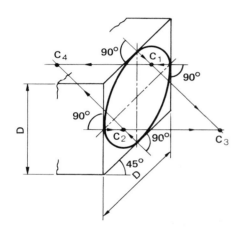

Receding axis drawn full size and at 45° to the horizontal.

Steps
The receding face is drawn D x D where D is the diameter of the circle of which the oblique view is required.
Horizontal and vertical centre lines are inserted carefully.
Lines are drawn, at 90° to the crate edge, from each of the four points of intersection of the crate edge and the centre lines to locate centres C_1, C_2, C_3 and C_4.
Small arcs are drawn from centres C_1 and C_2 and large arcs from centres C_3 and C_4, touching the edges of the crate, to complete the oblique circle.

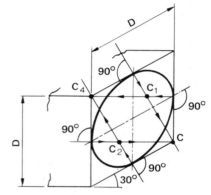

Receding axis drawn full size and at 30° to the horizontal

This method enables the "oblique circle" to be drawn relatively quickly — with compasses. The resulting elliptical shape is, however, only an approximation.
The positions of the arc centres depend upon the angle at which the receding axis is drawn. "Oblique circles" of very different shapes are produced by varying the angle of the receding axis, as can be seen by comparing the two views above.

Note The four-centre method can only be used when receding lines are drawn FULL size. It proves useful, therefore, for CAVALIER projection

(ii) The four-point ordinate method

An orthographic end view is drawn, full size and "crated".
Diagonals are drawn which cut the circle in four points, the distance of these points from the vertical centre line being W.
The oblique face is drawn D x D and centre lines and diagonals inserted.
Two ordinates are positioned at distance W from the vertical centre line.
The intersection of these ordinates and the diagonals produces four points on the requisite "oblique circle" (ellipse).

Note The "oblique circle" is plotted less accurately using this construction than it would be if the "Multiple-Ordinate" method had been used because here only two ordinates have been drawn.
If the lengths of receding edges are drawn less than full size then the ordinate spacing must be reduced accordingly.

The Multiple-Ordinate construction tends to be regarded as the basic method for plotting "circles" on oblique faces. It is commonly used, even though a tedious construction, because it is accurate and can be used to plot "circles" and/or part "circles" on receding faces drawn to any scale and at any angle.

4. CIRCULAR SOLIDS WITH INCLINED FACES

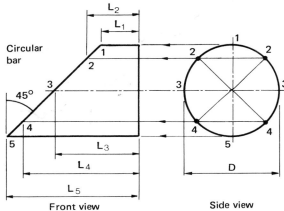

Circular bar

45°

Front view — Side view

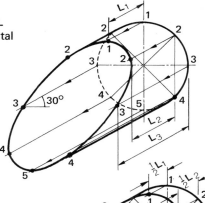

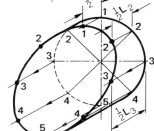

Receding lines are drawn FULL size and at 30° to the horizontal in this view.
The bar has been positioned with the shortest face at the front to enable the rear circle to be drawn with compasses.
Unfortunately this means that both the bar itself and the inclined face appear to be too long.

In this, alternative, view receding lines are drawn HALF size, at 30°, to minimise distortion.
Notice that both bar length and cut surface now seem to be better proportioned.

Steps
"Diagonals" are drawn in the side view and circumferential points 1, 2 etc. projected into the front view.
To start the oblique view a circle, diameter D, is drawn full size — WITH COMPASSES.
"Diagonals" are inserted and circumferential points numbered 1, 2, 3 etc. Lines are drawn at 30° from these points.
Appropriate lengths, from the front view, are stepped along these receding lines, as shown. For example, L_1 is stepped along the line drawn from point 1 in the top view; length $\frac{1}{2}L_1$ along the line from point 1 in the bottom view.
The plotted points are joined with a smooth curve to obtain the shape of the inclined face.

REMEMBER: In oblique projection (drawing), receding lines can be drawn at any angle and to any scale. They are usually drawn at 30° or 45° and either full size or half full size.
Minimise distortion by drawing the longest face at the front of the view and/or drawing receding lines at a reduced scale.
Draw circles at the front of the view wherever possible, with compasses, both for accuracy and to conserve time.

Points which should be memorized
(1) Receding lines on oblique views may be drawn at any angle and to any scale. They are, however, usually drawn at 32° or 45° and either full size or half size.
Where receding edges are drawn FULL size and at 45° the method of projection is known as CAVALIER.
Where receding edges are drawn HALF size, at any angle, the method of projection is known as CABINET.
(2) Distortion can be minimised by drawing the longest face of the component at the front of the oblique view, i.e. parallel to the front vertical plane, and/or receding lines at a reduced scale.
(3) Angles should never be transferred from orthographic views to oblique views. Points on inclined faces should be "plotted".
(4) Circles should be drawn at the front of the view wherever possible, with compasses, both for accuracy and to conserve time.
(5) Construction lines, including the oblique "crate", where utilized, should always be drawn feintly. They should NOT be erased in examination solutions — marks are awarded for correct construction lines.

Answers to exercise on page 74

1.	3C
2.	2B
3.	3B
4.	5C
5.	6A
6.	4A
7.	3A
8.	7B
9.	1C
10.	7A

INDEX